THE COMPLETE BOOK OF U.S. FIGHTING POWER

Andy Lightbody
Joe Poyer

Beekman House

Front cover—main image: USS *Iowa* battleship; **bottom, left:** M-1 Abrams Main Battle Tank; **bottom, center:** M-16 rifle; **bottom, right:** F-14 Tomcat.

Back cover, top: USS *Georgia,* **bottom:** M113 Armored Personnel Carrier. **Back cover, flap:** AH-64 Apache.

Contributing writers:
Andy Lightbody is coauthor of *The Illustrated History of Tanks* and *The Illustrated History of Helicopters*. He is also field/broadcast editor for *Armed Forces Journal International* and is co-host of the weekly military television magazine show *On Target*. Mr. Lightbody's articles appear frequently in the national and military trade press.

Joe Poyer, noted military affairs journalist and novelist, is coauthor of *The Illustrated History of Tanks* and *The Illustrated History of Helicopters*. He contributes regularly to numerous military publications, including *International Defense Images* and *International Combat Arms*.

PICTURE CREDITS:

Arms Communications: 20, 81 (center left), 111 (top), 145 (bottom), 224-225, 310, 314, 351 (center), 359, 376-377, 387 (bottom), 390, 414, 417, 424, 425, 428, 440, 443, 444, 446, 448-449, 488; **John Batchelor:** 15, 113 (bottom), 221 (bottom), 311 (top) 460; **Bath Iron Works Corporation:** 396, 397; **Bell Helicopter Textron:** 148; **Gary Bloomfield/PHOTRI:** 291 (top left); **Boeing Helicopters:** 119 (top); **R. Bossu/Sygma:** 193 (top), 215 (bottom left); **Robert Bruce/ International Defense Images:** 171 (top right), 174, 177 (top right, bottom right), 182 (top, bottom), 246, 247 (bottom left), 251 (bottom), 284 (bottom), 285 (top, bottom); **Rick Diaz/Arms Communications:** 41 (top); **Jeff Ethell/International Defense Images:** 108 (top), 109 (top, bottom left); **Robert Genat/Arms Communications:** 80, 107 (top); **Robert Genat/International Defense Images:** 81 (top); **Michael R. Green/Arms Communications:** 9 (bottom), 205, 227 (bottom), 253 (top), 256, 257 (bottom); **Hans Halberstadt/ Arms Communications:** 139 (top), 150-151, 172, 179 (bottom left, bottom right), 227 (top), 259 (top), 274 (top), 284 (top), 285 (center), 286-287; **Kirby Harrison/International Defense Images:** 40, 141 (bottom right); **David Hathcox/Arms Communications:** 44 (bottom), 95 (top right); **International Defense Images:** 8 (top), 139 (bottom left), 181 (bottom left), 337, 438 (bottom right); **Randy Jolly/Arms Communications:** 34-35, 44 (top), 63 (top left), 69 (top), 87 (top, center left, bottom), 91 (top, bottom left), 93 (center), 107 (bottom), 109 (bottom right); **Gary L. Kieffer/International Defense Images:** 93 (bottom), 95 (bottom left), 98, 100-101, 132-133, 180 (top), 181 (top right), 190, 196; **Kulik Photo/DOD/MGA:** Back cover (top), 8 (bottom), 21 (bottom), 25 (top, bottom), 43 (bottom), 45, 49 (top, bottom), 53 (bottom), 56 (bottom), 62, 63 (bottom), 66-67 81 (bottom), 82 (bottom), 86, 87 (center right), 94, 95 (top left), 99 (center right, bottom), 102 (bottom), 103 (bottom), 104-105, 110, 113 (center left), 116-117, 122, 126, 128-129, 131 (top), 135 (top), 139 (bottom right), 142-143, 144, 157 (bottom), 160, 161 (top left), 162, 163 (bottom), 175 (bottom right), 176, 179 (center right), 204, 252, 254-255, 261 (bottom), 288, 299 (bottom), 301 (bottom left, bottom right), 302, 316, 317 (top), 321 (bottom), 330-331, 338, 340-341, 351 (top), 383, 391 (bottom), 393 (top, bottom), 454-455, 456, 461, 464, 469, 472, 477 (top, bottom), 495; **McDonnell Douglas Helicopter Company:** 152, 153 (top, center left, center right, bottom), 154-155, 156, 157 (top left, top right); **Richard Mullen/International Defense Images:** 134, 136-137; **PHOTRI:** Front cover (top, bottom right), Back cover (bottom), 7 (top, bottom), 10 (bottom), 12-13, 14, 17, 19, 21 (top), 22-23, 26-27, 28, 29 (top, bottom), 30-31, 37 (bottom), 38-39, 41 (bottom), 43 (top), 46-47, 48, 50-51, 53 (top), 56 (top), 60, 64, 65 (top, center, bottom), 70-71, 72, 77 (top, bottom left, bottom right), 81 (center right), 82 (top), 83 (top, bottom), 84-85, 88-89, 92 (top, bottom), 93 (top), 95 (bottom right), 96-97, 99 (top, center left), 102 (top), 103 (top), 106, 108 (bottom), 114, 115 (center left, center right, bottom), 119 (bottom), 123 (top, bottom), 124-125, 131 (bottom), 135 (bottom), 141 (top left, bottom left), 145 (top), 146-147, 149 (bottom right), 161 (top right, center left, center right, bottom), 163 (top left, center left, center right), 164-165, 169 (bottom right), 175 (top), 183 (top, bottom left, bottom right), 187 (top), 191, 193 (bottom left), 197 (top), 208, 209 (top, bottom), 210, 212 (top, bottom), 214, 215 (top right, bottom right), 217 (top), 230-231, 232, 241 (bottom), 244, 249, 250, 253 (bottom), 264, 276-277, 279 (top), 282, 289 (top), 292-293, 295 (bottom left, bottom right), 297 (top, bottom), 298, 299 (top, center left, center right), 300, 301 (top right), 303 (top right, bottom left, bottom right), 304 (bottom), 307, 308-309, 311 (bottom), 312, 315, 317 (center, bottom), 318-319, 320, 321 (top), 322 (top, bottom), 323, 324, 325 (bottom), 326-327, 328, 329 (bottom), 332, 333 (top, center), 334 (top, center, bottom), 342, 346, 350, 351 (bottom), 352-353, 354, 356-357, 362, 363 (bottom left), 364-365, 367 (top, center, bottom), 370, 374, 375, 380-381, 382, 385, 387 (center), 388-389, 391 (top), 398, 402, 404 (top), 410, 411, 413, 427 (bottom), 429 (left), 430, 431 (bottom left), 433 (top, bottom), 434, 437, 438 (top right, bottom left), 439 (bottom), 452 (top, bottom), 453 (top), 459, 465, 466 (top, bottom), 470, 473, 476, 478-479, 482, 485, 492 (top, bottom), 494, 496, 497, 498, 499 (top); **David Polewski/International Defense Images:** 240, 259 (bottom); **Joe Poyer:** 266 (top, bottom), 267 (top, bottom); **Royal Ordnance:** 189 (top, bottom); **Mi Seitelman/International Defense Images:** 6, 16, 36, 42, 52, 54, 63 (top right), 90, 91 (bottom right), 111 (bottom), 112, 141 (top right), 248, 339 (top); **Frederick Sutter:** Front cover (bottom left), Back cover (flap), 18, 74-75, 149 (bottom left), 158-159, 169 (top, bottom left), 170 (bottom right), 173 (top), 184, 185 (top right, bottom left, bottom right), 192, 217 (bottom), 233, 234-235, 238, 245 (bottom left), 258, 261 (top), 275 (bottom left, bottom right), 279 (center right), 289 (center, bottom), 290; **Sygma:** 68, 73 (bottom), 170 (bottom left), 245 (bottom right); **Randy Taylor/Sygma:** 61 (top); **United States Air Force:** 58, 59, 113 (center right), 120, 121 (top, bottom left), 127 (bottom); **United States Army:** 179 (top left), 188; **United States Army Armament Munitions and Chemical Command:** 202-203; **United States Department of Defense:** Front cover (bottom center), 9 (top), 10 (top), 11, 24, 32, 33, 37 (top), 55, 57 (bottom), 69 (bottom), 73 (top), 76, 78, 79 (top, bottom), 113 (top), 115 (top), 118, 127 (top), 130, 138 (bottom), 140, 149 (top, center), 166-167, 168 (top, bottom), 170 (top), 171 (top left), 173 (bottom), 175 (bottom left), 177 (top left, bottom left), 180 (bottom), 185 (top left), 186, 187 (bottom), 193 (bottom right), 194, 195, 197 (bottom), 198, 199 (top, bottom), 200, 201, 206-207, 215 (top left), 216, 218 (top, bottom), 219, 220 (top, bottom), 221 (top), 222, 223 (top, bottom left, bottom right), 226, 228-229, 236-237, 241 (top), 242-243, 245 (top), 247 (top, bottom right), 251 (top), 257 (top), 260, 261 (center), 262-263, 268 (top, bottom), 269 (top, bottom left, bottom right), 270, 271 (top, bottom), 272, 273 (top, bottom), 274 (bottom), 275 (top), 278, 279 (center left, bottom), 280-281, 283 (top, bottom), 291 (top right, center left, bottom left), 294, 295 (top), 296, 304 (top), 305, 313, 322 (center), 325 (top), 329 (top), 333 (bottom), 335, 336, 339 (bottom), 343, 344-345, 347, 348 (top, bottom), 349, 355, 358, 360-361, 363 (top left, bottom right), 366, 368-369, 371, 372, 373, 378, 379, 386, 387 (top), 394, 395 (top, bottom), 399, 400-401, 403, 404 (bottom center), 405, 406, 407 (top left, center left, bottom left, bottom right), 408-409, 415, 418-419, 420, 421, 422, 423 (top, bottom), 426, 427 (top), 429 (right), 431 (bottom right), 432, 435 (top, bottom), 436, 439 (top), 441, 442, 447 (top, bottom), 450, 451 (top, bottom), 457, 458 (top, bottom), 462-463, 467, 499 (bottom); **United States Marine Corps:** 178, 179 (top); **United States Navy:** 445, 453 (bottom), 500; **K. Usher/International Defense Images:** 173 (center left, center right), 181 (top left); **Agostino von Hassell/Arms Communications:** 57 (top), 213, 412, 431 (top left); **Yogi, Inc.:** 471, 474-475, 480-481, 483, 486, 487, 489, 490-491, 493; **Doug Zalud/Arms Communications:** 121 (bottom right); **Tom Zimmeroff/Sygma:** 61 (bottom), 171 (bottom).

Louis Weber, C.E.O.
Publications International, Ltd.
7373 North Cicero Avenue
Lincolnwood, Illinois 60646

Manufactured in Yugoslavia.

h g f e d c b a

This edition published by Beekman House,
Distributed by Crown Publishers, Inc.,
225 Park Avenue South,
New York, New York 10003

ISBN 0-517-03298-8

CONTENTS

INTRODUCTION:

AMERICA'S MILITARY IN PEACE AND WAR 6

U.S. AIR POWER 12

FIGHTERS 18

F-4 Phantom II 20

F-14 Tomcat 24

F-15 Eagle 28

F-16 Fighting Falcon 32

F/A-18 Hornet 36

ATTACK PLANES 40

A-4 Skyhawk 42

A-6 Intruder 44

A-7 Corsair II 48

A-10 Thunderbolt II 52

AV-8B Harrier II 55

F-117A Stealth Fighter 58

BOMBERS 60

B-52 Stratofortress 62

F-111/FB-111 64

B-1 68

B-2 Stealth 72

RECONNAISSANCE AND ELECTRONIC WARFARE AIRCRAFT 76

U-2/TR-1 Series 78

E-2 Hawkeye 80

SR-71 Blackbird 82

E-3 Sentry (AWACS) 86

EF-111 Raven 90

TRANSPORTS 92

C-130 Hercules 94

C-141 Starlifter 98

C-5 Galaxy 102

AERIAL TANKERS 106

KC-135 Stratotanker 108

KC-10 Extender 110

UTILITY AND TRANSPORT HELICOPTERS 112

UH-1 Iroquois (Huey) 114

CH-47 Chinook 118

CH-3/HH-3 Jolly Green Giant 120

CH-46 Sea Knight 122

CH-53 Sea Stallion/HH-53 Super Jolly Green Giant 126

UH-60A Black Hawk/ SH-60B Seahawk 130

CH-53E Super Stallion/ MH-53E Sea Dragon 134

ATTACK HELICOPTERS 138

SH-3 Sea King 140

SH-2 Seasprite 144

AH-1 HueyCobra 148

530M Defender 152

AH-64A Apache 156

CRUISE MISSILES 160

AGM-86B Air-Launched Cruise Missile 162

U.S. LAND POWER 166

INFANTRY WEAPONS 172

Beretta Double Action, 9mm Sidearm 174

M16A2 Rifle 176

M21, M24, and M40A1 Sniper Rifles 178

M249 5.56mm Squad Automatic Weapon 180
M60 General Purpose Machine Gun 182
Mark 19-3 40mm Automatic Grenade Launcher 184
M29A1 81mm Mortar 186
M252 81mm Mortar 188
Shoulder-Launched, Multipurpose Assault Weapon 190
FIRE SUPPORT (ARTILLERY) 192
M101A1 105mm Towed Howitzer 194
M114 155mm Towed Howitzer 195
M102 105mm Towed Howitzer 196
M198 155mm Towed Howitzer 198
M119 105mm Towed Howitzer 200
M109 155mm Self-propelled Howitzer 201
M110A2 Self-propelled 203mm (8-Inch) Howitzer 208
105mm Artillery Ammunition 210
155mm Artillery Ammunition 210
203mm (8-Inch) Howitzer Ammunition 213
Lance Battlefield Support Missile (MGM-52C) 214
Multiple Launch Rocket System (MLRS) 216
Tactical Missile System (TACMS) 219
MAIN BATTLE TANKS 220
M-48 General George S. Patton Medium Tank 222
M-60 Main Battle Tank 226
M-1 and M-1A1 Abrams Main Battle Tank 232
120mm Tank Ammunition 239
105mm Tank Ammunition 239
ANTITANK WEAPONS 240
Tube-Launched, Optically Tracked, Wire-Guided (TOW) Missile (BGM-71) 244
M47 Dragon II Medium Antitank Weapon 246
AT-4 Light Antitank Weapon 249
ARMORED FIGHTING VEHICLES 250
M113 Armored Personnel Carrier 252
M2/M3 Bradley Infantry and Cavalry Fighting Vehicles 256
Marine Corps Light Assault Vehicle 25 258
M998 High Mobility, Multipurpose Wheeled Vehicle (HMMWV) 260
MINES 264
The Land Mine and Minelaying Systems 264
BATTLEFIELD ELECTRONICS 268
AN/PPS-5B Battlefield Surveillance Radar 269
AN/TPQ-36/37 Mortar/Artillery Fire Finder Radar 270
Laser Designators 272
AIR-DEFENSE SYSTEMS 274
MIM-23B Hawk Air-Defense Missile System 278
FIM-43A Redeye Antiaircraft Guided-Missile System 282
Vulcan Air-Defense System 284
M48A1 Chaparral Low-Altitude Self-propelled Surface-to-Air Missile System 288
FIM-92A Stinger 290
MIM-104 Patriot Tactical Air-Defense Missile System 294
Roland Air-Defense Missile System 296
LAND-BASED INTERCONTINENTAL BALLISTIC MISSILES 298
Minuteman III (LGM-30) Intercontinental Ballistic Missile 300
Peacekeeper (LGM-118) Intercontinental Ballistic Missile 302
CHEMICAL WARFARE 304
Chemical Warfare Capability 304

U.S. SEA POWER 308
AIRCRAFT CARRIERS 314
Midway-Class (CV) Aircraft Carriers 316

Forrestal-Class (CV)
Aircraft Carriers 320
Kitty Hawk-Class (CV)
Aircraft Carriers 323
Enterprise-Class (CVN)
Aircraft Carrier 328
Nimitz-Class (CVN)
Aircraft Carriers 332
BATTLESHIPS 336
Iowa-Class (BB) Battleships 338
CRUISERS 342
Long Beach-Class (CGN) Cruiser. 346
Leahy-Class (CG)
Guided-Missile Cruisers 350
Bainbridge-Class (CGN) and Truxtun-Class
(CGN) Cruisers. 354
Belknap-Class (CG) Guided-Missile Cruisers. . .358
California-Class (CGN)
Guided-Missile Cruisers 362
Virginia-Class (CGN)
Guided-Missile Cruisers 366
Ticonderoga-Class (CG)
Guided-Missile Cruisers 370
DESTROYERS 374
Forrest Sherman-Class
(DD) Destroyers 378
Charles F. Adams-Class (DDG)
Guided-Missile Destroyers 382
Farragut-Class (DDG)
Guided-Missile Destroyers 386
Spruance-Class (DD) Destroyers 390
Kidd-Class (DDG)
Guided-Missile Destroyers 394
Arleigh Burke-Class (DDG)
Guided-Missile Destroyers 396
FRIGATES. 398
Bronstein-Class (FF) Frigates 402
Garcia-Class (FF) Frigates 403
Brooke-Class (FFG)
Guided-Missile Frigates 406
Knox-Class (FF) Frigates 410
Oliver Hazard Perry-Class (FFG)
Guided-Missile Frigates 414
AMPHIBIOUS SHIPS 420
Iwo Jima-Class (LPH)
Amphibious Assault Ships 422
Tarawa-Class (LHA)
Amphibious Assault Ships 424
Wasp-Class (LHD)
Amphibious Assault Ships 426
Dock Landing-Class (LSD/LPD)
Amphibious Ships .428
Newport-Class (LST)
Tank Landing Ships 432
Charleston-Class (LKA)
Amphibious Cargo Ships 434
PATROL AND SPECIAL WARFARE CRAFT . . .436
Pegasus-Class Missile
Patrol Boats 437
WEAPONS AND SURVEILLANCE SYSTEMS. .440
Antiship Guns 441
Antiship Missiles 444
Antisubmarine Weapons. 446
Surface-to-Air Weapons 450
Radars and Surveillance Systems 456
SUBMARINES 460
Lafayette-Class (SSBN) and Benjamin
Franklin-Class (SSBN) Ballistic
Missile Submarines 464
Ohio-Class (SSBN) Ballistic
Missile Submarines 470
Permit-Class (SSN) Attack Submarines 476
Sturgeon-Class (SSN) Attack Submarines. 482
Los Angeles-Class (SSN) Attack Submarines . .486
SUBMARINE-LAUNCHED BALLISTIC
MISSILES. 494
UGM-73A Poseidon (C-3) Submarine-Launched
Ballistic Missile. 496
UGM-96 Trident I and II (C-4 and D-5)
Submarine-Launched Ballistic Missile 498

INDEX 501

INTRODUCTION: AMERICA'S MILITARY IN PEACE AND WAR

Since 1945, the United States of America has been the strongest military power on the globe. At the end of World War II, the United States was faced with a challenge from the Soviet Union. The choice was either the imposition of a communist dictatorship over most of the world or organized resistance in Central and Western Europe, the Middle East, and East Asia.

Above: The chassis of the M113 Armored Personnel Carrier has served as the basis for innumerable military vehicles.

AMERICAN MILITARY POWER

This book shall review the composition and makeup of the entire range of American military armament. The weapons systems used by the Army, Air Force, Marine Corps, and Navy will be examined, from the M9 Beretta pistol to the Peacekeeper intercontinental ballistic missile.

A short history of U.S. military forces helps to illustrate how these weapons fit the mission assigned to each branch of the service. The present force and composition of each service are also reviewed, as well as the overall command structure and how that command structure devolves downward from the National Command Authority, starting with the Commander in Chief—the President of the United States.

In the Air Power section, the important aircraft currently in operational service with the United States, ranging from the E-3 Sentry AWACS and the C-130 Hercules transport to the F-14 Tomcat and the new B-2 Stealth bomber, are discussed. Each profile provides a short developmental history, a description of the various systems (weapons, avionics, powerplant, and so on) of the aircraft, and important specifications.

The Land Power section takes a look at all major weapons used by the Army and the Marine Corps. This starts with personal weapons but also includes armored vehicles, artillery, electronics, and missile systems. The function of each weapon, its course of development, and present uses will be described, and specifications given.

In the Sea Power section, major ships and weapons of the United States Navy are examined. Carriers, battleships, cruisers, frigates, strategic nuclear submarines, attack submarines, and many others will be profiled. The role and function of each ship in the overall scheme of American naval strategy is detailed.

In short, every important fighting tank, armored vehicle, aircraft, naval vessel, rifle, pistol, and missile in the inventory of the United States Army, Air Force, Marine Corps, and Navy, will be discussed, analyzed, and illustrated. This book offers a thorough survey of American fighting power.

MILITARY MIGHT IN TODAY'S WORLD

The North Atlantic Treaty Organization (NATO) is an extension and expansion of the wartime alliance of Great Britain, France, and the United States. Organized and formalized in 1949, NATO welded 14 European and North American nations

Left: *The F-15 Eagle is an immensely capable jet interceptor.* Below: *The M60 machine gun has served with U.S. military forces since 1957.*

into a military alliance that halted Soviet expansionism in Europe along a line that ran from the Arctic Ocean to the Mediterranean Sea. A similar organization in the Middle East—the Central Treaty Organization (CENTO)—and one in the Far East—the Southeast Asia Treaty Organization (SEATO)—also helped to contain the Soviet Union in those regions. The Warsaw Pact is the Soviet Union's counterpart to NATO. The Warsaw Pact is an alliance of such Eastern European nations as Poland, East Germany, and Hungary with the Soviet Union.

Since the end of World War II, the United States has fought two major wars—Korea (1950–53) and Vietnam (1964–73)—and participated in a host of minor military conflicts in its efforts to contain communist expansion. For 45 years, America's nuclear umbrella, conventional military might, and will to resist aggression has kept Europe free of the wars that have plagued the continent for the past 1,000 years. Never has Europe enjoyed so long a period of peace nor the world gone so long without a major war.

Recent events in the Soviet Union and the Eastern Bloc seem to indicate that the Cold War may be coming to an end. The leadership of the Soviet Union appears to have realized that their weak and inefficient economy presents a far greater danger to their safety and well-being than any outside threat from another nation. Democracy is on the rise throughout the Eastern Bloc. The Warsaw Pact has become a shell of its former political and military self, and it is doubtful if the Warsaw Pact can ever again be as effective a military organization as it was even in the mid-1980s. As the threat and power of the Warsaw Pact declines, so too will the military aspects of the NATO alliance.

Significant numbers of American troops and equipment will probably be recalled from Europe during the 1990s. But this does not necessarily indicate a decrease in American military power. Should the Cold War resume, it will be necessary to make arrangements to return these and other forces to Europe. The Cold War with the Soviet Union does not represent the only danger to America's interests. The United States faces many other threats to its security and citizens. The United States must be ready at a moment's notice to protect its interests, as well as those of its allies, anywhere in the world.

The United States has remained free since 1776. For a nation to endure, it must be willing and able to accept combat to safeguard its rights and interests. The United States has been able to control its destiny because it has kept itself militarily strong.

Above: *The USS* Nimitz, *a nuclear-powered aircraft carrier, is the single most powerful weapons system in the world.* Left: *The UH-1 Huey proved to be the most successful helicopter flown during the Vietnam War.*

Right: *The M-1 Abrams Main Battle Tank was designed and built to meet the threat of Soviet tanks in a European war.* Below: *It is axiomatic that infantry troops must accompany tanks. The M2 Bradley was developed to provide the infantry with that capability.*

Above: *The F-16 Fighting Falcon was developed to replace the aging F-4 Phantom II.* Left: *The USS* Olympia *is a* Los Angeles-*class attack submarine. It preys on enemy strategic missile submarines and surface shipping.* Opposite: *The M198 howitzer is towed to its firing location and fires a 155mm round.*

U.S. AIR POWER

The F/A-18 Hornet, built by McDonnell Douglas, is the Marine Corps' latest and hottest jet fighter.

U.S. AIR POWER

Military power exists in any rational society for the purpose of defending that society, its people, and their interests. In the 1960s, the United States decided that nuclear power *alone* could serve the purpose of military power, and the development of conventional weapons lagged. But after the end of American involvement in Vietnam, military experts realized that conventional forces also had a role in America's defensive posture. The result of this realization has been the rebuilding of American conventional power, and air power is one of the most important aspects of that power.

AIR COMBAT FORCES OF THE UNITED STATES

The first military air activity in the United States took place during the Civil War. The first aeronautical branch of the United States Army was formed on July 1, 1891, as the Balloon Section of the U.S. Army's Signal Corps. This unit served in Cuba during the Spanish-American War in 1898 and was not very successful. The balloons were replaced in 1907 by Signal Corps Dirigible No. 1; although the dirigibles remained in service for two years, they were hardly more successful than the balloons.

In 1904, the British government offered the Wright brothers a significant sum of money for their new heavier-than-air flying machine. But the Wrights were patriots; they wanted the United States to benefit first from their invention. The United States government, however, was not interested. In a series of misunderstandings so obtuse as to seem deliberate, the government bureau in charge of military weapon acquisitions at that time, the Board of Ordnance and Fortifications, repeatedly turned the brothers down. Not until 1907, four full years after the Wrights' first flight at Kitty Hawk, North Carolina, was the government convinced that the Wright brothers had indeed invented an aircraft that could fly. The first fixed wing aircraft, the Wright Flyer, joined the Signal Corps on August 20, 1907.

Aviation remained the stepchild of the U.S. Army until World War I. By the time the United States entered the fray in 1917, aircraft had become a major weapon system. American pilots flew British and French aircraft because there were no American aircraft advanced enough to keep pace with German planes.

The period between the world wars saw military aviation advance at a moderate pace in most nations. In 1939, the swift conquest of Poland erased any doubt as to the aircraft's place in modern warfare. The image of war in the autumn of 1939 and again in the spring of 1940 was the Stuka dive bomber strafing military columns and civilian refugees alike. And it was England's Spitfire and Hurricane fighters during the Battle of Britain (July–September 1940) that saved the British people from being trampled under the Nazi boot. Some 750 fighter planes fought for and retained control of the skies over the English Channel and the English south coast, preventing a German invasion.

In 1942, American bomber aircraft joined the Royal Air Force in mounting round-the-clock bombing raids on the German homeland to destroy its production centers and communications networks. American and British fighter aircraft cleared the skies of Nazi fighters and bombers by mid-1944 and established an air umbrella over the invasion beaches of Normandy. Bombers continued to raid deep into Germany.

In the Pacific, carrier-based Navy and Marine and land-based Army Air Force planes slowly wrested control of the Pacific skies from the Japanese Air Force. B-17 and B-24 bombers, and then B-29s, whittled away at Japan's production capabilities. While the war was not won wholly in the air, air power played a vital role in ending the conflict.

After World War II, an expansionist-minded Soviet Union drew all of Eastern Europe behind the Iron Curtain and built a massive and capable air force. As the Cold War intensified, the Western powers responded with ever more advanced fighters, attack aircraft, transports, tankers, and bombers. In 1908, the Wright Flyer was capable of reaching speeds of 42 miles per hour. Today's fighters can travel at Mach 2—twice the speed of sound—and carry the most advanced weapons and surveillance systems available. Today's military aircraft go far beyond the dreams of the early pioneers in aviation.

THE ORGANIZATION OF U.S. AIR POWER

Within the fabric of American military power there are the three dimensions of land, sea, and air. While land and sea are generally mutually exclusive, the air element of the equation is present in operations involving the

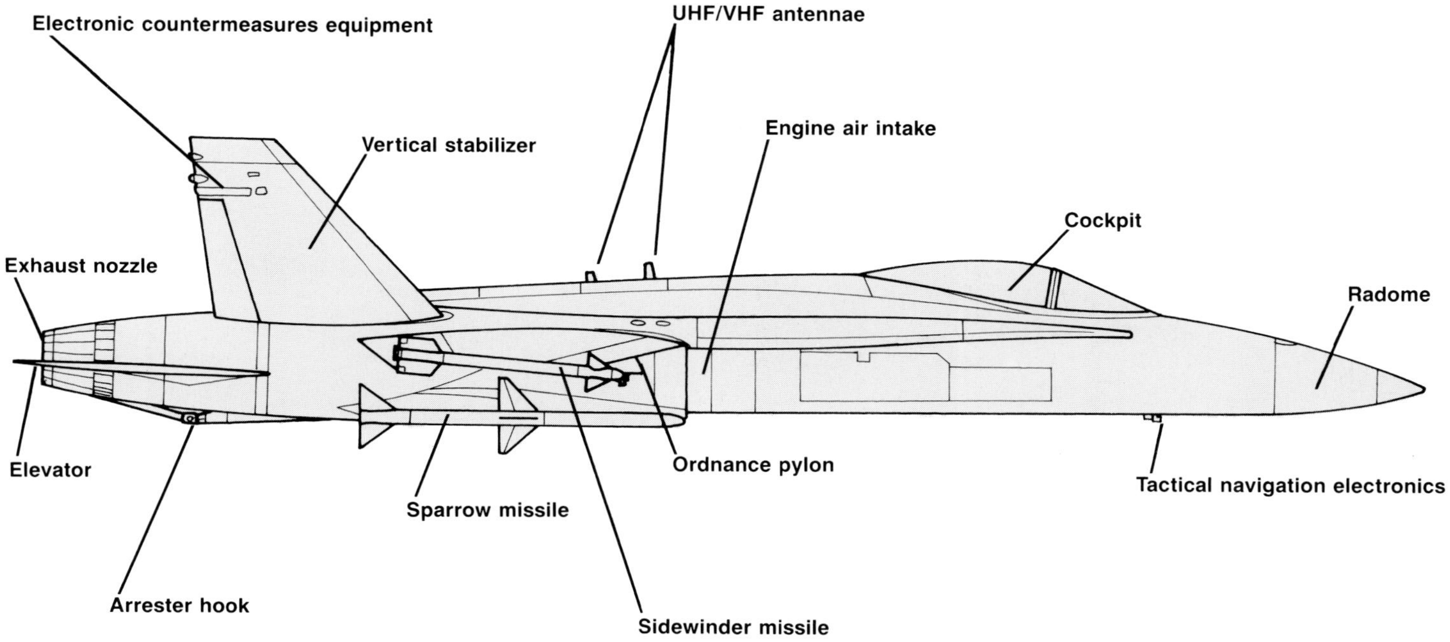

other two. Air power is not exclusive to the U.S. Air Force. The U.S. Army, U.S. Navy, and U.S. Marine Corps all possess aircraft of various types that are essential to their activities. Each of the four services regards air power in a different way.

Prior to 1947, when the Defense Department was created, there were two equal cabinet level departments of Navy and War, with the latter containing the Army and the subsidiary Army Air Forces (Army Air Corps until 1941). The cabinet level U.S. Department of Defense comprises three equal and independent executive departments: Army, Navy, and Air Force, with the Navy in turn containing the Marine Corps.

Since having been stripped of its Army Air Forces more than 40 years ago, the U.S. Army has had almost no fixed wing aircraft aside from a handful of light observation and utility planes. What the Army does have is one of the largest fleets of military helicopters in the world. Helicopters are, and have been since the Vietnam War, an integral part of the Army's image of itself as a highly mobile, highly flexible fighting force.

The U.S. Navy's concept of air power is very much tied to the deployment of its aircraft carriers. Indeed, the key element of naval operations is the carrier battle group (CBG), which consists of a number of surface vessels with a carrier as its centerpiece. Of the Navy's aircraft, 80 percent are assigned to its CBGs, with a second priority being shore-based, long-range antisubmarine patrols. The Navy possesses tactical combat aircraft whose roles parallel those of the Air Force, but the mobility of the aircraft carriers permits the Navy to reposition its air power with greater flexibility than is possible with land bases.

The Marine Corps serves as an all-purpose strike force capable of virtually any type of operation. These operations may include boarding an enemy ship on the high seas or conducting an amphibious landing on enemy territory. While the Marines depend upon the Navy for support, they also have the ability to provide their own air support in terms of transport as well as combat aircraft. The Marines operate fewer helicopters than the Army, but more fixed wing aircraft.

The Air Force evolved directly from the Army Air Forces that had grown during World War II to be the largest air service in history. Having once been part of the Army, the Air Force took on the commitment of providing air support for the Army as one of the

Opposite: *The SR-71 Blackbird is a high-altitude reconnaissance aircraft capable of speeds in excess of Mach 3 and altitudes above 90,000 feet.* Above: *An illustration of today's modern jet, showing weaponry, electronic gear, and design.*

conditions of its becoming completely independent in 1947, which is why the Army today has virtually no fixed wing aircraft. Today, the Air Force is much smaller than in the past; in terms of size it is second to that of the Soviet Union. But the Air Force owns the largest fleet of aircraft of any U.S. service, with more than three-quarters of all American military aircraft.

The Air Force's role is all-encompassing. It is responsible within the Department of Defense for long-range air transport and aerial refueling. Indeed, the Air Force has the overall responsibility of providing all but incidental air transport for the entire American defense establishment. Therefore, the Air Force possesses not only combat aircraft but also the largest fleet of military transport aircraft in the West.

MEETING THE CHALLENGE OF THE NEXT DECADE

Air power has become a universal factor in world military power, and it is an area in which the United Sates excels technologically. The Air Force has over 9,500 aircraft, a third of which are fighter/interceptor/attack types. About 17 percent are trainers. The primary slices of the remaining half of the pie are bombers, transports, aerial tankers, and reconnaissance aircraft. The Soviet Union has more than 13,000 aircraft in its Air Force/Air Defense Forces. However, while the Soviet Union has about 600 latest-generation fighters (MiG 29, MiG 31, and Su-27), the U.S. Air Force has nearly 2,000 F-15s and F-16s.

Both the Soviet Navy and the U.S. Navy have roughly 1,550 total aircraft (including helicopters), yet the U.S. Navy has 14 full-size aircraft carriers and 400 latest-generation F-14s, while the Soviet Navy has only one full-size carrier (the *Tbilisi*, presently conducting sea trials) and, as yet, no latest-generation combat aircraft. The U.S. Army has nearly 9,000 helicopters, compared with only about half that number in the Soviet Army, which has two-and-a-half times the personnel strength of the U.S. Army.

The aircraft described here are the basic building blocks of American air power, while the categories represent the roles these aircraft play in the total fabric of exercising that power. You'll learn about quick and agile fighters like the F-16. Read the latest on tough attack planes like the A-10 Warthog as well as such sophisticated electronic warfare aircraft as the E-3 AWACS, which can change the course of a battle without firing a single shot.

Maintaining the qualitative superiority of American air power is no easy task, nor is it inexpensive. It involves thoughtful planning in terms of specific aircraft and the way they are tailored to their missions. Together, these aircraft, each tailored for a specific mission, add up to U.S. air power, the most advanced and most effective flying force in the world today.

Above: *This F/A-18 Hornet, of Marine Corps Squadron 323, is stationed at El Toro, California. It is armed with Sidewinders on the wingtips, a stores carrier under the fuselage, and four Mark 83 general purpose bombs.* Right (top to bottom): *An F-15 Eagle, an F-16 Fighting Falcon, and an A-10 Thunderbolt II, the jets that make up the U.S. Air Force's triple threat.*

BT
10 TFS

FIGHTERS

The only job jet fighters have is to destroy enemy aircraft. To do this task, the fighter pilot's first rule is to be ready, willing, and able to kill any enemy aircraft sent against him. The second rule is to not get killed. Among fighter pilots, these rules have applied ever since somebody first used a revolver from an observation plane to fire on another observation plane. But over the decades, the nature of air-to-air combat has become more complex, more expensive, and more deadly.

The two primary variables of air-to-air combat have always been *armament* and *performance.* Armament began with the revolver in 1914 and quickly evolved to the machine gun, which remained the basic fighter plane armament for half a century. Although cannons were introduced as fighter plane armament in time for World War II, American aircraft designers generally favored the .50 caliber Browning with its faster rate of fire. Except for the Airacobra, which had a nose-mounted 37 millimeter cannon, American aerial cannons used in World War II were usually 20mm.

As early as 1915, experiments were made with free-flight rockets fired from aircraft, but reliability and performance were not improved enough to be practical until late World War II. After the war, the five-inch High Velocity Aerial Rocket (HVAR) was perfected; by 1950, the potent 2.75-inch Folding Fin Aerial Rocket (FFAR), known as "Mighty Mouse," was introduced. Both HVAR and FFAR were unguided rockets; they were carried in pods and fired in salvos. The AIR-2 Genie air-intercept rocket, larger but also unguided, came next. Some Genies were configured to carry a small nuclear warhead.

By the early 1950s, new electronics technology had made guided missiles possible. These new weapons were called "missiles" to distinguish them from unguided rockets. The first air-intercept missile was the AIM-4 Falcon, followed by the AIM-7 Sparrow and the AIM-9 Sidewinder. All were capable of speeds of roughly Mach 2 and were accurate up to 15 miles. The Sparrow and Sidewinder were used extensively in Vietnam and are still in production today.

Air-to-air missiles extend and enhance the ability of the modern fighter to do its job. Originally, air-to-air missiles were thought to be the only weapons fighters would ever need. Many fighters, such as the F-102, the F-106, and even the original F-4 Phantom II, were designed without provision for guns. But American fighter pilots discovered during the Vietnam War that dogfights did not take place at Mach 2 but at the same speeds as they had during the Second World War.

"Tight squeeze. . . MiG in sight. . . too close for a Sidewinder. . . . Oh, my kingdom for a Browning!" was the heartfelt prayer of pilots caught in a dogfight over North Vietnam.

Jets were retrofitted with 20mm cannons, and pilots were retrained in aerial combat techniques. A study done by the Air Force during the last year of the war showed that air-to-air missiles had a one-in-ten chance of scoring a kill, while 20mm cannon fire had a five-in-ten likelihood of killing an enemy aircraft.

Between the two world wars, fighter aircraft speeds increased from less than 200 miles per hour to more than 400 miles per hour. Turbo superchargers helped piston-engine aircraft fly higher than anyone had ever dreamed. And when jet fighters became operational, both speed and altitude capability improved again. Only four years after the first jet fighters became operational, they were flying faster than the speed of sound.

In the late 1950s, it was believed speed and altitude were everything. Again the Vietnam War proved this wrong. Maneuverability, not speed, became paramount. As a result, all Mach 3 fighters on the drawing board were canceled. Today's fighters can fly at Mach 2, but only to get to the aerial combat arena. Dogfights still take place at World War II speeds.

American fighters are distributed among the Navy, Marine Corps, and Air Force. The Navy has 14 operational aircraft carriers; each carrier contains an air wing with two fighter squadrons of F-14 Tomcats. Four of these carrier air wings also have one or two fighter-bomber squadrons of F/A-18 Hornets. The Marine Corps has a dozen fighter squadrons, about half with F/A-18s and the rest with F-4s. The Air Force has 12 major commands: six flying commands and six support commands. Four of the flying commands operate nearly 80 fighter squadrons: Tactical Air Command (based in the continental United States), Alaskan Air Command, U.S. Air Forces in Europe, and Pacific Air Forces. These fighter squadrons are backed by 48 Air National Guard and 11 Air Force Reserve squadrons. The Navy and Marines have nearly 500 F-14s and F/A-18s; the Air Force, Air Guard, and Air Force Reserves have nearly 2,000 F-15s and F-16s.

The next generation of fighters is taking shape. These new fighters will be flown by pilots who hope they will never have to kill enemy fighters. But these pilots will know that, if push comes to shove, they will have the aircraft to do the job.

Opposite: *These F-16s of the South Carolina Air Guard form the first line of defense against manned bombers.* Above: *The F/A-18 Hornet can handle a wide variety of weapons. This Hornet carries Sidewinder missiles (wingtips) and Harpoon antiship missiles (wings, inboard) in addition to its 20mm gun mounted in the nose.*

F-4 Phantom II

The F-4 Phantom was originally intended as a Navy attack aircraft in the early 1950s. Nearly 40 years later, the Phantom is still one of America's most important fighter aircraft. Nearly all enemy aircraft shot down during the Vietnam War were claimed by Phantom crews. The only five American pilots to become aces in the last 35 years did so in Phantom jets.

McDonnell Douglas Aircraft of St. Louis, Missouri, built the U.S. Navy's first carrier-based jet fighter, the FH-1 Phantom, in 1946. By 1954, McDonnell Douglas had added two other fighters—the F2H Banshee and F3H Demon—to the Navy's list. During the Korean War, the Navy saw a need for a carrier-based attack bomber, which would be designated AH-1. By 1955, when the new AH-1 was ready, the Navy had changed its mind and requested that the St. Louis plane maker reconfigure the AH-1 as a fighter. Redesignated F4H, the new plane was called the Phantom II.

The first of 696 F4Hs entered Navy service in 1961. In January 1962, the Air Force ordered 635 Phantoms under the F-110 designation. In September of 1962, Air Force and Navy numbering systems were merged; the Navy's F4H Phantoms were redesignated F-4A and F-4B, while Air Force Phantoms were redesignated F-4C. In 1964, the Air Force ordered 703 F-4Ds, which came equipped with a more powerful radar system. Air Force Phantoms were sent to Vietnam early the following year and scored their first aerial victories in July 1965.

It was during the Phantom's baptism of fire in Southeast Asia that a major shortcoming in the aircraft's armament was discovered. In the 1950s, when the plane had evolved, it was thought that all fighters should be equipped with air-to-air missiles rather than guns. But in the skies over Vietnam, air crews discovered that during close-in dogfights the missiles did not have time to arm themselves. The Air Force F-4Ds were hastily retrofitted with 20 millimeter cannon pods.

To improve combat superiority, the F-4E, designed in 1967, included an internally mounted 20mm cannon. The Air Force bought over 1,000 F-4Es. Unlike most fighters, the Phantom carries a crew of two, the pilot in the forward cockpit and the weapons system operator behind. The presence of the backseater aided in the adaptation of the Phantom to various configurations, including the RF-4C, the fighter-bomber, and the F-4G "Wild Weasel" antiradar.

The RF-4C, a variation of the F-4C, entered service in 1964 as a reconnaissance aircraft. Today, RF-4Cs are still configured to carry state-of-the-art reconnaissance equipment, including infrared target-locating sensors and electro-optical sensors in place of optical cameras. The F-4G "Wild Weasel" is a special Phantom configured as an antiradar plane. Other specialized Phantoms have been developed for West Germany (F-4F) and the United Kingdom (F-4K and F-4M).

Although the F-4 Phantom II is no longer a first-line air-superiority fighter, a great many of the more than 5,000 Phantoms that McDonnell Douglas built are still in service as fighters around the world. The venerable F-4 remains on active duty in the United States with Reserve and Air Guard units. The Phantom's versatility means that this venerable aircraft will remain in service with the Air Force, Navy, and Marine Corps until at least the turn of the century.

Above: *The venerable F-4 Phantom II has been in service with the U.S. Air Force, Navy, and Marines since 1960.* Right, top: *Ground crew members load a Sidewinder air-to-air missile aboard a Phantom II.* Right, bottom: *An F-4 Phantom II takes off from a U.S. aircraft carrier near the coast of Vietnam.*

McDONNELL DOUGLAS F-4E PHANTOM II

Wingspan:	38 ft., 5 in.
Length:	63 ft.
Height:	16 ft., 6 in.
Weight (maximum take-off):	58,000 lbs.
Engines:	Two General Electric J79-GE-17
Engine thrust:	17,900 lbs.
Operating altitude:	59,200 ft.
Top speed:	1,464 mph
Maximum range:	1,885 miles
Date of service:	1961

These F-4G Phantom II Wild Weasels from the 37th Tactical Fighter Wing, George Air Force Base, California, hunt for antiaircraft missile complexes.

WW

F-14 Tomcat

The F-14 Tomcat was designed as a fleet air-defense interceptor capable of serving into the 21st century. The Tomcat is the latest in a long line of Grumman "carrier cats" that date back to before World War II. In the infamous "Marianas Turkey Shoot" of June 19, 1944, United States Navy fighters ambushed a huge Japanese air armada and destroyed over 400 warplanes, it was the Grumman-designed-and-built Hellcat that did the lion's share of the shooting. Almost 40 years later, over the Gulf of Sidra in the Mediterranean Sea on August 19, 1981, a pair of F-14 Tomcats shot down two Libyan MiG-23s attempting to attack the USS *Nimitz.*

The F-14 evolved in the late 1960s, when the U.S. Navy dropped out of the multiservice, multipurpose TFX (tactical fighter, experimental) program and began work on an aircraft dedicated solely to fleet air defense. Since the F-14 was being developed by Grumman, it would be a "Cat," and since the man behind the project was Admiral Tom Connolly, then Deputy Chief of Naval Operations for Air, the new airplane was instantly called "Tom's Cat."

The Tomcat first flew in 1970. Four years later the first two F-14 carrier squadrons—VF-1 Wolfpack and VF-2 Bounty Hunters—became operational aboard the USS *Enterprise*. Nearly 400 Tomcats are operational today on U.S. Navy carriers throughout the world.

Like the TFX, which became the Air Force's F-111, the F-14 Tomcat has variable-geometry wings that can change shape in flight to match altitude conditions and speed needs. The wings may be swept forward to a nearly straight position for slow-speed operations like aircraft carrier landings, or swept back for such high-speed operations as supersonic dashes to catch enemy aircraft.

The Tomcat is a *big* but agile aircraft—a joy to handle according to its pilots. The F-14 is capable of out-turning and out-maneuvering the smaller and older F-4 Phantom. Like the Phantom, the Tomcat carries a crew of two. Like the F-4's weapons system operator, the Tomcat backseater operates the complex offensive radar and weapons systems. In terms of weaponry, the Tomcat—like all of America's post-Vietnam fighters—is armed with a 20 millimeter cannon, as well as an assortment of guided missiles. The latter includes the AIM-9 Sidewinder and the new AIM-120 AMRAAM. But the centerpiece of the Tomcat arsenal is its array of six AIM-54 Phoenix air-to-air missiles. The Phoenix was designed for, and is unique to, the F-14. Developed by Hughes Aircraft at the same time that Grumman was developing the Tomcat, the Phoenix has the longest range—over 100 miles—of any air-to-air missile in U.S. service. The combined range capability of the Tomcat and Phoenix means that enemy aircraft armed with antiship missiles could, theoretically, be intercepted and shot down before they could get close enough to endanger the American fleet.

The F-14 Tomcat is such a powerful, agile bird that few enemies have dared to knock the chip off the Tomcat's shoulder.

Below: *The F-14 Tomcat is the U.S. Navy's number one air-superiority fighter.* Right, top: *The F-14 Tomcat has been in service with the U.S. Navy since 1972.* Right, bottom: *The F-14 carries a crew of two: the pilot and a weapons officer, called a tactical air coordinator, or Taco.*

GRUMMAN F-14A TOMCAT

Wingspan (unswept):	64 ft., 1.5 in.
Wingspan (swept):	38 ft., 2.5 in.
Length:	62 ft., 8 in.
Height:	16 ft.
Weight (maximum take-off):	74,349 lbs.
Engines:	Two Pratt & Whitney TF30-P-414A turbofans
Engine thrust:	20,900 lbs.
Operating altitude:	50,000+ ft.
Top speed:	1,544 mph
Maximum range:	2,000 miles
Date of service:	1972

Two F-14 Tomcats from the aircraft carrier USS Enterprise *prowl the skies on routine patrol. They belong to the Black Lion Squadron (VF 213).*

F-15 Eagle

The F-15 Eagle is the best air-superiority fighter in the world. Some people may take exception to that notion, but certainly none of them could have been anywhere near Lebanon's Bekáa valley in June 1982, when Israeli F-15s tackled the best Soviet-built fighters in the Syrian Air Force and smoked 80 of them at no loss to themselves. Nowhere is the prowess of the Eagle better known than among the pilots who fly them, which is why "Eagle drivers" are frequently known as "ego drivers."

The F-15 is to the U.S. Air Force what the F-14 is to the U.S. Navy: the leading edge of fighter technology as defined by the mission requirements of that particular service. The F-15 flies from a multitude of places, but its pilots must always be ready to fly from unfamiliar fields. Air Force F-15s are based within striking distance of potential world conflict. They are stationed in Germany and Iceland as an integral part of the American commitment to NATO, and in Okinawa, where they provide air-defense coverage for South Korea and Japan. In Alaska they fly for the Air Force's Alaskan Air Command (AAC).

The 5,000-mile arc defended by the AAC is no idle venue when Soviet bomber bases are just 30 minutes flying time away. During 1987 and the first part of 1988, for example, the Soviet Air Force ran nuclear-strike training missions against Alaska at the rate of more than one per week, compared with less than once a month in the years before Mikhail Gorbachev took over as premier. These forays became cat-and-mouse exercises in which AAC Eagles had to intercept Soviet Tu-95 Bear bombers before they reached U.S. territory.

The missions flown by AAC Eagle drivers are exactly what the Air Force had in mind when it set out to develop a follow-up to the F-4 Phantom. The idea was to take everything that had been learned in air-to-air combat in Vietnam, add the best that modern emerging electronics technology had to offer, and build the best possible fighter to fulfill the Air Force mission. The first Eagles flew in July 1972, and the first F-15As entered squadron service four years later. The F-15C followed in 1979. By the early 1980s, Eagles had already begun to replace the F-4 Phantoms as the Air Force's first-line fighters.

Unlike the F-4, the F-15 has a crew of only one; the role of the backseater is taken over by a high-speed computer. Two-seat combat-capable F-15B and F-15D trainers do exist but, for the most part, the Eagle pilots fly alone.

The Eagle's armament includes a 20 millimeter cannon and AIM-7 Sparrow, AIM-9 Sidewinder, and AIM-120 AMRAAM air-to-air missiles. In 1984, two squadrons of F-15s were experimentally equipped with the ALMV/ASAT, a two-stage missile that could be fired into space to destroy satellites. After a successful test in 1985, Congress banned further testing of the system.

In 1987, the Air Force began taking deliveries of the F-15E, a long-range, two-seat fighter-bomber based on the F-15D. The speed and maneuverability of the Eagle made it the ideal airframe to adapt as the 21st century replacement for the aging F-111 fighter-bomber fleet. While the onrush of aviation technology will probably see the F-15C replaced as the Air Force's top air-superiority fighter by the turn of the century, the F-15E will probably be flying for another quarter century.

Above: *Pilots of F-15 Eagles must be highly skilled; two F-15 Eagles fly in close formation.* Right, top: *F-15 Eagles cross an Alaskan fjord on routine patrol. Note the AIM-120 air-to-air missiles on their inboard wing pylons.* Right, bottom: *Pilots love to barrel their F-15s down a canyon. The rock walls hide the jets from radar detection.*

McDONNELL DOUGLAS F-15C EAGLE

Wingspan:	42 ft., 9.75 in.
Length:	63 ft., 9 in.
Height:	18 ft., 5.5 in.
Weight (maximum take-off):	68,000 lbs.
Engines:	Two Pratt & Whitney F100-PW-100 turbofans
Engine thrust:	23,830 lbs.
Operating altitude:	60,000 ft.
Top speed:	Mach 2.5+
Maximum range:	3,570 miles
Date of service:	1974

Equipped with the AIM-7 Sparrow, the F-15 is the Air Force's top air-superiority fighter.

AF
76
119

F-16 Fighting Falcon

Named after the mascot of the U.S. Air Force Academy at Colorado Springs, Colorado, the F-16 is in service with 14 nations around the world as well as the U.S. Navy.

The idea behind the F-16 was to build a large number of lightweight, low-cost fighters to augment the squadrons of larger, more expensive (albeit more capable) F-15s. Several NATO countries were also shopping for such a plane to replace the Lockheed F-104. The new aircraft was to be coproduced by American and European factories as a NATO fighter. In 1974, the Air Force conducted a fly-off between the General Dynamics YF-16 and the Northrop YF-17 aircraft and picked the former.

The primary F-16 assembly line is at the General Dynamics plant in Fort Worth, Texas, but in 1978, European factories were opened by SONACA/SABCA in Belgium and by Fokker in the Netherlands. The first F-16 squadron was activated by the U.S. Air Force in 1979, and soon they were active in Belgium, Denmark, Norway, and the Netherlands, as planned when the program was launched. Israel was the next country to acquire the F-16, which had them in service as fighter-bombers in June 1981 when they were used to destroy the Iraqi nuclear plant at Osirak.

The Falcon is a jack-of-all-trades. Swift and agile yet capable of carrying heavy bomb loads, F-16s serve primarily as interceptors or fighter-bombers. And the U.S. Navy has selected the F-16 as an "aggressor" aircraft to be used in its realistic Top Gun air-combat training exercises.

To pilots familiar with older airplanes, such as the F-4, the Falcon is a pleasant surprise. Its control surfaces are entirely fly-by-wire, meaning that the work usually done by hydraulics is done in the F-16 by a computerized network of electric motors. This makes the F-16 much more responsive and has led to its nickname: "The Electric Jet."

Above: *The F-16 is a multirole, air-combat fighter that also has advanced capability as a ground-attack jet.*

Like its sister ship, the larger F-15, the F-16 Falcon is a one-seat aircraft, although a number of combat-capable two-seaters have been built that function as training aircraft. In its various combat configurations, the Falcon can carry the AIM-9 Sidewinder and AIM-120 AMRAAM air-to-air missiles in its interceptor mode. The Falcon can also carry a variety of air-to-ground ordnance in its fighter-bomber role. Air-to-ground ordnance includes conventional and nuclear bombs, the AGM-65 Maverick rocket, and the AGM-45 Shrike and AGM-88 HARM antiradar missiles. Like all post-Vietnam American fighters, the F-16 is also equipped with a 20 millimeter cannon.

The "Electric Jet" is a pilot's airplane. It is designed to function almost as an extension of the pilot's mind and hand, from the fly-by-wire avionics (the electrical devices and systems that control the

aircraft) to the cockpit canopy that is designed for an absolutely unobstructed forward view. While the contoured lines and advanced digital technology of the F-16 make it seem like something out of a science fiction movie, its selection for the Advanced Fighter Technology Integration program represents a merger of science fiction and reality. The Falcon provides a window on fighter technology of the 21st century.

GENERAL DYNAMICS F-16 FIGHTING FALCON

Wingspan:	31 ft.
Length:	49 ft., 3 in.
Height:	16 ft., 8.5 in.
Weight (maximum take-off):	37,500 lbs.
Engine:	One Pratt & Whitney F-100-PW-200 turbofan
Engine thrust:	25,000 lbs.
Operating altitude:	50,000 ft.
Top speed:	Mach 2+
Maximum range:	2,415 miles
Date of service:	1978

Above: *This F-16 belongs to the 474th Tactical Fighter Wing, based at Nellis Air Force Base, Nevada. Pilots and aircraft from the 474th form the Aggressor Air Force during Red Flag exercises.*

The F-16 Fighting Falcon is powered by a Pratt & Whitney F-100-PW-200 turbofan and can reach speeds of 1,305 miles per hour.

F/A-18 Hornet

The F/A-18 Hornet evolved from the Northrop YF-17, which was rejected by the Air Force in favor of the YF-16. The Hornet is the U.S. Navy's close-in air-superiority fighter that defends aircraft carrier task forces. The Hornet is the Marine Corps' premier attack aircraft, supporting its ground forces. Whether used by the Navy or the Marine Corps, the Hornet is the same plane; the "F" and "A" designations simply describe its role as a fighter jet or an attack jet.

The Hornet is a small, relatively low-cost, twin-engine jet aircraft, which makes it appealing to the Navy and Marines. The F/A-18 Hornet first flew in November of 1978 but did not officially enter service until 1983. Australia and Canada also selected the Hornet because of its low cost and versatility. Another factor in Canada's choice of the Hornet (designated CF-18) was that Canada—like the U.S. Navy—uses the "hose & drogue" method of aerial refueling, rather than the "flying boom" method used by the U.S. Air Force. (For more information on refueling methods, see Aerial Tankers.)

The Hornet's armament includes a 20 millimeter cannon mounted on the top center of the nose. This mounting differs from the F-14, F-15, and F-16, which mount the cannon on the side of the fuselage. In its fighter configuration, the Hornet, like the Falcon, carries AIM-9 Sidewinder air-to-air missiles on wingtip racks. Other weapons, such as the AIM-7 Sparrow, are carried underwing. For attack/fighter-bomber missions, the F/A-18 Hornet's armorer can select from conventional or nuclear bombs and AGM-88 HARM antiradar missiles or AGM-65 Maverick air-to-ground missiles. For its naval attack mission, the Hornet can also carry the AGM-109 Harpoon, a sea-skimming, antiship missile, which is the Navy equivalent of the French-built Exocet.

When projecting the future role of the Hornet, the Marine Corps motto "First to Fight" comes to mind. The Navy and the Marine Corps are the leading edge of American military power worldwide. If push comes to shove and the United States must "send in the Marines," the F/A-18 will be leading the way.

Below: *The F/A-18 Hornet flies at speeds in excess of 1,100 miles per hour.* Right, top: *The F/A-18 was designed to fill the carrier air patrol role, as well as provide ground support for the Marines.* Right, bottom: *An F/A-18 Hornet lands on the USS* America *during trials in late 1979.*

McDONNELL DOUGLAS F/A-18 HORNET

Wingspan:	37 ft., 6 in.
Length:	56 ft.
Height:	15 ft., 3.5 in.
Weight (maximum take-off):	36,710 lbs.
Engines:	Two General Electric F404-GE-400 turbofans
Engine thrust:	16,000 lbs.
Operating altitude:	50,000 ft.
Top speed:	Mach 1.8+
Maximum range:	2,303 miles
Date of service:	1983

An F/A-18 Hornet takes part in Top Gun exercises over the California desert.

ATTACK PLANES

Attack aircraft are servants of surface forces and are designed specifically for that role. (The term "surface" is used because attack aircraft operate against both land and sea targets.) Air Force attack aircraft support infantry and armored units. The Navy's carrier-based attack planes are responsible for bombarding land targets for Marine Corps operations ashore and for attacking enemy ships or submarines in support of friendly vessels or on-shore positions.

The attack role takes three forms. The first is *close air support,* where the aircraft is within a one-mile radius (or less) of the troops it's supporting. The second is *battlefield interdiction,* where the aircraft attack targets that are in the general area but are not yet engaged with friendly forces. The third is *deep interdiction,* where an attack bomber may fly up to 500 miles into enemy territory to attack targets, such as bridges, airfields, and traffic choke-points, which may not have an immediate relation to the current battle, but whose destruction can prevent reinforcements from reaching the battlefield. Deep interdiction is a role attack planes share with bombers.

Generally, attack planes are the slowest of combat aircraft, although there are exceptions. But pound for pound, attack planes generally carry the greatest weapons load. This load can include air-to-ground ordnance ranging from simple high-explosive bombs to complex radar-guided "smart" bombs or special delayed-action munitions specifically designed to destroy thick concrete bunkers or put deep craters in runways. Air-to-ground missiles (AGM) are also part of the arsenal, and each missile is tailored to a particular task. The AGM-65 Maverick, for example, is a basic "fire-and-forget" missile equipped with either a television guidance system or an imaging infrared seeker. Maverick is designed to take out specific targets with a higher degree of pinpoint accuracy than possible with a "dumb" iron bomb, or even a smart bomb.

A second type of AGM is the anti-radiation, or antiradar, missile (ARM), which can seek out radar sites and surface-to-air missile sites that use radar to guide their antiaircraft missiles. The original AGM-45 Shrike of the Vietnam era is still in service, complemented by the newer AGM-88 HARM (High Speed ARM) and the AGM-136 Tacit Rainbow. Initially developed for use by surface ships against other surface ships, the versatile RGM/AGM-84 Harpoon has evolved into both a submarine-launched and air-launched antiship missile.

Attack squadron organization parallels that of fighter squadrons. Each of the Navy's 14 carriers has a carrier air wing with at least two fighter squadrons (VF) and one to three attack squadrons (VA) that fly either A-6s or A-7s. Some air wings are being transformed into strike-fighter squadrons (VFA), which are organized around the F/A-18 Hornet. There are also reserve and training VAs and VFAs at naval air stations ashore. The Marine Corps has 13 active attack squadrons, which fly A-4s, A-6s, and AV-8s.

The Air Force has designated its attack squadrons as fighter squadrons and has distributed them throughout the world as part of the four tactical combat commands: Tactical Air Command (TAC), Alaskan Air Command (AAC), U.S. Air Forces in Europe (USAFE), and the Pacific Air Forces (PACAF). Of the approximately 500 attack planes in the Air Force, 90 percent are A-10s, while 70 percent of those in the Air National Guard and the Air Force Reserve are A-7s and the remainder A-10s.

It is axiomatic in modern warfare that air power is a vital component of any winning team. There is no phase of modern warfare where air power/land power teamwork is more evident or more important than the attack role.

Opposite: *The AV-8B Harrier II is an attack jet that can take off and land vertically.* Left: *The A-10 Thunderbolt II attack plane has been nicknamed the Warthog.* Below: *The A-4 Skyhawk, one of the most successful attack jets ever in U.S. military inventory, entered service in 1954. It still flies with the Marine Corps today.*

A-4 Skyhawk

Since it was to be based on aircraft carriers, the A-4 Skyhawk was designed to carry the maximum weapons load for the minimum weight and size. Designed by the Douglas Aircraft Company's famed Ed Heinemann, the "Hot Rod," as the A-4 was quickly nicknamed, first flew under the A-4D designation in 1954. In 1962, the A-4D was redesignated the A-4. The aircraft weighed four tons empty, but it could *carry* three tons of weapons, including nuclear bombs. In production for an incredible quarter of a century, a total of 2,960 Skyhawks rolled off the Douglas assembly line before production ceased.

In August 1964, when American destroyers were attacked by North Vietnamese patrol boats, A-4s were among the first American aircraft to participate in the counterstrike. Skyhawks continued to play an important role as part of the U.S. Navy strike force throughout the duration of the war against North Vietnam.

Still in service today with U.S. Marine attack squadrons, the Skyhawk remains a tireless, heavy-hitting war bird. Equipped with a 20 millimeter cannon and AIM-9 Sidewinders for air defense, the A-4 can also carry a variety of air-to-ground munitions as part of its three-ton load. These include "iron" bombs, radar-guided "smart" bombs, AGM-62 Walleye television-guided missiles, and AGM-65 Mavericks. It also carries launchers for unguided 2.75-inch rockets. A-4s can refuel one another in flight.

After seeing nearly a decade of combat in Vietnam, the A-4 continued in U.S. Navy service until 1987, during which time Skyhawks were assigned to be used by the Navy's world-renowned Blue Angels.

In almost any other context, it would be hard to imagine an attack plane being part of an aerobatic team like the Blue Angels. However, because of the Skyhawk's stunning maneuverability, there is little to wonder about; it is easy to picture how and why these remarkable little planes have been so effective for so many air services for so many years.

Below: *The Skyhawk was designed as a carrier-based aircraft for the Navy and Marine Corps.* Right, top: *The A-4 is half the weight of the original 1954 Navy specification for a new carrier-based attack jet.* Right, bottom: *The A-4M Skyhawk can be identified by the large hump aft of the cockpit that houses the Angle Rate Bombing System that makes the plane an extremely accurate bombing aircraft.*

DOUGLAS A-4F SKYHAWK	
Wingspan:	27 ft., 6 in.
Length:	41 ft., 4 in.
Height:	15 ft.
Weight (maximum take-off):	24,500 lbs.
Engine:	One Pratt & Whitney J52-P8A turbojet
Engine thrust:	9,300 lbs.
Operating altitude:	58,600 ft.
Top speed:	646 mph (loaded)
Maximum range:	2,000 miles
Date of service:	1956

586
NAVY
NP
VA55

ARBS
Smart Hawk
RESCUE
DANGER
MARINES

A-6 Intruder

The A-6 Intruder grew out of the Navy's need for an all-weather attack plane with an eight-ton bomb load that could support both Navy and Marine Corps operations. Built by Grumman, the preeminent builder of American carrier-based aircraft for the last half century, the Intruder was first flown in April 1960. Today, new Intruder acquisitions are still part of the Navy's budget.

The basic version was the A-6A, of which 484 were built. Many of these, in turn, were converted or adapted for roles other than ground attack, including 58 that were converted to KA-6D aerial tankers. Today, the A-6E is the U.S. Navy's standard medium-attack aircraft and carries a nine-ton bomb load.

The A-6E was born in 1970 as a converted A-6A. Eventually, more than 300 new A-6Es were ordered. This variant evolved into the A-6E/TRAM (Target Recognition and Attack Multisensor) standard by 1980, to which all previous A-6Es were converted and to which all current production types have been built. TRAM's electronics are carried in a turret located under the nose and include infrared- and laser-targeting sensors and multimode radar. The lasers are used in conjunction with laser-guided weapons. The TRAM system is multifaceted in that an A-6E can illuminate a target with its laser while a second A-6E launches its weapons against it, using the first A-6E's laser to guide the projectile. In addition to laser-guided munitions, the A-6E can carry "iron" bombs and AGM-84 Harpoon antiship missiles. The A-6E can also pack AIM-9 Sidewinders to defend itself from hostile aircraft.

A second major A-6 variant in service with the U.S. Navy today is the EA-6B. This electronic warfare version, called Prowler, accompanies A-6E strike forces and uses highly sophisticated electronics to jam enemy radar.

The Intruder carries its crew of two in a side-by-side seating arrangement typical of much larger planes. The pilot occupies the left seat, with the weapons system operator/navigator on the right. In order to accommodate an additional pair of crew members who operate the electronic countermeasures hardware, the Prowler is five feet longer than the Intruder.

Attack missions flown by Intruders against targets protected by radar-directed missiles—especially enemy surface ships—would include a Prowler to confuse the enemy and give the A-6Es a chance to slip in and do their work. The Intruder/Prowler team, because they use the same basic aircraft, are an ideal carrier-borne combination from the standpoint of maintenance as well as operations.

Top: *The A-6 Intruder's wings fold up for compact storage on the cramped quarters of an aircraft carrier.* Bottom: *The A-6E Intruder is the Navy's all-weather, day/night medium-attack aircraft.*

GRUMMAN A-6E INTRUDER	
Wingspan:	53 ft.
Length:	54 ft., 9 in.
Height:	16 ft., 2 in.
Weight (maximum take-off):	60,400 lbs.
Engines:	Two Pratt & Whitney J52-P-8B turbojets
Engine thrust:	9,300 lbs.
Operating altitude:	42,400 ft.
Top speed:	806 mph
Maximum range:	2,740 miles
Date of service:	1963

Below: *More than 700 Intruders of all configurations have been built, and production continues today.*

The two-seat A-6E Intruder can carry up to 30 500-pound bombs.

02
KC
157003
VMAT (AW) 202
MARINES

A-7 Corsair II

The A-7 Corsair II's older cousin was the Vought F8U Crusader, which served as one of the Navy's top carrier fighters before and during the Vietnam War. Aside from the F-4 Phantom II, Crusaders claimed more enemy MiGs in Vietnam than any other American aircraft.

The Corsair II was built as a light attack plane to complement the Navy's A-4 Skyhawk. Vought, which had merged with Ling-Temco in 1961, won the contract by suggesting a compact, scaled-down aircraft based on the F-8. Even as A-7 deliveries to the Navy were getting under way, the Air Force was discovering that it had a need for attack aircraft in Vietnam that could not be fully met by fighter-bombers. The Air Force decided to join the Navy program and acquire A-7s as well.

The first Corsair II mission in Vietnam was flown by Navy A-7As from the USS *Ranger* in December 1967, and the last was actually the final American combat mission of the war, flown by Air Force A-7Ds against targets in Cambodia on August 15, 1973. The A-7 proved to be a very reliable, stable performer. The Air Force, for example, flew 12,928 Corsair II missions in Southeast Asia—including many against targets in heavily defended North Vietnam—with only four losses.

The Corsair II is a single-seat aircraft, although 60 of them have been converted to two-seat combat-capable trainers that could be used in the attack role in an emergency. The aircraft's armament consists of nearly eight tons of bombs, and AGM-65 Maverick and AGM-88 HARM missiles or AIM-9 Sidewinder air-to-air missiles for self-defense. For general all-around use, Corsair IIs carry a 20 millimeter cannon.

Today, Corsair IIs remain the principal component in U.S. Navy carrier-based light attack squadrons, having replaced the A-4 Skyhawk. On the Air Force side, A-7s are now used by the Air National Guard, which furnishes 70 percent of the nation's air-defense and ground attack capability. The A-7 equips more Guard units than any other combat aircraft. Despite the Corsair II's age, the A-7's durability will almost certainly make it a valuable asset for years to come.

Below: *The A-7 Corsair II has been flown by the Air Force, Navy, and Marine Corps. Shown here is an Air Force A-7D.* Right, top: *The A-7 Corsair II, now being replaced by the F/A-18 Hornet, was a workhorse for the Navy during the Vietnam War.* Right, bottom: *The Corsair II carries a 20mm Gatling gun in its nose.*

LING-TEMCO-VOUGHT A-7E CORSAIR II

Wingspan:	38 ft., 9 in.
Length:	46 ft., 1.5 in.
Height:	16 ft., 0.75 in.
Weight (maximum take-off):	42,000 lbs.
Engine:	One Allison TF41-A-2 turbofan
Engine thrust:	15,000 lbs.
Operating altitude:	37,910 ft.
Top speed:	691 mph
Maximum range:	2,861 miles
Date of service:	1966

The A-7 Corsair II can be equipped with the Sidewinder missile or up to 15,000 pounds of bombs.

06
00
306
NAVY
01
NAVY

A-10 Thunderbolt II

Above: *The A-10 Thunderbolt II looks as tough on the ground as it does in the air.*

Nobody calls the A-10 the "Thunderbolt." Even its friends call it the "Warthog." Ugly and misshapen though it may be, it is the nastiest ground-attack aircraft in any nation's air force.

The A-10 can unleash a withering thunderbolt of destructive power, which is its sole reason for existence. The Vietnam War made clear the need for a ground-attack/close support aircraft. In Vietnam, the Air Force was forced to use a combination of World War II aircraft, converted trainers, fighter-bombers, and borrowed Navy fighters for the task. So, in 1972 the Air Force considered both the Northrop A-9 and the Fairchild Republic A-10 aircraft, and chose to put the A-10 into full-scale squadron service. The last of 713 Warthogs was delivered in 1984.

Today, Warthogs are in service with the Tactical Air Command and with Air Guard and Reserve units in the continental United States, as well as with Air Force units in Korea and Alaska. The largest concentration of A-10s, however, is in western Europe, where they form an integral part of any resistance to an invasion by Warsaw Pact forces.

The Warthog is one of the "hardest" aircraft flying. The pilot sits in a titanium-armor "bathtub" that can withstand incoming rounds from 23 millimeter cannons. Control lines are duplicated and stretched through widely separate parts of the aircraft. The heavily armored engines are located high and to the rear of the fuselage for maximum shielding from ground-launched heat-seeking missiles. The A-10 can fly on one of its engines or with half its tail shot away.

The offensive characteristics of the Warthog are equally impressive and have earned it the additional nickname of "tank-buster." The centerpiece of the A-10's suite of armaments is the huge GAU-8 Avenger 30mm rotary cannon. The largest forward-firing aerial cannon in the Air Force, the seven-barrel Avenger packs nearly 1,200 rounds of extra-long (six-inch), extra-potent, high-velocity slugs with depleted uranium tips. Depleted uranium is no longer radioactive and is used because it is heavier than lead or steel and thus will slam its way through a thicker slab of armor plate. The Avenger is, by itself, capable of taking out an enemy battle tank. Indeed, the simplicity of its rounds makes the Avenger more reliable than many other antitank weapons.

In addition to its Avenger, the A-10 can carry eight tons of air-to-ground munitions, from "iron" bombs to "smart" bombs and cluster bombs to AGM-65 Mavericks. Electronic countermeasures equipment can also be carried on the A-10's eight underwing pylons, as can AIM-9 Sidewinders for defense against hostile aircraft.

Left: *The Warthog can carry a maximum weight of 28,480 pounds of fuel, ammunition, bombs, and rockets.* Below: *In response to increasingly advanced Soviet antiaircraft defenses, the A-10's avionics, as reflected by the complexity of the cockpit, have grown more sophisticated since the aircraft entered service.*

FAIRCHILD REPUBLIC A-10A THUNDERBOLT II	
Wingspan:	57 ft., 6 in.
Length:	53 ft., 4 in.
Height:	14 ft., 8 in.
Weight (maximum take-off):	50,000 lbs.
Engines:	Two General Electric TF34-GE-100 turbofans
Engine thrust:	9,065 lbs.
Operating altitude:	37,800 ft.
Top speed:	439 mph
Maximum range:	2,454 miles
Date of service:	1975

Above: *The A-10 Thunderbolt's main task is tank busting. Its nose-mounted 30mm cannon can punch through the armor of any main battle tank today.*

AV-8B Harrier II

Soon after World War II, a number of nations began to develop a vertical takeoff and landing (VTOL) combat aircraft that could operate like a helicopter with fixed wing performance. Success was achieved in 1960 by Hawker aircraft in England, with the test flight of their Model P.1127. Produced as the Kestrel, its performance did not live up to expectations. But it was the first operational VTOL aircraft in the world.

By 1968, the Kestrel had evolved into the Harrier, a more practical and versatile VTOL aircraft. The following year, Royal Air Force Harriers took part in the *Daily Mail* London–New York air race. Although their six-hour time did not set any speed records, it was presentable. More importantly, the Harriers were the only planes in the race to land *in* Manhattan.

The U.S. Marine Corps was very interested in using VTOL aircraft for close air support of amphibious operations. A VTOL aircraft could be based on assault ships as well as aircraft carriers. The Marines ordered 110 Harriers, which entered service in 1971 as the AV-8A Harrier. In 1975, McDonnell Douglas developed an improved Harrier; a larger wing nearly doubled the aircraft's range and payload. By 1982, a joint manufacturing agreement had been worked out between British Aerospace (which had absorbed Hawker) and McDonnell Douglas whereby the American company would produce the up-rated VTOL aircraft as the AV-8B Harrier II. The Marine Corps AV-8B can be armed with a 25 millimeter cannon, a four-ton bomb load, or a variety of guided air-to-ground munitions, as well as the AIM-9 Sidewinder air-to-air missile.

In April 1982, Argentina invaded the British-owned Falkland Islands. The Harrier "jump jets" of the Royal Navy and Air Force were the only fixed wing air combat element the British could bring to the area. These Harriers flew more than 2,000 attack missions and in the fighter role, shot down at least 20 enemy aircraft without a single loss.

Today's U.S. Marine Corps AV-8B Harriers would fly and fight in much the same way the British Harriers did in the Falklands: in support of a joint Navy/Marines amphibious assault landing or in the context of Marine operations ashore.

Below: *The AV-8B Harrier II derives from the original British Harrier, which served with distinction during the Falkland Islands War in 1982.*

Left: *The Harrier II's ability to take off and land vertically allows it to be serviced and maintained within a few miles of the forward edge of the battle; thus, massive, swift ground support can be launched within minutes.*
Below: *The AV-8B is flown by the Marine Corps. It will replace the A-4 Skyhawk in eight Marine squadrons.*

McDONNELL DOUGLAS AV-8B HARRIER II

Wingspan:	30 ft., 3.5 in.
Length:	42 ft., 10 in.
Height:	11 ft., 3.5 in.
Weight (maximum take-off):	29,750 lbs.
Engine:	One Rolls-Royce F402-RR-402 turbojet
Engine thrust:	21,500 lbs.
Operating altitude:	51,000 ft.
Top speed:	662 mph
Maximum range:	1,550 miles
Date of service:	1983

Above: *The AV-8B's ability to take off and land vertically makes it ideal for carrier-based operations.*
Left: *The AV-8B can carry up to 9,200 pounds of weaponry mounted on external racks under the wings.*

F-117A Stealth Fighter

The F-117A Stealth fighter was actually in service for six years before the Air Force even admitted its existence. Not since the early 1960s, when the A-11—the predecessor to the SR-71 Blackbird—was being flight tested, has a military aircraft been kept such a closely guarded secret for so long.

The F-117A was born in 1978 at Lockheed's famous "Skunk Works" in Burbank, California, which has developed so many other state-of-the-art aircraft for the Air Force. Although originally conceived as a fighter interceptor, it was quickly changed to an attack jet, which explains the "A" designation following the series number.

The F-117A was designed to be as invisible to radar as possible, as well as difficult to see visually. Its shape is somewhat like a large, flat delta—or perhaps an arrowhead. It appears to have a vertical stabilizer above and below the fuselage and a horizontal stabilizer that projects upward at a severe angle.

The F-117A is a single seat, twin-engine aircraft. The cockpit is set low in the front of the fuselage. The engines, buried in the wing roots and deeply recessed to minimize their infrared signature, are located above the fuselage centerline. The engines are believed to be the General Electric F404 model and are not equipped with afterburners. A lack of afterburners, coupled with the F-117A's awkward shape, suggests that the aircraft does not have supersonic capability. The wing span is thought to be 40 feet. The skin covering is composed of panels of small, flat surfaces that reflect radar signals in every direction. Almost all of the external surface is coated with radar-absorbent material.

Little information of any other sort has been released to the public. The Air Force first flew the F-117A in 1981, and from 1981 to 1989 the F-117A was flown only at night to maintain secrecy. Rumors of its existence and capabilities were rife for several years. But except for the aircraft's actual existence, most of the rumors, including its F-19 designation, turned out to be wrong.

At least one unit of 59 F-117As is known to exist; the 4450th Tactical Group based at the Tonopah Test Range Air Base, Tonopah, Nevada. Also joining the 4450th as training aircraft are 18 specially modified A-7Ds.

The F-117A received its baptism of combat in December 1989, when two F-117As flew from Nellis Air Force Base to Panama. The aircraft dropped several 2,000-pound bombs with pinpoint accuracy on the headquarters of the Panamanian Defense Forces 6th and 7th Infantry Division at Rio Hato, 75 miles from Panama City. This created a diversion while American paratroopers of the 82nd Airborne launched the main attack.

With its wings folded or removed, at least two, and perhaps as many as four, F-117As can be carried in a C-5 Galaxy transport. The F-117A is equipped with fly-by-wire controls, which suggests that the aircraft is unstable in flight and needs the constant attention of the flight control computer to keep it flying. The fly-by-wire controls would account for observers' reports of the aircraft's extraordinary maneuverability, and its instability would account for the nickname bestowed by its pilots, the "Wobbly Goblin."

The Air Force has not made a final decision, but the primary mission of the aircraft will probably be low-level precision attack on high-priority targets with air-to-surface missiles stowed in internal bays. Thus, although the F-117A is called a fighter, it is likely to fly in the attack role.

The Wobbly Goblin is a true stealth aircraft. Every aspect of its design is intended to make the aircraft invisible to radar, even at the expense of flying characteristics. Some military observers have suggested that the radar cross section of the F-117A is about the same as that of a radio-controlled model airplane.

Above: *The YF-117A became operational with the U.S. Air Force in 1983 but remained a closely held secret until 1989. It flew its first combat mission in December 1989 against Panamanian Defense Forces.*

Above: *This artist's rendering of the F-117A shows some of its stealth features: engines mounted above the wings to shield inlets and exhausts from radar and infrared detection, angled surfaces to deflect radar beams, and radar- and infrared-absorbing composite skin coverings.*

LOCKHEED F-117A STEALTH FIGHTER

Wingspan:	Believed to be 40 ft.
Length:	Classified
Height:	Classified
Weight (maximum take-off):	Classified
Engines:	Believed to be two General Electric F404-GE-400 turbofans
Engine thrust:	16,000 lbs.
Operating altitude:	Classified
Top Speed:	Classified
Maximum range:	Classified
Date of service:	1983

BOMBERS

The role of the bomber is to destroy the enemy's capability and will to wage war. To do so, fleets of aircraft carrying hundreds of tons of bombs penetrate enemy airspace to destroy manufacturing and transportation capabilities, command and control centers, administrative facilities, and food and fuel production and processing facilities. They also terrorize enemy civilian populations in an effort to break morale.

All bombers in the U.S. military belong to the U.S. Air Force's Strategic Air Command (SAC), which dates from 1946. SAC is a continuation of the huge bomber force built up during World War II to attack the Axis powers. SAC was the largest bombing air fleet in the world until the mid-1960s, when the Soviet Air Force Long Range Aviation surpassed it in numbers. The Strategic Air Command today consists of more than 250 B-52G and B-52H heavy bombers, 60 FB-111s, and 100 B-1Bs. They will soon be joined by the B-2 Stealth aircraft, which will begin to replace the aging B-52s.

The strategic bombing force forms one leg of America's strategic nuclear triad, combining with the intercontinental ballistic missile force and the nuclear-powered strategic submarine fleet. All are capable of delivering nuclear weapons in such quantity that they have, hopefully, made war obsolete between the major powers. But the Vietnam War reminded the United States that there remains a need for conventional bombs and bombers. This realization played a key role in the design of the B-1B bomber and the B-2 Stealth bomber.

While SAC bombers still carry gravity—unpowered—bombs, they also carry the sophisticated AGM-86 air-launched cruise missile (ALCM). This 21-foot-long pilotless aircraft is armed with a nuclear warhead and can be released by a bomber 1,500 miles from its target. The ALCM is capable of flying at very low levels, thus penetrating enemy territory below radar coverage.

More than 100 B-52s have been modified to carry a dozen ALCMs each. The B-1B can carry 12 ALCMs externally and another eight inside its weapons bay in a rotary launcher. For conventional missions, B-52s, B-1Bs, and FB-111s can carry an assortment of quarter-ton and half-ton unguided "gravity," or "iron," bombs, or GBU-series guided "glide" bombs (also known as "smart" bombs). Also available are 14-foot AGM-69 Short Range Attack Missiles (SRAM). SRAMs are the original standoff weapon. Like the ALCM, the pilot can release SRAMs before the plane is over a target to avoid antiaircraft artillery and missiles. The SRAM has a much shorter range—about 100 miles—than the ALCM and lacks the low-level, terrain-hugging "mind" of the ALCM. But the SRAM is more than twice as fast as the ALCM.

Combining the firepower and versatility of hard-to-track, low-flying aircraft such as the ALCM and SRAM with positioning by the mind and hand of a human being makes the modern strategic bomber a very powerful weapon indeed.

Opposite: *The Big Ugly Fat Fellow (BUFF) has been in service with the Strategic Air Command since 1954.* Above: *The B-1B bomber is smaller than the B-52 but carries a larger weapons payload because of improved engines and design.* Left: *The radar cross section of the B-1B bomber is said to be less than one square meter.*

B-52 Stratofortress

The Boeing B-52 Stratofortress has survived in front-line service for *three* generations. There are crew members flying aboard B-52s whose grandfathers flew B-52s.

Boeing Aircraft built the B-17 Flying Fortress and the B-29 Superfortress, two of the most important warplanes of World War II, and the B-47 Stratojet, the first all-jet, swept-wing bomber. These were the predecessors to the B-52. Development of the plane that would become the B-52 began in the late 1940s, when the Air Force foresaw the need for an all-jet bomber that could carry both nuclear and conventional bombs more than 4,000 miles.

The B-52 made its first flight in 1952 and entered service with the U.S. Air Force's Strategic Air Command (SAC) in 1954, a year after the Soviet Union exploded its first hydrogen bomb. Aside from a handful of B-52s assigned to the Air Force Systems Command for testing, all 744 Stratofortresses Boeing built between 1951 and 1963 served with SAC. All told, two prototypes—447 B-52As through B-52Fs with tall tails, and 193 B-52Gs and 102 B-52Hs with low tails—were built. The H model is powered by eight turbofan engines instead of the eight turbojet engines of the previous models. The B-52H turbofans deliver an aggregate of 110,000 pounds of thrust, versus 80,000 pounds of thrust from the turbojets of the B-52A through B-52G models.

In 1957, as a demonstration of their intercontinental capabilities, three B-52s flew nonstop (with aerial refueling en route) 24,325 miles around the world. Five years later, a B-52H flew 12,532 miles nonstop without refueling, setting a distance record that stood until the flight of the *Voyager* 25 years later.

In 1965, SAC B-52s went to Vietnam to conduct Operation Arc Light, carpet-bombing raids on suspected Viet Cong strongholds. In 1972, SAC B-52s based in Guam and Thailand conducted an 11-day series of strategic bombing missions against Hanoi (during Operation Linebacker II) that forced the North Vietnamese government to return to the Paris negotiating table, helping lead the way to a cease-fire. Since 1984, only the low-tailed B-52G and B-52H models have remained in service, and there is every indication that the B-52H (and perhaps the B-52G as well) will serve until the mid-1990s, or even beyond.

Known familiarly as the "Big Ugly Fat Fellow" (BUFF), the B-52 of today is a far different airplane than the B-52 of three generations ago. Electro-optical viewing system screens have replaced a myriad of instruments to provide visual data from the forward-looking infrared sensor (FLIR) and low-light television (LLTV) cameras that protrude from the chin of today's BUFF. The FLIR sensors provide an image of daylight clarity even during periods of low visibility, while the LLTV camera provides a clear image even by starlight. These systems combine with advanced terrain-avoidance radar to permit low-level B-52 missions under virtually any condition.

Once a high-altitude strategic bomber only, today's B-52 can conduct numerous missions. The newly acquired low-level capability permits extremely long-range penetration beneath enemy radar, while the same long-range capability that made the B-52 a wonder in the 1950s permits today's BUFF to launch cruise missile missions thousands of miles from its base.

The B-52 is a venerable warhorse, but it's hardly ready to be put out to pasture.

Above: *There are 261 B-52 bombers still in operation with the U.S. Air Force.*

BOEING B-52H STRATOFORTRESS

Wingspan:	185 ft.
Length:	160 ft., 11 in.
Height:	40 ft., 8 in.
Weight (maximum take-off):	488,000 lbs.
Engines:	Eight Pratt & Whitney TF33-P-3 turbofans
Engine thrust:	13,750 lbs.
Operating altitude:	55,000 ft.
Top speed:	595 mph
Maximum range:	10,145 miles
Date of service:	1954

Above, left: *Nose art, popular with World War II bomber crews, has undergone a revival, thanks to the B-52.* Above, right: *A B-52 copilot programs the inertial navigation system. The pilot and the flight engineer will also enter the same flight data, and the computer will compare all three sets of data for accuracy.* Left: *The B-52 can reach altitudes of 55,000 feet and can fly at 595 miles per hour.*

F-111/FB-111

The F-111 Aardvark was born in the early 1960s when the Defense Department under Secretary Robert McNamara conceived the idea of a tactical fighter-bomber that could be used by both the Air Force and the Navy; it was called the TFX (tactical fighter, experimental). The prototype made its first flight in December 1964, but the needs of the two services had grown so far apart that the aircraft was unable to fill the requirements of both.

In 1968, the Navy dropped out of the project, and the Air Force ordered 141 F-111As. These were followed over the years by 296 F-111D, E, and F aircraft (with improved systems) through 1976. For the most part, these F-111s went into service with the U.S. Air Force's Tactical Air Command (TAC). The Strategic Air Command (SAC), meanwhile, acquired 76 F-111s to use as medium bombers under the designation FB-111.

When the F-111s entered combat in Vietnam in 1967, the results were disastrous. There were structural defects traceable to years of fiddling with the design. There were also serious problems with the then-experimental terrain-following radar that was supposed to permit extremely low-level bombing missions deep in North Vietnam. The F-111 was withdrawn, and when it was reintroduced in 1972, it was a changed aircraft. The Viet Cong called it "whispering death" because it came in so fast and so low that the first sound enemy troops heard was that of exploding bombs. Having proved itself in the last full year of American involvement in Vietnam, the F-111 went on to become the airplane of choice for TAC units specified to perform long-range, deep-interdiction attacks against targets within enemy territory. Gradually, the F-111 earned the respect of its aircrews and won the nickname "Aardvark."

With a Mach 2 speed, the Aardvark is faster than other American bombers, a characteristic that, when combined with a range exceeding that of American fighters, makes it a unique and valuable airplane. Its bomberlike cockpit features side-by-side seating for the pilot and weapons systems operator. The F-111 can carry 12 tons of bombs and missiles of various types and in various combinations. The FB-111 can carry a 16-ton nuclear or conventional bomb load or 13 tons of bombs and four AGM-69 Short Range Attack Missiles carried on swiveling pylons located beneath the variable-geometry wings. The wings can be changed in flight from nearly straight for a slow, level cruise to a delta configuration for a high-speed dash.

In the spring of 1986, Libya was implicated in the terrorist bombing of a West German nightclub that killed several American soldiers. This was only the latest in a series of terrorist attacks aimed at the United States by Libya and other countries in the Middle East. Eighteen Aardvarks made a 5,750-mile bomb run on April 15, 1986 (with the support of U.S. Air Force aerial refueling planes), and dropped more than 70 tons of unguided and laser-guided bombs on Libya. One aircraft and crew were lost. Terrorist attacks against Americans around the world virtually ended for several years after this.

Above: *The F-111 Aardvark is so named because of its large nose.*

Top: *The pilot and copilot are seated side by side in the F-111.* Center: *The FB-111A can deliver "smart" weapons, such as these Mark 82 parachute-retarded bombs, with pinpoint accuracy.* Bottom: *This FB-111A from the 48th Tactical Fighter Wing, Royal Air Force Lakenheath, England, is taking part in Red Flag exercises.*

GENERAL DYNAMICS F-111F	
Wingspan (unswept):	63 ft.
Wingspan (swept):	32 ft.
Length:	73 ft., 6 in.
Height:	17 ft.
Weight (maximum take-off):	91,500 lbs.
Engines:	Two Pratt & Whitney JF30-P-100 turbofans
Engine thrust:	25,100 lbs.
Operating altitude:	57,900 ft.
Top speed:	1,453 mph
Maximum range:	3,378 miles
Date of service:	1967

The F-111 became operational with the U.S. Air Force in 1967.

B-1

As potential successors to the B-52 bomber, the B-58 and B-70 came and went without success. Then in 1962, the Air Force undertook the Advanced Manned Strategic Aircraft (AMSA) program to develop a new strategic bomber.

The huge Mach 3 XB-70 was perceived as too much airplane for too much money, so AMSA would have to be a lesser airplane. The contract was won in 1970 by the North American Division of Rockwell International, which had developed the XB-70. Built under the designation B-1, the new strategic bomber made its maiden flight in December 1974. By 1977, three of the billion-dollar bombers had been built when President Jimmy Carter made good on a campaign promise and canceled the program. Four years later, however, when a replacement for the B-52 still had not been found, President Ronald Reagan revived the program under the designation B-1B.

The B-1B program produced a new bomber that included redesigned engine air intakes to reduce the aircraft's radar profile to far less than that of the 162-foot B-52. The B-1B appears on radar with an apparent size of only 20 inches. Because of its radar profile, a B-1B can, theoretically, penetrate enemy airspace with a 99 times better chance than a B-52 of getting through a radar net. The redesigned intakes cut the speed of the B-1B to just over Mach 1, compared with double that for the B-1A, but this is still half again faster than the B-52.

The first B-1B rolled out of the factory in September 1984 and made its initial flight the following month. The first full B-1B squadron became operational with the U.S. Air Force Strategic Air Command (SAC) in October 1986. The 100th—and last—B-1B was completed under budget and ahead of schedule in April 1988.

The actual range and speed of the B-1B are classified. Despite the B-1B's smaller size, its bomb load is larger than that of the B-52. This translates to roughly half again more bomb tonnage and the internal capacity to carry 24 AGM-69 Short Range Attack Missiles (compared with 20 in a B-52H), plus another 14 on external racks under the fuselage. The B-1B is configured with a unique rotary launcher that can accommodate eight AGM-86B air-launched cruise missiles (ALCM) in the internal weapons bay and another 12 outside.

The B-1B bomber handles like a fighter. It can accelerate fast and turn quickly. On more than one occasion, it has climbed out of a low-level, Mach 0.9 flight so rapidly that accompanying fighters were left behind. While the B-52 was designed for high-altitude flight and later modified for low-level missions, the B-1B was initially designed for low-level flight to penetrate enemy radar nets.

The task of preventing a nuclear first strike against the United States falls to SAC and its bombers, and the B-1B will do its part until the turn of the century and beyond.

Above: *The B-1B is the Strategic Air Command's frontline bomber. B-1Bs are based at Dyess Air Force Base (AFB), Texas; Ellsworth AFB, South Dakota; Grand Forks AFB, North Dakota; and McConnell AFB, Kansas.*

ROCKWELL INTERNATIONAL B-1B

Wingspan (unswept):	136 ft., 8.5 in.
Wingspan (swept):	78 ft., 2.5 in.
Length:	147 ft.
Height:	34 ft.
Weight (maximum take-off):	477,000 lbs.
Engines:	Four General Electric F101-GE-102 turbofans
Engine thrust:	30,000 lbs.
Operating altitude:	60,000 ft.
Top speed:	Mach 1.25 (estimated)
Maximum range:	7,455 miles (estimated)
Date of service:	1986

Left: *Many of the B-1B's performance specifications are classified, but its range is intercontinental and it can fly at supersonic speeds.* Below: *The B-1B is designed to carry a larger payload of bombs and cruise missiles than the B-52.*

The B-1B bomber can be refueled in midair from the KC-135 aerial tanker.

B-2 Stealth

Intended to complement the B-1B bomber force, the Northrop B-2 Stealth bomber is designed to be a nearly undetectable, long-range, hard-to-see aircraft. The "radar invisible" B-2 would be capable of penetrating the Soviet Union's extensive air-defense system, and then finding and striking everything from hardened targets to mobile missiles with near impunity.

The B-2 Stealth bomber is, without question, the most expensive aircraft in aviation history. As of federal fiscal year 1989, the B-2 program is expected to cost in excess of $71 billion dollars to acquire 132 aircraft. The Stealth bomber remains the center of a great deal of political jockeying in virtually all arenas within Congress, the Pentagon, and the Air Force. But expense is just part of the controversy surrounding this plane. Other major questions, from its actual need in light of recent world developments to doubts concerning the "invisible" technologies themselves, give rise to often long and heated debate.

Similar in appearance to the old Flying Wing of the late 1940s, the modern B-2 is said to be 50 percent more efficient aerodynamically than the B-1B. The B-2 uses the latest in high-technology components and will be difficult to detect on radar screens. The "stealthiness" of the B-2 results from a combination of manufacturing technologies. First, the shape of the aircraft itself eliminates all sharp angles and protrusions that radar beams could hit and bounce off of. Its winglike head-on profile provides a very small front view and a very low radar cross section. Second, the aircraft is made of composites and a host of secret coatings. Thus, radar waves are often "absorbed" by the plane itself instead of deflecting back. Third, a host of electronic countermeasures and electronic warfare "black boxes" help to keep the large bomber looking like little more than a sea gull or small cloud on an enemy radar screen.

Above: *The B-2 Stealth bomber is designed to penetrate heavy antiaircraft defenses.*

The B-2 has a two-member cockpit and a highly sophisticated flight panel. There are more than 200 computers on board, and more lines of software coding are used than in the space shuttle. Powered by four General Electric F-110 non-afterburner turbofan engines buried deep inside the aircraft's wings, the B-2 has an estimated top speed of Mach .85 and an operational ceiling of 50,000 feet. With a full load of weaponry, its unrefueled high-altitude range is 7,500 miles.

While the Air Force contends that the B-2 could be used as a conventional bomber and carry a full load of iron bombs and conventional weaponry, its frontline mission is to carry nuclear weapons. These weapons could include Short Range Attack Missiles (SRAM) and nuclear gravity bombs carried in side-by-side internal weapons storage bays. It is thought the B-2 can carry up to 16 nuclear gravity bombs or SRAMs in each full load.

Supporters of the controversial aircraft contend that no other plane in the world can accomplish the high-stakes deterrence mission for which this plane was designed. Supporters also contend that the Soviets will have to spend hundreds of billions of dollars to counter stealth technology. Critics say the cost is simply too high, as are the overall risks. The controversy is sure to continue, and the total number of aircraft that will eventually join the Strategic Air Command remains open to debate. The first operational aircraft are due in the early 1990s.

NORTHROP B-2 STEALTH

Wingspan:	172 ft.
Length:	69 ft.
Height:	17 ft.
Weight (maximum take-off):	240,000 to 376,000 lbs.
Engines:	Four General Electric F-110 non-afterburner turbofans
Engine thrust:	19,000 lbs.
Operating altitude:	50,000 ft.
Top speed:	Mach .85
Maximum range:	7,500 miles
Date of service:	1991 (expected)

Top: *The B-2 bomber is expected to become operational with the Strategic Air Command in mid- to late-1991.* Bottom: *The B-2 makes use of the latest state-of-the-art technology in aircraft design, including extensive use of carbon fiber skin coverings to reduce radar visibility.*

The B-2 bomber is 69 feet long, 17 feet high, and has a wingspan of 172 feet.

RECONNAISSANCE AND ELECTRONIC WARFARE AIRCRAFT

Battles can be won and lost without a shot being fired. Secrets that took years to weave—and nearly as long to disguise—can be compromised in split seconds. Intelligence operations—"spying"—is the domain of the mental rather than the physical. But as the 20th century nears its end, technology has supplemented and enhanced intelligence gathering. At the beginning of the 20th century, intelligence gathering consisted primarily of sending men to watch the enemy, tapping into the enemy's telephone wires, or spying on enemy movements from tethered balloons. By the beginning of World War I, the airplane was ready to supplant the vulnerable balloon. Now, three-quarters of a century later, satellites watch with unfailing attention and specially designed-and-built aircraft can slip across the enemy's frontiers and battle areas for closer views.

Reconnaissance aircraft evolved from observation aircraft, a role to which military airplanes were assigned even before the term "warplane" was coined. At first, the pilot used only his eyes for observation, straining through the oil and dust on his goggles for surface features far below. By 1917, hand-held cameras were recording observations for later interpretation on the ground. By World War II, the large-format cameras carried by reconnaissance aircraft were highly specialized and very accurate. The photos the cameras provided proved to be an essential element in planning and executing the Allied strategic bombing missions that ultimately turned the tide of the war. Reconnaissance photos also provided vital information for surface operations and were particularly useful in planning amphibious operations.

The idea of using aircraft for electronic warfare began in the post-war period. As the technical complexity of radar defenses expanded, the necessity of countering it also grew. During the Vietnam War, the U.S. Air Force discovered that defense was as important as offense during bombing missions over heavily defended North Vietnam. The Air Force found they were dealing with sophisticated electronic defenses supplied to the North Vietnamese by their Russian allies. To meet this threat, and to be equally prepared to tackle well-defended potential targets in Europe, the Air Force converted about 20 B-66 tactical bombers to electronic warfare aircraft. Equipped with radar, electronic countermeasures hardware, and a large amount of aluminum foil "chaff" (to fool enemy radar), the EB-66s accompanied American fighter-bombers on their raids.

The aerial reconnaissance chore in the Vietnam War was handled by converted warplanes. In the early part of the war, the RF-101 flew reconnaissance missions. The RF-4C, the reconnaissance version of the F-4 Phantom II fighter, replaced the RF-101 after 1967. And today, the RF-4C remains an excellent low-level, day-to-day tactical reconnaissance aircraft.

While converted aircraft can often do an admirable job, aircraft specifically designed to accomplish a particular task can do a better job. This is the case with today's reconnaissance aircraft—the Lockheed U-2/TR-1, the Grumman E-2 Hawkeye, the Lockheed SR-71 Blackbird, the Boeing E-3 Sentry (AWACS), and the Grumman EF-111 Raven.

Opposite: *The TR-1 is a modification of the original U-2 high-altitude reconnaissance aircraft.* Right: *The SR-71 was America's highest flying and fastest reconnaissance aircraft.* Bottom, left: *The EF-111 Raven is the tactical electronic jamming version of the F-111 fighter.* Bottom, right: *The E-2C Hawkeye is an Airborne Early Warning aircraft based aboard aircraft carriers.*

U-2/TR-1 Series

More than a quarter of a century after one of these top-secret aircraft was shot down over the Soviet Union, the name U-2 is still synonymous with the phrase "spy plane." The U-2 was developed at Lockheed's secret "Skunk Works" advanced-projects facility. The plane was to perform very high-altitude, long-range reconnaissance missions. Because great speed was not necessary, designer Kelly Johnson based the airframe on that of a glider, giving the new plane superior soaring capability at high altitudes. The U-2 first flew in 1955, and was in service a year later. It was able to fly higher than Soviet air defenses could reach, making missions over Moscow possible. But by 1960, the range of Soviet surface-to-air missiles had improved to the point where the U-2 was vulnerable, as U-2 pilot Gary Powers found out on May Day over an ICBM site near Sverdlovsk.

The U-2, however, continued in service. It flew reconnaissance missions over Cuba and Vietnam, as well as performing more routine aerial-mapping missions over the United States for NASA and the Department of Agriculture. It has not been disclosed how many U-2s were built, but it is known that 25 of them (about half the total) were rebuilt under the U-2R designation. The U-2R has improved avionics (the electrical systems that control the aircraft) and longer wings that promote more fuel capacity and greater range.

In 1980, it was decided that the assembly line should be reopened to build 26 all-new U-2Rs, which would be delivered under the newer and more appropriate designation TR-1 (tactical reconnaissance, first). One of these "Dragon Ladies" had been delivered to NASA as an earth-resources survey aircraft under the designation ER-2. The U-2Rs and TR-1s are owned by the U.S. Air Force Strategic Air Command. Although they are based at Beale Air Force Base in California, the U-2Rs and TR-1s are continuously deployed at other American bases around the world.

The basic TR-1, like most U-2s before it, is a single-seat aircraft. The aircraft is capable of flying 17 miles above potential battlefields or enemy territory. The flat-black bird with indistinct markings melts into the darkness at the edge of space, ten miles above the tracks of most other planes. Electronic countermeasures gear unheard of in Gary Powers' day protect the pilot while over the target. Indeed, due to advances in technology, there is no need to glide precisely *over* the target.

Below: *The TR-1 is powered by one Pratt & Whitney J75-P-13B, which provides 17,000 pounds of thrust.* Opposite, top: *The original U-2 was designed by Kelly Johnson in the early 1950s.* Opposite, bottom: *The TR-1 can be distinguished from the U-2 by the two large wing pods that hold extra fuel and various electronic packages.*

LOCKHEED U-2

Wingspan:	80 ft.
Length:	49 ft., 7 in.
Height:	15 ft.
Weight (maximum take-off):	17,270 lbs.
Engine:	One Pratt & Whitney J75-P-13 turbojet
Engine thrust:	17,000 lbs.
Operating altitude:	80,000 ft.
Top speed:	430 mph
Maximum range:	4,000 miles
Date of service:	1956

LOCKHEED TR-1

Wingspan:	103 ft.
Length:	63 ft.
Height:	17 ft.
Weight (maximum take-off):	40,000 lbs.
Engine:	One Pratt & Whitney J75-P-13B turbojet
Engine thrust:	17,000 lbs.
Operating altitude:	90,000+ ft.
Top speed:	430 mph
Maximum range:	3,000 miles
Date of service:	1981

E-2 Hawkeye

Above: *A squadron of four E-2C Hawkeyes is always stationed aboard each aircraft carrier when at sea.*

Radar beams travel in a straight "line of sight"; they do not reflect off the ionosphere as do most radio waves. Therefore, the higher the radar transmitters, the farther the radar system can "see." An aircraft carrier's radar mast can stand as high as a 15-story building. But the E-2 Hawkeye's radar transmitter stands as high as a 2,500-story building.

The Hawkeye aircraft manages the entire field of action for a carrier battle group from a vantage point high in the sky. The idea of managing a battlefield from a command post in the sky was explored in both world wars, but the technology was lacking. It was not until the mid-1950s that communications and radar technology developed to the point where airborne battle management was feasible.

The first such aircraft was the land-based Lockheed WV-2 (EC-121 after 1962) Warning Star and the carrier-based Grumman WF-2 (E-1 after 1962) Tracer. Both Navy and Air Force EC-121s served in Vietnam, where they refined the techniques for large-scale airborne battlefield control that ultimately led to the E-3 Sentry Airborne Warning and Control System (AWACS).

Based on the S-2 Tracker, the E-1 Tracer demonstrated the concept of a carrier-based Airborne Early Warning (AEW)/ flying command post. The concept was limited both by the state-of-the-art of radar technology and the lack of room aboard the Tracer for the high-speed digital computer necessary to sort out the haze of blips on the radar screen. In 1957, the Navy selected Grumman to develop a larger and more capable aircraft. The result was a turboprop-powered airplane with only a passing resemblance to the Tracer. It was called Hawkeye and made its first flight in 1960.

Originally designated the W2F, Hawkeye was redesignated the E-2 in 1962. The current standard Hawkeye is the E-2C, which entered service aboard the Navy's carriers in 1964. More than 100 of this version have been built, and more are on the way. The Hawkeye's most distinguishing feature is its huge, saucerlike radome (the housing unit for the antenna of the radar) perched delicately above its fuselage. To compensate for the airflow from this unusual appendage, Grumman engineers gave the plane a tail with not one, but four vertical tail surfaces. The 24-foot radome revolves once every ten seconds, while providing its own lift.

Beneath the spinning dome, a three-member AEW crew works, while a two-member flight crew flies the Hawkeye. The crew—including an air traffic controller—can see more than 200 miles in any direction with the APA-171 radar. It has a surveillance envelope of three million cubic miles. The system can handle more than 600 airborne targets and can track ships and ground vehicles at the same time. The AEW crew can control and direct 40 intercept operations simultaneously.

Typically, each carrier air wing will have an AEW squadron equipped with four Hawkeyes. There are additional AEW squadrons at land bases ranging from Japan to California. Hawkeyes are beginning to serve in civilian functions, such as law enforcement. In Florida, Hawkeyes have been assigned to detect drug smugglers.

Top: *The Hawkeye's distinctive radome revolves six times per minute.* Center, left: *These E-2C Hawkeyes are flying out to their aircraft carrier at the beginning of a cruise.* Center, right: *The Hawkeye's radar can handle up to 600 aircraft at once.* Bottom: *The E-2C Hawkeye can remain in the air for six hours before refueling.*

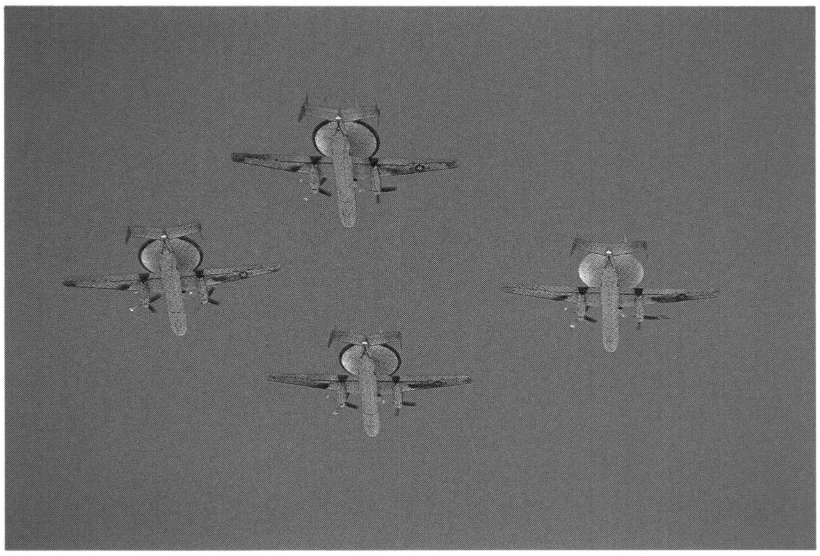

GRUMMAN E-2C HAWKEYE

Wingspan:	80 ft., 7 in.
Length:	57 ft., 6.75 in.
Height:	18 ft., 3.75 in.
Weight (maximum take-off):	51,933 lbs.
Engines:	Two Allison T56-A-425 turboprops
Engine horsepower:	4,910
Operating altitude:	30,800 ft.
Top speed:	372 mph
Maximum range:	1,605 miles
Date of service:	1964

SR-71 Blackbird

The SR-71 Blackbird is said to be faster than a "speeding bullet," and that is literally true. After more than two decades of service, the Blackbird is still the fastest airplane in the world. Although the Blackbird has held the world's absolute speed record of 2,193.167 miles per hour for over a decade, its actual top speed is much faster and highly classified. Aircrews of SR-71s wear shoulder patches that say "Mach 3-plus," and the emphasis is on the plus.

The Blackbird evolved from a Mach 3 interceptor, which had itself evolved from a CIA spy plane developed in the early 1960s. The CIA's mysterious Model A-12 reconnaissance airplane, which first flew in 1962, was a product of Lockheed's secret "Skunk Works." The Air Force decided to take a look at a Mach 3 interceptor version of the A-12 for its Air Defense Command (ADC). The YF-12 interceptor was the fastest such airplane ever flown and could cruise comfortably at three times the speed of sound. The YF-12 was mothballed when it was decided that the Soviets didn't have bombers fast enough to justify its expense.

The Strategic Air Command (SAC) thought the new YF-12 was exactly what they needed as a new "Reconnaissance/ Strike" airplane and ordered it as the RS-71. By the time SAC's airplane flew in 1964, reconnaissance was its sole function, and so its designation was changed to SR-71 for "Strategic Reconnaissance."

The SR-71 Blackbird is like no other aircraft. The materials used in its construction were experimental at the time. The overall design and shape of the fuselage (which provides most of the lift) were engineering breakthroughs. The turbo-ramjet engines, designed especially for this plane by Pratt & Whitney, are also unique, as they must be to sustain speeds of above Mach 3. The SR-71 is the only airplane in the world known to burn JP-7 fuel, a concoction so *non*volatile that it can't be lit with a match. A chemical reaction is needed to get the engines started.

Left: *The SR-71 was the fastest manned, operational aircraft in service anywhere in the world.* Below: *The SR-71 Blackbird is also known as the Habu, after a small, poisonous Okinawan snake.*

There are two crew members: The pilot flies the aircraft and the electronics officer operates the cameras, sensors, and reconnaissance hardware. The crew members wear the same flight suits worn by space shuttle astronauts. The heavy lids that secure the two cockpits are cranked down, the JP-7 is ignited, and the SR-71 shrieks down the runway. The Blackbird takes off almost vertically and is out of sight in seconds.

Missions are routinely flown from Kadena Air Base on Okinawa. A typical mission may take the aircraft up the Pacific coast of China, across North Korea, and along the Soviet coast as far as the Bering Strait; or the SR-71 may fly across the southern coast of India to the Persian Gulf and then northwest into the Mediterranean. These birds will fly anywhere deemed necessary by those responsible for U.S. national security. The Blackbird made its last operational flight in 1990.

Always watching, looking, and listening, the SR-71 has gathered millions of pieces of data in the years since it was first deployed. That data provided the intelligence services of the United States with a better appreciation of the capabilities and intentions of those inimical to the United States.

LOCKHEED SR-71 BLACKBIRD

Wingspan:	55 ft., 7 in.
Length:	107 ft., 5 in.
Height:	18 ft., 6 in.
Weight (maximum take-off):	172,000 lbs.
Engines:	Two Pratt & Whitney J58 turbo-ramjets
Engine thrust:	32,500 lbs.
Operating altitude:	100,000 ft.
Top speed:	Mach 3.5+
Maximum range:	3,250 miles
Date of service:	1966

Left: *The SR-71 was withdrawn from operational service with the Air Force in January 1990.* Below: *Refueling capability provides the SR-71 with virtually unlimited range.*

The SR-71 flew thousands of reconnaissance missions over Vietnam in the late 1960s and early 1970s in support of the American effort in that war.

U.S. AIR FORCE

E-3 Sentry (AWACS)

The E-3 Sentry is the most sophisticated airborne command post ever devised. A handful can and do control all flight operations throughout Europe.

During the Vietnam War, the U.S. Air Force flew its *College Eye* EC-121Qs and the remarkable *Igloo White* EC-121R Batcats over Laos and the Gulf of Tonkin, where they had great success in controlling and directing air operations against North Vietnam. After the Vietnam War, a revolution in electronics made possible far more sophistication in much less space.

The airframe chosen for the new airborne command post was the Boeing Model 707, which was similar to the airframes of the Air Force's KC-135s, RC-135s, and EC-135s. This airframe was designed to be configured with state-of-the-art electronics inside and topped with a 30-foot rotating radome. The big skunk-striped "rotodome" is similar to, though larger than, the one on Grumman's E-2 Hawkeye. The Sentry's radome is backed up by a greater information-processing capability than the Hawkeye. The result is the Air Force's Airborne Warning and Control System (AWACS).

The first of two dozen E-3A Sentrys was delivered in 1977, and all 24 went into service on January 1, 1979. Though owned and flown by the Air Force Tactical Air Command (TAC), their first, and continuing, assignment is with the joint U.S./Canadian North American Air Defense Command (NORAD), which guards the North American continent.

An improvement program begun in 1984 will see the A model superseded by the E-3B and the E-3C. The improvements have included a larger number of situation display consoles (SDC), a better Have Quick radar jamming system, and an upgraded Joint Tactical Information Distribution System (JTIDS) and Tactical Digital Information Link (TADIL).

As the world discovered when an Iranian airliner was shot down by mistake in the Persian Gulf in 1988, battlefield electronics are only as good as the people who operate them. Decisions are only as good as the precision of the information upon which they are based. This makes IFF (Identification, Friend or Foe) recognition a vital part of the AWACS task, and one made all the harder by the theaters in which the E-3 must operate. North America has heavy concentrations of air traffic, but the areas of concern to TAC and NORAD are on the periphery, where traffic is lighter.

In Europe, however, the situation is vastly more complex. Here, the air forces and airlines of two dozen nations are divided into friendly and unfriendly systems in the center of the heaviest air traffic on Earth. To complicate matters, commercial flights can cross the line between West and East at certain points, but military flights cannot. Problems arise when trying to tell if the blip that crossed at point A is an airliner or an unfriendly military flight.

Most of the world's E-3s operate in Europe. NATO owns 18 of them; both Britain and France have them on order. In time of war, these planes would form an interlocking, yet noninterfering, network of command posts able to manage the hundreds of NATO warplanes that would be airborne at any given moment. The E-3s would have to distinguish enemy from neutral aircraft. To do so, the IBM CC-2 computers, which are the heart of each Sentry's data processing capability, perform 250,000 operations per second.

Below: *The E-3 Sentry is the successor to various earlier EC-121 versions.*

Top: *The AWACS aircraft is based on the commercial Boeing 707-320 airliner.* Center, left: *The large radome is mounted on two 11-foot struts and is 30 feet in diameter.* Center, right: *The E-3 Sentry can remain aloft for up to 11 hours, 22 hours with in-flight refueling.* Bottom: *The E-3 Sentry's radars are capable of spotting enemy ships as well as aircraft.*

BOEING E-3 SENTRY (AWACS)

Wingspan:	145 ft., 9 in.
Length:	152 ft., 11 in.
Height:	41 ft., 9 in.
Weight (maximum take-off):	325,000 lbs.
Engines:	Four Pratt & Whitney TF33-PW-100/100A turbofans
Engine thrust:	21,000 lbs.
Operating altitude:	29,000 ft.
Top speed:	530 mph
Maximum range:	7,475 miles
Date of service:	1979

The E-3 Sentry is flown by the U.S. Air Force and by NATO; Egypt and Saudi Arabia also fly the Sentry, but with highly classified equipment removed.

USAF
50556

EF-111 Raven

During the Vietnam War, the radar environment over North Vietnam was so thick that American F-105 fighter-bombers were accompanied by EB-66 electronic countermeasures aircraft whose sole purpose was to jam enemy radar. Based on the success and experience of these operations, the Air Force decided in the early 1970s to refine the concept and develop a successor to the EB-66.

The F-111 airframe was picked for its low-level capability, its geometric wing flexibility, and the fact that the jamming aircraft would probably be escorting F-111 and FB-111 bombers. With basic engines and airframes in common, the jammer and its bombers could be maintained by the same team. Grumman, with its expertise in developing the E-1, E-2, and EA-6 for the Navy, was chosen to rewire and modify more than 40 older F-111s.

Flight testing began in 1977, and the EF-111 Ravens were deployed to the Upper Heyford Royal Air Force Base in England in 1984 as components of the 42nd Electronic Combat Squadron. Two years later, in April 1986, when F-111s were sent against bases in Libya, three EF-111s went along. Although the intended mission of the F-111/ EF-111 team is deep interdiction within Eastern Europe, they performed well over Libya, and could do so in other parts of the world as well.

Above: *The EF-111 Raven's task is to jam enemy radar and communication systems while the FB-111 and other bombers attack.*

GRUMMAN EF-111A RAVEN

Wingspan (unswept):	63 ft.
Wingspan (swept):	31 ft., 11.5 in.
Length:	76 ft.
Height:	20 ft.
Weight (maximum take-off):	88,948 lbs.
Engines:	Two Pratt & Whitney TF30-P-30 turbofans
Engine thrust:	18,500 lbs.
Operating altitude:	45,000 ft.
Top speed:	1,412 mph
Maximum range:	2,303 miles
Date of service:	1984

Top: *The EF-111 Raven version of the F-111 made its first flight on March 10, 1977.* Left: *The Raven, shown here being readied for a flight, carries a crew of two.* Above: *The crew sits side by side, pilot on the left, systems operator on the right.*

TRANSPORTS

The transportation of matériel and personnel—the science and art of logistics—is essential to any military operation. Supplying U.S. military forces overseas is the responsibility of both the U.S. Navy's Military Sealift Command and the U.S. Air Force's Military Airlift Command (MAC).

MAC's primary responsibility is for the air resupply of America's far-flung military commitments. They also are responsible for search and rescue operations anywhere in the world involving American military, or even civilians. And MAC also has responsibility for all special warfare operations that involve the placement of Army, Marine, or Navy special forces by air.

MAC has over 900 aircraft in its fleet; three-quarters of that number are exclusively for hauling cargo. The C-130 Hercules, the C-141 Starlifter, and the C-5 Galaxy, all built by Lockheed, are the most important and most numerous transports in that fleet. The remaining aircraft are primarily military versions of civilian airliners: the McDonnell Douglas C-9 ambulance, which is based on the DC-9 jetliner; the Beechcraft C-12, based on the Super King Air 200; the Grumman C-20, based on the Gulfstream II; the C-21, the Learjet 35; the C-22, the Boeing 727 jetliner; and the C-23, an all-freight version of the Shorts 300 small regional airliner.

An important part of MAC's job—outside the military airlift role—is to provide executive transportation for government officials, most notably the President of the United States. This task is carried out by MAC's 89th Military Airlift Wing at Andrews Air Force Base near Washington, D.C. Any airplane that carries the President is assigned the call sign *Air Force One.* In 1989, the 89th Military Airlift Wing received two Boeing 747s (designated VC-25s) to serve as the primary and backup presidential transports.

Today's MAC hauls cargo for all the military services, including the Coast Guard. But the Navy, Marines, and Coast Guard still employ the venerable C-130 for specialized cargo deliveries. The Navy also flies the C-9 ambulance plane and a few C-12s for utility purposes. Other transports peculiar to the Navy include the Grumman C-1 Trader, which is based on the old S-2 Tracker and has a cargo capacity of less than two tons, and the C-2, a variant of the E-2 Hawkeye that can carry five tons of payload. These unique transports are used for carrying supplies and personnel between aircraft carriers and shore bases.

The Lockheed C-130, C-141, and the C-5A/B aircraft were carefully designed to meet the need for "medium," "large," and "extra large" transports. The C-130 can carry 25 tons, the C-141 Starlifter handles 45 tons, and the extra-large C-5 Galaxy can haul up to 150 tons of payload. Each has a specific role in airlift operations. The C-141 might ferry personnel and routine cargo over long distances, such as from the United States to Europe or Japan. The C-5 would be used to haul both personnel and very large or heavy cargo over equally long distances. The C-130, with its special ability to land on short, unimproved landing strips, takes the job of carrying supplies to the front lines. All three aircraft can be used to carry paratroopers, their equipment, and their vehicles.

MAC is developing, with McDonnell Douglas, a new transport aircraft, the C-17. The C-17 will have a cargo compartment as wide and as high as a C-5, a total capacity greater than that of a C-141, and an ability to land at airfields previously accessible only to C-130s.

Left, top: *The C-5 Galaxy is the largest cargo transport in the U.S. Air Force.* Left, bottom: *The nose of the Galaxy lifts up and the rear doors open, allowing easy cargo loading.* Right, top: *The C-130 Hercules became operational with the Air Force in 1956.* Center: *The C-141 Starlifter is the workhorse of the Air Force.* Bottom: *More than 1,800 C-130s have been built for the U.S. Air Force, air forces of other nations, and commercial organizations.*

C-130 Hercules

The C-130 has been in production at Lockheed's plant in Marietta, Georgia, for 35 years. More than 1,800 C-130s have been delivered. The C-130 has played a role in virtually every American military operation since its introduction in the 1950s. The Hercules has delivered supplies under withering ground fire in Vietnam and in near-blizzard weather conditions at the South Pole.

The turboprop-powered Hercules made its first flight in 1954. The Air Force, Marines, Navy, and Coast Guard all purchased the C-130, as did more than 50 foreign air forces from Abu Dhabi to Zaire. Lockheed has also developed a nearly identical commercial freighter called L-100, which has been sold to customers in more than a dozen countries.

There are now about 700 C-130s in the Air Force, divided about equally between active Military Airlift Command (MAC) units and Reserve and Air Guard units assigned to MAC. Most of these are C-130B and C-130E transports, along with some newer C-130Hs and HC-130Hs that are assigned to MAC's Rescue and Recovery Service. The Navy, Marines, and Coast Guard operate about 100 Hercules in various roles, ranging from the Coast Guard's own HC-130H rescue aircraft to the ski-equipped Navy LC-130s used in Antarctica. The Marines also fly the KC-130 for aerial refueling of fixed and rotary winged aircraft.

Nor is this the extent of the "Herk's" many-faceted repertoire. While the majority of America's C-130 fleet is moving cargo or performing one of many routine tasks, others are unobtrusively, and often secretly, completing nearly unimaginable missions:

- Somewhere over the Pacific, a JHC-130 snares a film capsule in midair from a spy satellite streaking through the Earth's atmosphere.
- In a world trouble-spot, a DC-130 is an airborne aircraft carrier, clutching four one-ton remote-control airplanes beneath its wings. On cue, these unmanned drones silently fly off into the twilight to snap photos by infrared light of guerrillas in a jungle. Subjected to small arms fire, the drones may die, but the DC-130 will be long gone.
- Deep in hostile territory, an MC-130 Combat Talon—belonging to an Air Force Special Operations Squadron—pushes through a nighttime rainstorm to retrieve a friendly operative from a hiding place. The MC-130 comes in very low, extends huge scissorslike whiskers from its nose, and tightens a cable. The MC-130 snatches a second cable that is attached to the secret agent and held aloft by a helium balloon. With a sudden snap, he's off the ground and airborne beneath the MC-130.
- In a hurricane's eye, all is quiet. Suddenly, a form emerges from the fury of the hurricane's 150 miles per hour winds. A WC-130 makes a routine penetration of the storm to obtain weather-forecasting data.

A variation of the Hercules is the Spectre gunship, which was born in Vietnam. In 1965, the Air Force needed an aircraft that could pour a concentrated wall of gunfire at ground targets. To meet this

Above: *C-130 Hercules transports are powered by two Allison T-56-A-15 turboprops.* Opposite, clockwise from upper left: *The Air Force's Aerospace Rescue and Recovery Service operates this specialized HC-130P Hercules. The Hercules has probably delivered more paratroopers than any other aircraft in history. The rear doors and cargo ramp of the C-130 make it easy to load and unload troops and equipment. The C-130 was the backbone of the invasion of Grenada.*

need, the Air Force first developed the Spooky, known as "Puff the Magic Dragon" (or "Dragon Ship") because of the smoke it breathed. Spooky was originally a 30-year-old C-47 transport with side-firing cannons and machine guns. The Dragon Ships were able to concentrate their firepower by orbiting the target in a circular pattern so that the lines of fire were focused—like the spokes of a wheel—on a single target for up to 20 minutes at a time. In 1967, building on the concept of the Spooky, AC-130 Spectre gunships were deployed. They carried 20 millimeter, 40mm, and even 75mm cannons. After the war, the AC-130s remained and evolved. Today, the AC-130H is equipped with a 105mm howitzer that augments its 20mm Gatling guns. In the early 1990s, the new AC-130U will be on line with a deadly combination of 25mm, 40mm, and 105mm cannons directed by sophisticated low-light TV and infrared target locators.

From transport to gunship, from electronic warfare to airborne battlefield control, this 35-year-old turboprop is the prime candidate for a one-airplane air force.

LOCKHEED C-130H HERCULES

Wingspan:	132 ft., 7 in.
Length:	97 ft., 9 in.
Height:	38 ft., 3 in.
Weight (maximum take-off):	155,000 lbs.
Engines:	Four Allison T56-A-15 turboprops
Engine horsepower:	4,508
Operating altitude:	33,000 ft.
Top speed:	375 mph
Maximum range:	4,894 miles
Date of service:	1956

Rocket-assisted take-off units make it possible for the C-130 to operate from short fields and unimproved landing sites.

812

C-141 Starlifter

A typical Starlifter mission begins at Norton Air Force Base (AFB) near San Bernadino, California, with an early morning flight to Travis AFB near San Francisco, home of the 60th Military Airlift Wing. There the C-141—Flight 807—picks up passengers and cargo bound for points west. The C-141 stops at Hickam AFB in Hawaii—where the crew ends its day. But less than three hours later, the C-141 is on its way across the international date line bound for Andersen AFB in Guam. It's tomorrow without a sundown.

A new crew takes over, and the next stop is Clark Air Base (AB) in the Philippines. After another crew change, the aircraft is bound north, to Kadena AB on Okinawa, Japan. Three hours later, the Starlifter is airborne once again with a new crew and flies on to Yokota AB in Japan. Once again, the crew changes and the C-141 begins its return flight, arriving back at Norton AFB some 44 hours after its first takeoff. The flight crews, traveling in rotation, will take ten days to return.

This type of long-haul cargo run is called a channel flight. Flight 807, and its return, Flight 808, are daily occurrences for the Military Airlift Command (MAC). There are numerous other such channel flights to other parts of the world, from Dover AFB, Delaware, or McGuire AFB, New Jersey, to RAF Alconbury, Great Britain, or Rhein-Main AB, West Germany, or even as far as Diego Garcia in the middle of the Indian Ocean. The Starlifter may be one of the least glamorous birds in the Air Force, but MAC could not do its job without the C-141. It is the everyday airliner of the military.

The Starlifter was designed in the early 1960s to be an airlifter in the same size and weight class as the largest commercial jetliners of the day. It was built with high, shoulder-mounted wings for operation from less than perfect runways. The cargo bay has very small windows and a ramp at the rear of the fuselage. The C-141 was designed to accommodate the weight and bulk of the Minuteman intercontinental ballistic missile (ICBM). Lockheed built a total of 285 Starlifters before production ended.

The Starlifter entered service in 1965, just as the Vietnam War was heating up and it became necessary to have an airlifter that could fly nonstop from California to Saigon. The C-141 was sold only to MAC. No other nation has the need for such a long-haul aircraft.

Due to its limited cargo space, the C-141 was hauling much less than its full payload capacity. In 1976, every C-141 in the fleet was stretched 23 feet by adding sections to the fuselage ahead and behind the wing roots. By 1982, all 267 remaining Starlifters had been lengthened, retrofitted with hardware to make them aerial refuelable, and redesignated C-141B. Cargo space was thus increased so the payload weight started living up to the Starlifter's capability. In foul weather or fair, the Starlifter is there—meeting the schedules, hauling the goods, dropping paratroopers, and fulfilling MAC's commitments around the world.

Below: *The C-141 Starlifter's tremendous cargo-carrying capacity enables it to haul complete artillery pieces.* Right, top: *The Starlifter's safety record is unparalleled in American military service.* Center, left: The C-141 is large enough to carry a complete Minuteman III ICBM. Center, right: *The Starlifter has flown to every continent in the world.* Bottom: *The C-141's rear clamshell doors, which can be opened in flight, make it possible to air-drop troops or supplies.*

LOCKHEED C-141B STARLIFTER

Wingspan:	159 ft., 11 in.
Length:	168 ft., 3.5 in.
Height:	39 ft., 3.5 in.
Weight (maximum take-off):	344,900 lbs.
Engines:	Four Pratt & Whitney TF33-P-7-turbofans
Engine thrust:	21,000 lbs.
Operating altitude:	25,000 ft.
Top speed:	570 mph
Maximum range:	4,080 miles
Date of service:	1965

A C-141 Starlifter performs one of its many functions, dropping special cargo.

C-5 Galaxy

For 17 years, the Galaxy was the largest airplane in the world. Only the Soviet Union's Antonov An-124, which entered service in 1985, is longer, by five feet. There is enough room inside the C-5 for 16 army trucks, 36 standard shipping pallets, two 63-ton M-1A1 Abrams tanks, six Apache attack helicopters, ten Pershing missiles, or two Minuteman ICBMs. The Military Airlift Command (MAC) has even hauled some of the Navy's smaller submarines in a C-5. The C-5's immense cargo bay has a ramp at either end to increase the speed of loading and unloading.

There's also plenty of room for people. The after passenger compartment above the cargo hold and behind the cockpit can carry the same number of passengers as a Boeing 727. The climb from the floor of the cargo bay to the flight deck is three stories. The flight deck has a galley and dining area reminiscent of a Pullman car. There are enough bunks for a complete extra flight crew and a rest area for 15 crew members. The pilot, copilot, and flight engineer sit in a cockpit almost as large as a standard-size living room.

The remarkable Galaxy was born amid controversy over its cost and performance, and made its first flight in 1968. This was the first aircraft of its size ever built (the Boeing 747 was still under construction) and low price estimates proved costly for Lockheed. Delays and cost overruns resulted, and Congress wound up funding only 81 of the originally planned 115 C-5As. Nevertheless, the first C-5s reached MAC squadrons in time for limited service during the Vietnam War.

By the end of the 1970s, the C-5A had proved itself. The entire fleet logged 400,000 hours and hauled four billion tons of cargo. In 1980, the C-5A fleet was retrofitted with new wing components to give each airframe another 30,000 hours of flight time. Despite the increased longevity being built into the C-5A, there was still a serious need for more heavy airlift capacity within the MAC fleet. In 1982, Congress agreed to let the Air Force buy 50 more Galaxys. Designated C-5B, the new planes are similar in appearance to the C-5As but have stronger wings, bigger engines, and improved avionics (the electrical systems that control the aircraft). The first C-5B joined MAC in 1986, the 50th in 1989.

The combined Galaxy fleet can airlift a total of 19,000 tons. It is this sheer load-carrying power that will make the Galaxy an integral part of MAC for the rest of the century. And the Galaxy and all its Lockheed brethren will continue to make MAC the most potent military airlift force in the world.

Left, top: *The C-5 Galaxy can air-drop four Sheridan tanks and 70 paratroopers on the same mission.* Left, bottom: *This Galaxy, clad in NATO camouflage, taxies off to begin another flight.* Above: *The C-5 Galaxy's cargo bay is large enough to carry three Marine Corps CH-53D Sea Stallion helicopters.* Right: *The C-5 is flown by a crew of five: pilot, co-pilot, flight engineer, and two loadmasters. On air-drop missions, a navigator is also carried.*

LOCKHEED C-5B GALAXY

Wingspan:	222 ft., 8.5 in.
Length:	247 ft., 10 in.
Height:	65 ft., 1.5 in.
Weight (maximum take-off):	837,000 lbs.
Engines:	Four General Electric TF39-GE-1C turbofans
Engine thrust:	43,000 lbs.
Operating altitude:	35,750 ft.
Top speed:	564 mph
Maximum range:	6,469 miles
Date of service:	1969

The C-5 Galaxy has a range of 5,589 miles when carrying 100,000 pounds of cargo.

AERIAL TANKERS

The concept of refueling one aircraft from another in the air had been considered almost from the beginning of fixed wing flight. But the payload capacity and reliability of aircraft was not sufficient to allow the technique to be developed until after World War I. By 1929, aerial refueling techniques had improved to the point where U.S. Army Air Corps fliers were able to fly nonstop from Oakland to New York using a Boeing Model 95 mail plane called *Hornet Shuttle*. Several Boeing Model 40Bs had been equipped with extra large-capacity fuel tanks and long hoses and positioned at Elko, Nevada; Cheyenne, Wyoming; Omaha, Nebraska; and Cleveland, Ohio. The *Hornet Shuttle* was met by a Boeing Model 40 in flight, which dropped a hose. The observer in the other aircraft grabbed the hose and fuel was pumped into the Boeing 95.

This stunt remained the high-water mark for aerial refueling for nearly two decades. During World War II, the U.S. Army Air Force considered the development of an operational aerial refueling capability but other more pressing concerns intervened. After World War II, the concept was revived and tested using two Boeing B-29s. It immediately became evident that some means of controlling the refueling hose was needed.

In 1948, the Boeing company developed the "flying boom," a rigid pipe that could be extended to connect the tanker to the aircraft to be refueled. The boom operator in the tanker held the long refueling boom steady while the pilot in the other aircraft slowly moved in to hook up.

With the development of an intercontinental bomber force, aerial refueling became a necessity of paramount importance. The Strategic Air Command (SAC) converted B-29s into KB-29 tankers; then came the famous KC-97 tankers, a variation of the Stratocruiser airliner. Although the KC-97 remained in service with reserve units until the 1970s, it was superseded in the mid-1950s by the KC-135. Today, the U.S. Air Force owns the largest aerial refueling fleet in the world. Nearly all of its 700 KC-135s and 59 new KC-10s are assigned to SAC, which has managed all Air Force tankers since they were consolidated into one command in 1965.

Rather than the flying boom, the U.S. Navy uses the "hose and drogue" method of refueling. The hose and drogue is a variation on the 1929 Air Corps experiment that was refined by the RAF in the late 1940s. With the hose and drogue method, the refueler unreels a hose with a cup (drogue) at the end. The airplane to be refueled slides a probe into the cup and fuel begins to flow. With this system, the tanker can refuel several aircraft at one time.

In the last four decades, aerial refueling has shown itself to be one of the most important innovations in the deployment of combat aircraft. These huge, lumbering tankers help extend the range of smaller aircraft and give larger aircraft virtually unlimited range.

Above: *The KC-10A Extender is the Air Force's aerial tanker version of the DC-10 wide-body jetliner.*

Above: *The KC-10A Extender can serve as both an aerial refueler and a cargo transport aircraft.* Left: *The KC-135R version of the Stratotanker has been equipped with more powerful, fuel efficient engines.*

KC-135 Stratotanker

The twin sister of the world's first successful jetliner, the KC-135 has refueled more airplanes in midair than most airports have refueled on the ground.

Since the end of World War II, the appearance of commercial jet airliners had been expected. But the realization of such aircraft proved elusive, particularly after several British-built Comet jetliners crashed mysteriously. Boeing decided to tackle the commercial program; it based the new jetliner on an aircraft built for the Air Force.

The prototype Boeing jetliner was designated the Model 367-80, or "Dash Eighty," and developed into two aircraft types. One version of the "Dash Eighty" series would become the Model 707 jetliner. The other version entered military service as the C-135 and eventually became the tanker version, designated the KC-135. The KC-135 is often incorrectly identified as a "military 707," but it is really a Model 717.

The 717 arrived on the scene just as the bulk of the Strategic Air Command's (SAC) B-52 fleet was coming on-line. The older Boeing KC-97 tankers could not keep pace with the B-52s, but the 717 could. Given the name Stratotanker, the KC-135 entered service with SAC in 1957. During the Vietnam War, KC-135s were the deciding factor in countless missions over North Vietnam. Though equipped with a flying boom, the Stratotanker can also deploy a hose and drogue for refueling U.S. Navy aircraft, a characteristic that proved very useful in Southeast Asia.

The KC-135 fleet, owned entirely by SAC, supports not only the Air Force but the Navy and the Marine Corps as well. Since 1982, the original KC-135As have been receiving major systems modifications and are being retrofitted with more efficient and quieter General Electric/SNECMA turbofan engines. As each KC-135A is modified, it is redesignated KC-135R. Other KC-135As that are assigned to SAC reserve units are being reengined with surplus Pratt & Whitney turbofans and redesignated KC-135E. There are also several dozen (the exact number is a secret) Stratotankers designated KC-135Q that carry the special JP-7 fuel used only by the SR-71 reconnaissance aircraft.

The basic 707/717 airframe is as durable today as it was revolutionary 40 years ago. Its versatility led to the EC-135 and RC-135 and, ultimately, to the E-3 Sentry AWACS. But its real significance to the Air Force lies in the way KC-135 tankers have enhanced the ability of all the other aircraft to do their jobs more effectively.

Top: *Although all KC-135s are owned by the Strategic Air Command, they provide refueling service for all Air Force commands as well as the Navy and Marines.* Bottom: *The Stratotanker can carry a crew of five and up to 80 passengers.*

BOEING KC-135R STRATOTANKER

Wingspan:	130 ft., 10 in.
Length:	136 ft., 3 in.
Height:	38 ft., 4 in.
Weight (maximum take-off):	322,500 lbs.
Engines:	Four General Electric/SNECMA F108-CF-100 turbofans
Engine thrust:	22,000 lbs.
Operating altitude:	41,000 ft.
Top Speed:	530 mph
Maximum range:	5,000 miles
Date of service:	1957

Top: *KC-135 Stratotankers have been continually upgraded and are expected to remain in service until 2020.* Bottom, left: *The KC-135 serves as the Air Force's primary refueling aircraft.* Bottom, right: *The KC-135R can carry more fuel farther than earlier models.*

KC-10 Extender

In the KC-135 Stratotanker, the refueling boom is operated by a crew member lying face down on a cramped leather couch and peering through a small window. In the KC-10 Extender, the operator sits in a large, comfortable chair before a picture window. The KC-10 is a far larger and more capable tanker than the venerable KC-135. The KC-10 can not only carry a full refueling load but also a full cargo load.

The KC-10's basic airframe is identical to that of the commercial DC-10 airliner. The major differences are, of course, the boom, the boom operator's station, and the near complete absence of windows. What would be the passenger area in the DC-10 is fitted with a standard cargo floor with provisions for bolting in portable seats or tying down cargo pallets. Along the entire lower deck of the KC-10 are huge fuel bladders with a total capacity of 200,000 pounds of jet fuel.

The KC-10 first flew in 1980, a decade after the first DC-10s went into commercial service. Because the KC-10 is based on the DC-10, parts and support facilities are available in emergency situations at commercial airfields around the world. The commonality between the DC-10 and KC-10 also means that Air Force Reserve KC-10 pilots who fly airline DC-10s in civilian life can make an easy transition to the refueler. A total of 59 KC-10 Extenders were built.

Above: *With a full cargo load, the KC-10 Extender has a maximum range of 4,370 miles.*

McDONNELL DOUGLAS KC-10 EXTENDER	
Wingspan:	165 ft., 4.5 in.
Length:	181 ft., 7 in.
Height:	58 ft., 1 in.
Weight (maximum take-off):	590,000 lbs.
Engines:	Three General Electric CF6-50C2 turbofans
Engine thrust:	52,500 lbs.
Operating altitude:	33,400 ft.
Top speed:	610 mph
Maximum range:	11,500 miles
Date of service:	1981

Above: *The KC-10 Extender can refuel an Air Force aircraft with the flying boom system. When using the hose and drogue method, the Extender can refuel up to three Navy or Marine Corps aircraft at one time.* Left: *From his position inside the KC-10, the boom operator controls the refueling boom—or hose—with joysticks.*

UTILITY AND TRANSPORT HELICOPTERS

It was not until the late 1930s that practical helicopters first appeared, and they essentially remained a novelty until the 1950s. The U.S. Army had helicopters during World War II, but they were not widely used overseas because they were considered too slow for most observation missions, too delicate for combat, and too small to have the load-carrying ability to serve as transports. They were referred to as "utility helicopters" because the most they could carry was two or three people.

As it had been with airplanes four decades earlier, the development of helicopters depended on figuring out what they could do and then deciding what to use them for. By the Korean War, it had been determined that the limited capacity of helicopters could be used for search and rescue or medical evacuation missions.

By the 1950s, three major manufacturers had come to the forefront of American helicopter technology. Bell was building small helicopters, Sikorsky was building middle-size machines, and Piasecki (later to become Boeing Vertol) was building large transport helicopters that could carry big loads.

In the 1960s, the Vietnam War saw the helicopter emerge as a major weapons system in the same way that the airplane had come of age during World War II. The CH-47 Chinook proved itself an important cargo hauler; the HH-3 Jolly Green Giant saved many lives deep in enemy territory; and the UH-1 Huey became the single most important motorized vehicle of the entire war.

The American experience in the Vietnam War has been the major factor affecting development of military helicopters since. At the present time, medical evacuation and search and rescue are still important roles for the helicopter, but the payload capacities of today's helicopters far exceed those of Korean War-era transport aircraft. The speed and agility of today's helicopters make them the modern equivalent of a swift cavalry horse.

The largest user of military helicopters in the world today is the U.S. Army, with nearly 9,000 helicopters. The vast majority of these are observation, transport, and utility helicopters; the remainder are attack helicopters. The U.S. Navy and Marine Corps have about 400 helicopters, with roughly one-half assigned to reconnaissance or transport functions. The U.S. Air Force operates fewer than 200 helicopters, which are mostly assigned to utility and rescue work. The U.S. Coast Guard has just over 100 helicopters, all of them assigned to search and rescue.

The helicopter offers the Army the flexibility and air mobility to meet a variety of threats. That the Army relies so much on the helicopter shows how their faith in the helicopter has evolved since the Vietnam War.

Opposite: *The SH-60B Seahawk is the Navy's Light Airborne Multipurpose System (LAMPS) III helicopter.* Left: *The CH-47 Chinook is the Army's heavy-lift helicopter.* Center, left: *A CH-53E Super Stallion, the Navy's heavy-lift helicopter, takes off from the carrier USS* Coral Sea. Center, right: *The HH-53 Super Jolly Green Giant, the Air Force's heavy-lift helicopter, has been in service since 1968.* Bottom: *An illustration of today's modern helicopter, showing elements common to most helicopters.*

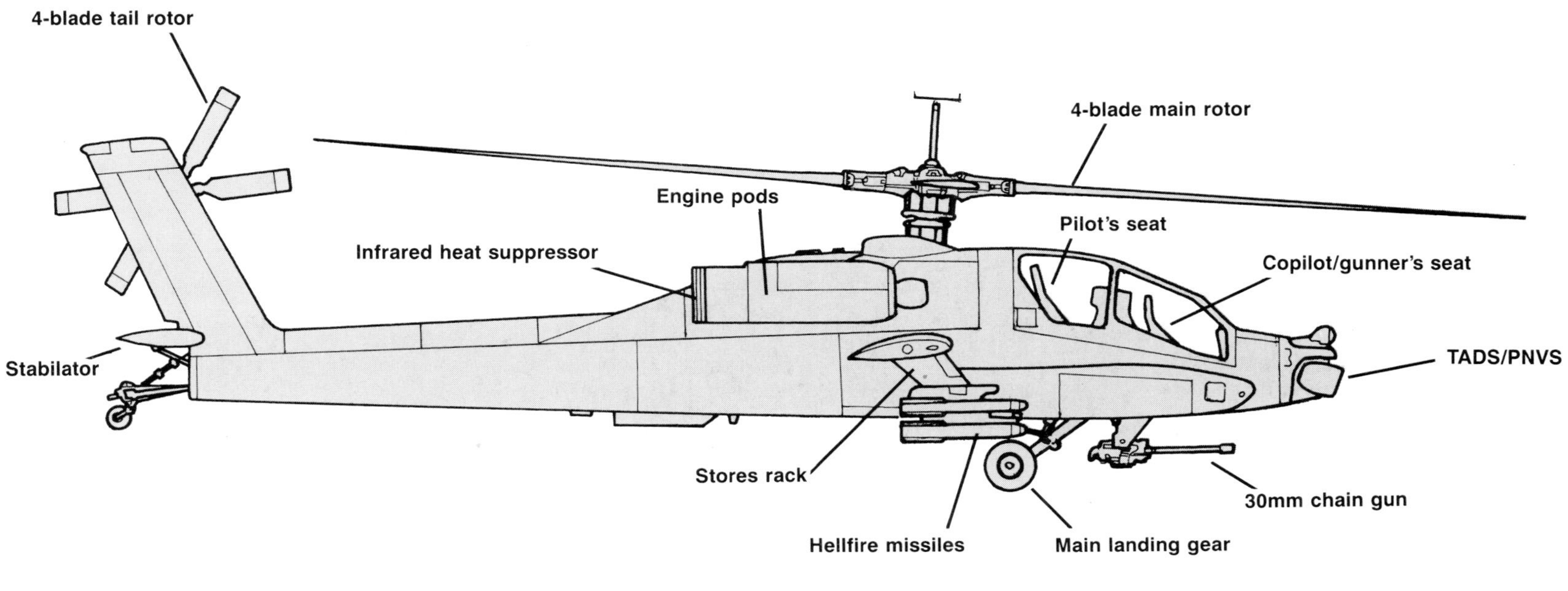

UH-1 Iroquois (Huey)

(BELL MODEL 204)

The UH-1 Huey, the mainstay of American and Army of the Republic of Vietnam forces during the Vietnam War, first flew in 1956 as Bell Helicopter's Model 204. The Model 204 was originally designed as a light utility helicopter to meet the specifications of the United States Army's XH-40 program. The Huey entered military service as the HU-1A and went to Vietnam as an air ambulance in 1962.

The Huey was the first production helicopter equipped with a gas turbine engine. The original was a Lycoming T33 capable of producing 770 horsepower. The overall weight of the Huey in its original A configuration was 5,800 pounds. Lycoming engineers improved the T33 engine until it was capable of producing 1,100 horsepower. With a more powerful engine, Bell engineers were able to build an even larger airframe, the UH-1H. The UH-1H could carry up to 14 fully equipped troops or six stretcher casualties, compared with the eight soldiers or three stretchers of earlier UH-1s.

The UH-1H (Bell civilian designation: Model 205) is powered by a T53-L-13 gas turbine engine. The Huey was the first U.S. military helicopter to have an engine mounted on top of and behind the cabin roof. This type of mounting eased the problems of gearing the main shaft and tail rotor and left the cargo and cockpit space clear of drive shafts and engine bulkheads. Five separate fuel tanks hold a total of 223 gallons of fuel. The rotor (the assembly that turns the helicopter's blades) derives from the successful system developed by Bell. The rotor blades originally were extruded aluminum spars laminated together but are now being replaced by stronger blades of glass fiber composite over a Nomex honeycomb core construction. The trailing edge of the blade is also glass fiber. The leading edge of the blade has a polyurethane covering over a stainless steel sheath, which enables the blade to cut through unexpected obstructions like small tree branches when the aircraft is flying at low altitudes. A twin-engine version of the Huey, the UH-1N Iroquois, is powered by the Pratt & Whitney Canada T400-CP-400 Turbo "Twin Pac."

Since more than 7,000 UH-1s of various configurations have been purchased by more than a dozen nations, the Bell UH-1 has been armed with every type of weaponry a helicopter of its weight and payload capacity can carry. Unless operating in a war zone, most Hueys on military service are unarmed. But if there is a standard weapon load for the Huey, it is three 7.62 millimeter NATO M60 machine guns, one mounted on each skid and one in a door mount operated by the crew chief. The Huey can carry various-sized containers of 2.75-inch free-flight rockets, 20mm and 25mm cannons in pod mounts, 7.62mm NATO miniguns, .50 caliber machine guns, launchers for rockets up to 3.2 inches, 40mm grenade launchers, various antitank missiles, various air-to-ground missiles, and for naval service depth charges and torpedoes.

The famed Huey has been flying for U.S. military services since the early 1960s and will continue to do so well into the 21st century, performing resupply, troop carrying, electronic warfare, medical evacuation, and mine dispersing operations as needed. Today's Huey is far more capable than the first UH-1As and UH-1Bs that saved so many lives in Vietnam. The Hueys of tomorrow will be even more capable when they have been fitted with new composite blades, radar altimeters, infrared jammers and suppressors, new chaff and flare dispensers, and improved avionics (the electrical systems that control the aircraft) and communications gear. No other aircraft has been built for military service in any country in such quantity since the end of World War II.

Below: *The UH-1 Huey's first assignment was as a medical evacuation helicopter.* Right, top: *The "H" version of the Huey was the most numerous production model.* Center, left: *The official name is Iroquois, but the UH-1 is more commonly known as Huey, a nickname derived from the initials of its original service designation.* Center, right: *The Huey and its crews earned an enviable reputation in Vietnam as "can-do" aircraft.* Bottom: *More than 7,000 UH-1 Hueys have been built by Bell Helicopter.*

BELL UH-1H IROQUOIS (HUEY)

Main rotor diameter:	48 ft.
Tail rotor diameter:	8 ft., 6 in.
Length:	57 ft., 9.5 in.
Width:	9 ft., 6.5 in.
Height:	11 ft., 9.75 in.
Weight (maximum take-off):	9,500 lbs.
Maximum altitude:	12,600 ft.
Top speed:	127 mph
Maximum range:	318 miles
Date of service:	1959

The UH-1H Huey can carry a fully equipped infantry squad of 12 soldiers plus weapons.

CH-47 Chinook

(VERTOL MODEL 114)

Above: *The CH-47A Chinook can lift up to eight tons on its external cargo hooks.*

The United States Army in the mid-1950s developed specifications for a helicopter that would be able to operate in all weather conditions and carry the Pershing medium-range guided missile. The Army design specifications also required that the new medium transport helicopter carry a payload of 4,000 pounds internally and 16,000 pounds externally on a sling, accommodate 40 fully equipped troops, and have a cargo ramp and rear clamshell doors that could be opened wide enough to permit light vehicles to drive on and off.

The Vertol Company submitted a stretched and up-engined version of their CH-46 Sea Knight. The first orders for test helicopters were placed in mid-1959. The new helicopter, later called the Chinook, was designated the YH-1B. In 1962, in line with a complete renumbering of all American military aircraft, the craft was redesignated the CH-47. By 1963, the first Chinooks were deployed for active duty with the 1st Cavalry (Airmobile) Division. In September 1965, the 1st Cavalry was ordered to Vietnam with its complement of CH-47A Chinooks.

Four models of the Chinook have been developed since 1963. The A model was powered by two 2,650 horsepower Lycoming T55-L-7 turboshaft engines. The B model was equipped with two 2,850 horsepower T55-LC turboshaft engines and had improved rotor blades. Model C uses two 3,750 horsepower T55-L11C turboshaft engines, and the D model is powered by two T55-L-712 turboshaft engines, each putting out 4,500 horsepower.

The CH-47 Chinook is similar in appearance and design to the CH-46 Sea Knight. The two can be differentiated by the pod-like fairings along both sides of the CH-47 in place of the stub wings on the CH-46. Like the CH-46, the CH-47's twin main rotors turn opposite to one another and are mounted on twin fore-and-aft pylons. Each main rotor has three blades that can be folded alongside one another for transportation by fixed wing aircraft or surface ships. The blades used in the D model are of glass fiber and Nomex honeycomb construction. The two engines are mounted in pods on either side of the rear pylon and drive both rotors. Either engine can power both rotors.

The fuselage is a monocoque construction, a light metal structure covered with sheet metal and glass fiber panels. The bottom half of the fuselage is sealed for on-the-water activities. The rear cargo ramp can be completely lowered while the helicopter is on the ground, in flight, or on the water. For water surface operations, a plastic dam is inflated when the cargo ramp is opened. The cabin, or cargo, area is 30 feet two inches long, seven feet six inches wide, and six feet six inches high. Up to 44 fully equipped soldiers or 24 stretchers can be carried inside. Hooks slung beneath the aircraft enable it to carry bulky cargoes outside—from water tanks to D5 bulldozers (24,750 pounds) to the M198 155 millimeter howitzer (15,600 pounds).

The approximately 493 CH-47A/B models that remain in United States Army service will be converted to the D model configuration by 1993.

BOEING CH-47D CHINOOK

Rotor diameter:	60 ft. (both)
Length:	51 ft.
Width:	12 ft., 5 in.
Height:	18 ft., 7.8 in.
Weight (maximum take-off):	50,000 lbs.
Maximum altitude:	15,000 ft.
Top speed:	185 mph
Maximum range:	115 miles
Date of service:	1963

Top: *The most powerful version of the Chinook is the D model, with engines putting out 4,500 horsepower each.* Bottom: *The CH-47 Chinook's forward and after blades rotate in opposite directions to eliminate the effects of torque.*

CH-3/HH-3 Jolly Green Giant

(SIKORSKY MODEL S-61R)

The "Texas Towers" were built in the late 1950s to provide platforms in the Atlantic Ocean on which to mount early warning radar systems. At that time, the Air Force lacked a helicopter with sufficient range and cargo capacity to resupply the crews of these towers, so they borrowed three SH-3 Sea Kings from the Navy. Air Force personnel involved with the project were so pleased with the Sea King's performance that they borrowed three more.

The following year, the Air Force asked Sikorsky to build an Air Force version of the SH-3. A more powerful set of engines, the General Electric T58-GE-1 turboshaft engines delivering 1,300 horsepower each, was installed. A double-wheel tricycle landing gear and a rear ramp/door that opened and closed hydraulically for drive-on/drive-off vehicle loading were also added. Other changes the Air Force requested included pressurized rotor blades, self-lubricating hubs on both the main and rear rotors, an auxiliary power unit to supply electrical and hydraulic power while on the ground, and a winch and hoist with a 2,000-pound capacity.

The first test flight for the new helicopter took place in June 1963, and the first operational CH-3Bs were delivered in December of that same year. In February 1966, up-rated T58-GE-5 turboshaft engines delivering 1,500 horsepower each were installed in new aircraft. Subsequently, all CH-3Bs were converted to the new engine. Helicopters with the T58-GE-5 engines received the designation CH-3E.

The Air Force Aerospace Rescue and Recovery Service also flew CH-3Es, which they redesignated as the HH-3E, for search and rescue. They were armed with two 7.62 millimeter NATO miniguns, fitted with armor, a rescue hoist, self-sealing fuel tanks, and a retractable in-flight refueling probe. The HH-3E made history as the Jolly Green Giant during the early 1970s with a series of deep-penetration raids into North Vietnam, Laos, and Cambodia to rescue downed American fliers during the Vietnam War. All HH-3E search and rescue helicopters are now assigned to Air Force Reserve and Air National Guard units.

Below: *This Air Force HH-3E Jolly Green Giant is equipped for rescues at sea.*

SIKORSKY CH-3E/HH-3E JOLLY GREEN GIANT

Main rotor diameter:	62 ft.
Tail rotor diameter:	10 ft., 4 in.
Length:	57 ft., 3 in.
Width:	15 ft., 9.5 in.
Height:	18 ft., 1 in.
Weight (maximum take-off):	22,050 lbs.
Maximum altitude:	14,700 ft.
Top speed:	166 mph
Maximum range:	465 miles
Date of service:	1964

Top: *This HH-3E has been equipped with two 450-gallon auxiliary fuel tanks and a refueling probe.* Bottom: *The Air Force originally ordered the HH-3 in 1966 as a special operations version of the CH-3.* Right: *The Air Force, using Jolly Green Giants, plucked hundreds of downed pilots out of enemy-held territory in Vietnam.*

CH-46 Sea Knight

(VERTOL MODEL 107)

The Boeing Sea Knight is a further development of the tandem rotor concept that began in United States military service with the Piasecki HRP-1 "Flying Banana." In 1956, Vertol Helicopter Company began to design an improved medium-lift helicopter, designated the Vertol Model 107. The United States Army ordered ten prototypes—the YHC-1A—for testing, but found them too small. But the Marine Corps and Navy found the Model 107—equipped with a slightly more powerful set of General Electric GE-8B engines—acceptable as a medium assault and transport helicopter. They adopted the Sea Knight as the HRB-1 in February 1961. The following year, in a reordering of all United States military aircraft designations, the Sea Knight was given the Marine Corps designation CH-46. The Navy designation is HH-46 when equipped for search and rescue and RH-46 when set up for mine countermeasures or mine clearing. CH-46 Sea Knights reached Marine Corps squadrons in early 1965 and were promptly sent to active duty in South Vietnam.

The Sea Knight is a twin rotor, twin engine medium-lift helicopter. The two three-bladed rotors turn in opposite directions to eliminate torque (the tendency of a helicopter to spin out of control, caused by the turning of the main rotor), and so the helicopter does not need a tail rotor. The twin General Electric T58-16 turboshaft engines deliver 1,870 horsepower each in the current E model but only 1,400 horsepower in the earlier D and F models. The engines are mounted on either side of the after pylon. The forward rotor, which is mounted on the front pylon, is linked to the engines by a high-speed drive shaft running through a tunnel atop the stressed-skin fuselage. Either engine can drive either rotor, and one engine can drive both.

The cockpit seats the pilot and copilot side by side. The cargo hold is 24 feet long, six feet wide, and six feet high. The cargo hold is equipped with a large side door and a rear ramp. The CH-46 can carry 25 fully equipped troops. Light vehicles can be driven into the cargo hold. When used as a medevac helicopter, as many as 15 stretchers can be accommodated.

While the CH-46 is normally unarmed, for protection while in combat zones it can be equipped with either a 7.62 millimeter NATO or a .50 caliber door-mounted machine gun manned by the crew chief. The Navy's RH-46 Sea Knight can be fitted with Mark 44 or Mark 46 antisubmarine torpedoes.

The United States Navy and Marine Corps purchased 624 Sea Knights before production ended in the early 1970s. A series of upgrade programs has been instituted to allow the Sea Knight to continue to fly well into the next century. All earlier D and F models are slated to be up-rated to the more powerful E model. The CH-46 in its numerous variations is flown by the United States Marine Corps and Navy as well as the military services of Canada, Japan, Sweden, and Thailand.

Above: *Both the Navy and Marine Corps fly the CH-46 Sea Knight.*

Above: *The CH-46 Sea Knight serves with the armed forces of a dozen other nations. It is seen here in the colors of the Canadian Armed Forces.*
Right: *The CH-46 Sea Knight is capable of landing on a variety of ships.*

BOEING CH-46E SEA KNIGHT	
Rotor diameter:	51 ft. (both)
Length:	44 ft., 7 in.
Width:	12 ft., 8 in.
Height:	16 ft., 9 in.
Weight (maximum take-off):	21,400 lbs.
Maximum altitude:	10,000 ft.
Top speed:	166 mph
Maximum range:	222 miles
Date of service:	1965

The CH-46 Sea Knight is the medium-lift and chief troop-carrying helicopter of the U.S. Marines.

CH-53 Sea Stallion/HH-53 Super Jolly Green Giant

(SIKORSKY MODEL S-65)

When the United States Marine Corps needed a new assault and transport helicopter, they turned to Sikorsky Aircraft. Sikorsky developed the basic design for a large cargo-carrying helicopter, the CH-53 Sea Stallion (Sikorsky model designation S-65).

The CH-53 has a watertight hull with a rear-opening ramp to permit loading of bulky cargo. The cargo hold, equipped with reversible skid-roller strips set into the titanium floor, is 30 feet long, seven feet six inches wide, and six feet six inches high. Light vehicles and artillery pieces up to the size and weight of a 105 millimeter howitzer can be winched into the hold. A total of 37 fully equipped troops, 24 stretchers loaded on special racks, or up to 8,000 pounds of cargo can be carried. With its rotors turning, the CH-53 Sea Stallion can operate directly on the water, and its rear cargo ramp can be lowered after an inflatable waterproof dam is erected.

Above: *The CH-53D Sea Stallion provides the major heavy-lift capacity for the Marine Corps.*

The CH-53 uses the "boom and pod" fuselage on which the rear stabilizer and tail rotor are mounted. The cockpit seats three crew members: pilot, copilot, and crew chief in the jump seat behind the pilot and copilot. The CH-53's blades are pressurized to warn of cracks. Since the CH-53 operates from aircraft carriers and assault landing ships, the main rotor blades and the end of the tail boom, which carries the vertical/horizontal stabilizer and tail rotor, fold hydraulically.

Normally, the CH-53 is not armed, but it can be configured to carry a fairly wide variety of weaponry. In a combat zone, the minimum armament would be a door-mounted .50 caliber machine gun or a 7.62mm NATO minigun or machine gun.

The CH-53A entered service with the Marine Corps in September 1966 and was sent to Vietnam in January of the following year. The new heavy-lift helicopter moved troops and equipment around the country and hauled combat-ready soldiers into hot landing zones until U.S. forces ceased military operations there in 1973. In the years since, CH-53s have formed the backbone of the Marine Corps' heavy-lift capability.

The CH-53 has been extensively up-rated since the introduction of the initial A model, which was powered by two 2,850 horsepower General Electric T64-6 turboshaft engines. In 1966, the United States Air Force ordered a more powerful version of the CH-53A, powered by twin 3,080 horsepower T64-GE-3 turboshaft engines, to supplement its HH-3 Jolly Green Giants. Designated the HH-53B, they flew long-range search and rescue missions during the Vietnam War and came to be called "Super Jolly Green Giants." An up-rated version now in use, the HH-53C, employs two T64-GE-7 engines delivering 3,925 horsepower each. The HH-53Cs are also equipped with auxiliary fuel tanks, a retractable in-flight refueling probe, a rescue hook, and an external hoist capable of lifting 20,000 pounds.

The current version of the CH-53 used by the Marine Corps is the CH-53D, which entered service in March 1969.

SIKORSKY CH-53D SEA STALLION/HH-53C SUPER JOLLY GREEN GIANT	
Main rotor diameter:	72 ft., 3 in.
Tail rotor diameter:	16 ft.
Length:	67 ft., 2 in.
Width:	15 ft., 5 in.
Height:	24 ft., 11 in.
Weight (maximum take-off):	36,400 lbs.
Maximum altitude:	6,500 ft.
Top speed:	196 mph
Maximum range:	257 miles
Date of service:	1966

The CH-53D has a unique cargo handling system that permits one person to load the aircraft. The more powerful T64-GE-413 turboshaft engines deliver 3,925 horsepower each and give the helicopter a maximum speed of 196 miles per hour. The T64-GE-413 engine is also far easier to maintain. The CH-53D can carry 55 fully equipped troops.

The CH-53 is also operated by the United States Navy as a minesweeping helicopter. Designated the MH-53D, it possesses a variety of mineclearing equipment and electronics. Four MH-53Ds aboard the USS *Shreveport* took part in the 1984 Red Sea operation to clear mines placed by Libya in an attempt to shut down that waterway.

To upgrade the capability of the Air Force's Special Operations Forces, 33 HH-53s have been converted to the MH-53J PAVE LOW III Enhanced configuration. They have been equipped with terrain-following and terrain-avoidance radars, communications equipment for secure communications, titanium armor, and mountings for either a .50 caliber machine gun or the 7.62mm NATO minigun.

Sikorsky's CH-53/HH-53 series has a long and honorable history of service with the Marine Corps, Navy, and Air Force. It has compiled one of the best safety records of all military aircraft flying today.

Top: *This Sea Stallion is equipped for the mine clearing role.* Left: *The CH-53D Sea Stallion can deliver 37 fully armed troops into the battle zone.*

This Sea Stallion belongs to HM-14 Squadron and is equipped for mineclearing; the mineclearing gear is deployed on the rear ramp.

53

UH-60A Black Hawk/SH-60B Seahawk

(SIKORSKY MODEL S-70)

In the early 1970s, the United States Army identified a need for a more advanced utility helicopter than the UH-1 Huey that would perform a variety of roles into the next century. The Utility Tactical Transport Aircraft System (UTTAS) program to develop such a craft was started, and in 1972, two companies—Sikorsky and Boeing Vertol—were selected to supply prototypes. In late December 1976, the Army selected Sikorsky as the prime contractor; the first deliveries of the new UH-60A Black Hawk were made in 1978.

The Black Hawk has a single main rotor and a boom-mounted tail rotor. The main rotor can survive hits from .50 caliber or 23 millimeter armor-piercing shells. The rotor hub uses elastomeric bearings that do not need lubrication and require far less maintenance than traditional metal bearings. The blade tips are swept back 20 degrees, and the trailing edges have tabs to improve airflow. The blades are made of hollow titanium spars, Nomex honeycomb cores, graphite trailing edges, and glass fiber leading edges, all covered with glass fiber and epoxy skins. The leading edges are sheathed in titanium.

Two General Electric T700-700 turboshaft engines provide 1,543 horsepower each and drive a single transmission. The Black Hawk also carries a Solar auxiliary power unit—a small, 90 horsepower gas turbine engine—for operations independent of ground support. The fuel system was designed to be crashworthy—that is, in most crashes the fuel is not expected to catch fire or explode. The fuselage is sufficiently armored to withstand hits from .30 caliber weapons.

The Black Hawk can be armed with one or two side-mounted machine guns, Hellfire guided missiles, 2.75-inch rockets, and the M56 mine-dispersing system. The helicopter carries a crew of three, and the pilot's and copilot's seats are armored. The aircraft can also carry a full infantry squad (11 troops), but as many as 14 soldiers can be crammed into the main cabin in what Sikorsky denotes as "high-density seating." Eight of the seats can be replaced with racks for four stretchers. The Black Hawk is equipped with an external cargo hook with an 8,000-pound cargo capacity. Despite its capacity, the Black Hawk is small enough that one can be carried in a C-130 Hercules, two in a C-141 Starlifter, and six in a C-5 Galaxy transport aircraft.

Since its introduction in 1978, the UH-60A Black Hawk has undergone a number of modifications for specialized missions. The Army developed the EH-60A to carry Quick Fix IIB electronic countermeasures equipment for disrupting and monitoring enemy battlefield communications. The EH-60A can be identified by the four dipole antennae that project above and below the boom and the whip antennae attached beneath the fuselage.

The Air Force ordered a version of the UH-60A, known as the HH-60A Night Hawk, for use as a combat rescue helicopter. The Night Hawk is armed with 7.62mm NATO machine guns. The Air Force is also purchasing a second version of the UH-60A, known as the MH-60G Pave Hawk that will be fitted with special instrumentation, including radar, electronic map displays, tactical air navigation systems, and .50 caliber machine guns.

The Marine Corps has purchased nine VH-60A Black Hawks to replace its VH-1N

Above: *The UH-60 Black Hawk was designed to replace the UH-1 Huey as an all-purpose utility helicopter.*

SIKORSKY UH-60A BLACK HAWK/SH-60B SEAHAWK

Main rotor diameter:	53 ft., 8 in.
Tail rotor diameter:	11 ft.
Length:	50 ft., 0.75 in
Width:	7 ft., 9 in.
Height:	16 ft., 10 in.
Weight (maximum take-off):	16,260 lbs.
Maximum altitude:	19,000 ft.
Top speed:	184 mph
Maximum range:	373 miles
Date of service:	1978

Hueys in the Executive Flight Detachment of Marine Helicopter Squadron 1, the unit that flies the President and other administration officials.

The Navy has also purchased a variation of the Sikorsky S-70, designated the SH-60B Seahawk, for their Light Airborne Multipurpose System (LAMPS) Mark III program. The Navy's version differs from the Army's in having gas turbine engines specially constructed for operation in humid and salty environments, chin pods, pylon mounts to hold either two Mark 44 or Mark 46 homing torpedoes or extra fuel tanks, magnetic anomaly detection equipment, a fourth crew space for the sensor operator, greater fuel capacity, rescue hoist, automatic blade-folding devices for the main and tail rotors, and a haul-down device for landing the helicopter on small ships in rough seas. The Seahawk is to be deployed on all *Oliver Hazard Perry*-class frigates, *Spruance*-class and *Kidd*-class destroyers, and *Ticonderoga*-class cruisers.

Another Navy version of the Seahawk, the SH-60F, is being deployed as an antisubmarine warfare (ASW) helicopter to patrol the "inner zone" of an aircraft carrier battle group. The SH-60F carries specialized ASW instrumentation, including dipping sonar and Mark 50 homing torpedoes. The Navy has also ordered a combat search and rescue version, the HH-60H, that can support Navy Sea-Air-Land (SEAL) commandoes and Underwater Demolition Team special forces.

Top: *The SH-60 Seahawk is the Navy's version of the Black Hawk.* Bottom: *The MH-60G Pave Hawk is the latest Air Force version of the Black Hawk. The Air Force uses the Pave Hawk as a rescue helicopter.*

The Black Hawk's power and maneuverability make it an excellent helicopter for over-the-water rescues.

CH-53E Super Stallion/MH-53E Sea Dragon

(SIKORSKY MODEL S-80)

With the advent of the over-the-horizon concept of amphibious landings (amphibious landings originating from beyond the horizon), a powerful and fast helicopter was needed to carry massive amounts of supplies and large numbers of fully equipped troops into amphibious landing zones from ships far out at sea. The Marine Corps and Sikorsky evolved the CH-53E Super Stallion version of the heavy-lift CH-53 Sea Stallion; it flew for the first time in March 1974.

From a distance, the two helicopters look identical, but a closer look reveals four distinct differences. First is the third General Electric T64-416 turboshaft engine mounted on the transmission fairing above and slightly behind the starboard engine which helps the CH-53E reach a top speed of 193 miles per hour. This is fast enough that it can be refueled in flight by a KC-130 Hercules tanker.

The second difference is the extra wide and thick sponsons jutting from either side of the fuselage that serve to stabilize the huge helicopter when conducting on-the-water operations. The sponsons also function as fuel tanks, giving the CH-53E a total internal capacity of 1,017 gallons. Additional external drop tanks holding 650 gallons of fuel each can be mounted on the sponsons.

The third difference is the vertical stabilizer and a larger tail rotor, which are cocked to the left. The horizontal stabilizer forms a gull-like wing and is supported by a strut. The fourth and final difference is found in the blades of the seven-bladed main rotor, which are made of titanium and glass fiber. The earlier CH-53A/D models used a six-bladed main rotor. The CH-53E's blades are attached to the main hub by extension straps that make it appear as if the main rotor is greater in diameter than that of the A/D models.

Above: *The CH-53E Super Stallion is one of the most powerful heavy-lift helicopters outside the Soviet Union.*

The extra blade on the CH-53E required modifications to the main rotor assembly, particularly the hub, which nearly doubled in size. The main hub is manufactured of steel and titanium and uses elastomeric (a synthetic, flexible material) rather than mechanical bearings. As in the CH-53A/D series, the blades are pressurized to warn of cracks.

The three General Electric T64-416 turboshaft engines are rated at 4,380 horsepower each. The seventh blade, coupled with the new engines, nearly doubles the lifting power of the CH-53E over that of the CH-53A/D, making the Super Stallion one of the most powerful heavy-lift helicopters outside the Soviet Union.

The cargo hold, or main cabin, is about the same size as that of the CH-53A/D Sea Stallion, but more cargo can be carried because of the more powerful engines. The CH-53E can carry a maximum payload in excess of 36,000 pounds

SIKORSKY CH-53E SUPER STALLION/MH-53E SEA DRAGON

Main rotor diameter:	79 ft.
Tail rotor diameter:	20 ft.
Length:	73 ft., 4 in.
Width:	13 ft.
Height:	18 ft., 7 in.
Weight (maximum take-off):	73,500 lbs.
Maximum altitude:	9,500 ft.
Top speed:	193 mph
Maximum range:	1,290 miles
Date of service:	1981

compared with the 8,000-pound payload of the CH-53A/D Sea Stallion. Instead of 37 fully equipped troops, the Super Stallion can carry 55. The CH-53E can also carry up to seven standard cargo pallets. Using its winch and cargo hook, the Super Stallion can carry one LAV-25 (Light Armored Vehicle), which weighs 27,500 pounds, plus add-on fuel tanks.

The cockpit of the CH-53E is similar to that of the CH-53A/D and carries a crew of three. But the instrumentation and flight controls have been uprated. The Super Stallion uses two computers and a new autopilot in addition to the latest in automated navigation equipment.

The United States Navy flies the MH-53E Sea Dragon in the mine countermeasures role. The Navy version can be instantly recognized by the extremely large sponsons that carry additional fuel to enable the MH-53E to operate for long periods of time. The MH-53E is powerful enough to tow mechanical, acoustical, or magnetic hydrofoil sleds to detect various types of submerged mines.

Normally, the CH-53E and the MH-53E are not armed, but a variety of weapons systems from depth charges to AIM-9 Sidewinder missiles for air-to-air combat can be fitted. In an active combat zone, whether serving in the assault/transport role or on search and rescue duties, the CH-53E would be expected to carry either a .50 caliber machine gun or the 7.62 millimeter NATO minigun as a bare minimum.

Top: *The Super Stallion is a three-engine version of the earlier CH-53A/D Sea Stallion.* Bottom: *This Sea Dragon is equipped with extra-capacity sponson fuel tanks for mineclearing missions.*

After dropping its load of combat-ready troops, a Marine Corps CH-53E Super Stallion lifts off.

ATTACK HELICOPTERS

To distinguish between attack helicopters and utility and transport helicopters, it is necessary to see attack helicopters as the fighters and bombers of the helicopter world. Most military helicopters are capable of carrying guns. Some, such as the UH-60A Black Hawk, can even carry Hellfire missiles. But the distinguishing feature of attack helicopters is that combat is their primary, and in most cases, only role.

Before World War I, no one had a clear idea of the offensive potential of the airplane. Before the war in Vietnam, no one considered the helicopter a serious offensive weapon. That thinking began to change in 1964, when UH-1 Huey utility helicopters in Vietnam were armed with machine guns to protect other Hueys transporting troops into battle. But even with machine guns, the UH-1 Huey was still a big and lumbering target. The next step was the AH-1 HueyCobra gunship, whose sole job was to provide suppressing fire while UH-1 Hueys went about the business of moving troops and supplies. The HueyCobra became the model for all attack helicopters flying today.

The helicopter has established an undisputed place on the modern battlefield. With its unique capability for vertical flight and low-and-slow loitering, the helicopter has become indispensable to any modern army. Today, attack helicopters have essentially two roles to perform in support of ground combat elements. First, they provide fire support for friendly ground troops against either enemy troop concentrations or enemy armor. In light of the advances made in main battle tanks and armored fighting vehicles in the last three decades, this task has taken on major importance. Second, helicopters are developing a role in securing air superiority over the battlefield.

This second role is a new one. It first attracted serious attention after the 1982 Falkland Islands War. While slow-flying helicopters are relatively immune to speedier fixed wing aircraft, three Argentinean helicopters fell victim to British Harrier jump jets; Harriers can match the helicopter's ability to hover and fly slow and low. If a Harrier can shoot down a helicopter, the thinking of military experts went, then another helicopter should be able to do the same.

The phenomenon of air-to-air combat between helicopters was reported during the Iran-Iraq war but has not been documented in detail (at least publicly). In 1983, the Army and Marine Corps conducted extensive testing, both in the air and on computers, of various helicopters in the air-combat role. The results were more than promising. Like World War I fighter planes, the helicopter that can turn inside the other in a climbing, spiraling dogfight has the edge. Armed with fire-and-forget missiles and 25 millimeter or 30mm chain guns, the air-combat helicopter will be a potent addition to the weapon systems of any army.

From little-used utility helicopters during World War II through medical evacuation operations in Korea to the first gunships of Vietnam, the helicopter continues its evolution toward greater attack capabilities. Air-to-air combat helicopters have defined the newest genre of combat aircraft on the modern battlefield.

Opposite: *The Bell AH-1 HueyCobra developed from the famed UH-1 Huey.* Left: *The AH-64A Apache is the world's toughest gunship; its special task is tank busting.* Bottom, left: *The SH-2F Seasprite is the Navy's Light Airborne Multipurpose System I helicopter.* Bottom, right: *The SH-3H Sea King serves the Navy as a specialized antisubmarine warfare and sea rescue helicopter.*

SH-3 Sea King

(SIKORSKY MODEL S-61)

While the Sikorsky Model S-58 proved to be quite a bit more powerful and versatile than its predecessor, the S-55, it still could not carry a sufficient payload to enable it to operate alone in the antisubmarine warfare (ASW) mode. In 1957, the United States Navy asked for a new ASW-capable helicopter that could carry out both the hunter and killer roles. Previously, two SH-34 Seabats had been used as a team, one serving as the hunter, the other as the killer.

The new helicopter, designated Model S-61, was a further improvement on the S-58. The S-61 was developed as an amphibious, all-weather craft that could also serve in the transport and search and rescue roles. Powered by two General Electric T58-GE-8 engines, the new helicopter could carry a full complement of ASW electronics, including a Bendix AQS-13B, AQS-13F, or AQS-18 dipping sonar; doppler radar and radar altimeter; active and passive sonobuoys; smoke markers and smoke floats; and Texas Instruments' AQS-81(V) Magnetic Anomaly Detector. The S-61 can also carry 840 pounds of weapons, including the Mark 44 or Mark 46 homing torpedo. Weapons capacity has been up-rated in later versions to nearly 8,000 pounds. In September 1961, the first deliveries of the SH-3 Sea King were made to the Navy's VHS-3 Squadron at Norfolk, Virginia, and VHS-10 Squadron at San Diego, California. The SH-3 Sea King thus became the first practical ASW helicopter in service anywhere in the world.

The SH-3 is capable of landing on water and remaining stable even in fairly heavy seas as long as the rotors are turning. Two pontoonlike floats carried in pods extending from either side of the fuselage provide additional support to the amphibious hull. The SH-3 has both a fully functional autopilot and autostabilization system, which are linked to the doppler radar and the radar altimeter. This allows the pilot to program a set course for the helicopter to fly while hunting a submarine.

Above: *This SH-3 Sea King is about to deploy its Bendix AQS-13B sonar probe to search for a submarine.*

Current models of the Sea King have up-rated T58-GE-8R turboshaft engines that deliver 1,500 horsepower each. This up-rating improves performance when carrying a full weapons load, which can include the MB57 Mark 1 Nuclear Depth Charge. The engines are mounted above the cockpit and drive the five-bladed rotors. Since the SH-3 was designed primarily for shipboard use, the rotor blades fold automatically. The tail rotor also folds for storage.

The S-61 has found a variety of uses that its designers probably did not foresee. The Air Force liked the large cargo compartment as well as the powerful 1,500 horsepower engines. They acquired the S-61 for search and rescue operations at a time when long-range penetration of North Vietnam to rescue downed American fliers had become a growing concern. In addition, the Navy has used the S-61 as a minesweeper (RH-3A) and has armed it with a 7.62 millimeter NATO minigun, extra fuel capacity, armor, and a high-speed rescue hoist for its search and rescue mode. The S-61 also forms part of the fleet of helicopters belonging to the Executive Flight Detachment in Washington, D.C., which is responsible for transporting the President as well as other senior administration executives.

SIKORSKY SH-3D SEA KING

Main rotor diameter:	62 ft.
Tail rotor diameter:	10 ft., 7 in.
Length:	54 ft., 9 in.
Width:	16 ft., 4 in.
Height:	16 ft., 10 in.
Weight (maximum take-off):	18,626 lbs.
Maximum altitude:	4,900 ft.
Top speed:	166 mph
Maximum range:	625 miles
Date of service:	1961

Top, left: *Until recently, the VH-3A Sea King was used to transport the President and other high-ranking officials of the United States.* Top, right: *The SH-3 Sea King has a range of 625 miles and a maximum speed of 166 miles per hour.* Bottom, left: *The rugged Sea King has been chosen by several foreign military forces as their antisubmarine warfare helicopter. This one wears the colors of the Canadian Armed Services.* Bottom, right: *The yellow-finned magnetic anomaly detector, behind the right landing gear of this SH-3 Sea King, is used for antisubmarine warfare operations.*

The SH-3 Sea King has served as the Navy's standard carrier-based antisubmarine helicopter since 1961.

745 NAVY
743 NAVY
742 NAVY
HS-12
741 NAVY
HS-12

SH-2 Seasprite

(KAMAN MODEL K-20)

Above: *A total of 192 SH-2 Seasprite helicopters were built by Kaman. After a lapse of 15 years, 48 more were ordered by the Navy.*

The Kaman Seasprite has one of the longest records of service of any United States military helicopter. Charles H. Kaman, a former Sikorsky employee and one of the foremost American helicopter pioneers, developed a flight control system for helicopters that did not angle the blade to change pitch. (Pitch is the angle at which the rotor blade meets the air.) In his system, hinged trailing-edge flaps, or "servo tabs," on the outer portion of each blade moved to change the blade's angle of attack pitch. Kaman won a mid-1950s Navy competition to design a high-speed, all-weather helicopter. He used the more traditional single main and tail rotor design but included his servo tab blade-control mechanism. The result was the HU-2 Seasprite.

The Seasprite had retractable landing gear, a watertight hull, and a small fuselage that could carry 11 passengers. The helicopter was fitted with folding rotor blades and a cable haul and tie down system, first pioneered by the German Navy during World War II. The nose could be folded back to reduce the aircraft's length when stowed aboard ships or aircraft carriers. The Seasprite has been in United States Navy service since its introduction in December 1962.

The initial production UH-2A (the designation was changed to SH-2A in the 1962 renumbering of all military aircraft) was powered by a single 1,250 horsepower General Electric T58-GE-8B turboshaft engine mounted ahead of the main rotor. Initial shipboard service in 1963 on the USS *Independence* and the USS *Albany* showed that the craft was underpowered, and in 1965 two GE T58 engines in outboard mountings were substituted. These engines provided much improved performance plus the safety of an additional engine for operations over water. All single engine SH-2A/Bs have been converted to the twin engine model SH-2C.

SH-2Cs conducting search and rescue missions (designated HH-2C) were armed with a 7.62 millimeter NATO minigun in a chain turret, .50 caliber or .30 caliber machine guns mounted in the waist doors, and armor plating at all critical areas. A subsequent HH-2D version was left unarmed and unarmored.

Two HH-2Ds were further modified by installing radar systems under the helicopter's nose to detect surface ships and surfaced submarines. This led to the Light Airborne Multipurpose System (LAMPS) program to convert all SH-2s to SH-2F standards and deploy them for antisubmarine warfare, antiship surveillance and targeting, and search and rescue operations.

The main rotor hub is made of titanium, and the blades, which can be folded, are of aluminum and glass fiber. The tricycle landing gear has two wheels per side in front that fold forward. The fixed rear landing gear has a single tire and is steerable. Two General Electric 1,350 horsepower T58-GE-8F turboshaft engines provide the power. The SH-2F can carry 476 U.S. gallons of fuel. It can also be fitted with two external tanks and can be refueled ship-to-helicopter, while the aircraft is hovering.

The SH-2F carries a crew of three: pilot, copilot/tactical coordinator (also known as a Taco), and sensor operator. When fitted for the LAMPS role, the electronics of the SH-2F include surveillance radar; tactical navigation systems; UHF radios; magnetic anomaly detector; sonobuoy receiver, recorder, and data link; sonobuoys; eight Mark 25 smoke markers; up to two Mark 46 torpedoes; cargo hook; and rescue hoist.

Above: *This SH-2F LAMPS I from the Navy's HSL-31 Squadron carries a Mk 46 torpedo.* Left: *The SH-2F carries a pilot, copilot, and an antisubmarine warfare systems operator.*

KAMAN SH-2F SEASPRITE

Main rotor diameter:	44 ft.
Tail rotor diameter:	8 ft.
Length:	40 ft., 6 in.
Width:	12 ft., 3 in.
Height:	13 ft., 7 in.
Weight (maximum take-off):	13,500 lbs.
Maximum altitude:	22,500 ft.
Top speed:	165 mph
Maximum range:	431 miles
Date of service:	1963

This SH-2F refuels while airborne; the helicopter's LN-66 radar is visible in the round housing under the nose.

NAVY

AH-1 HueyCobra

(BELL MODEL 209)

Above: *The SuperCobra is a later development of the AH-1 HueyCobra, the first gunship helicopter in U.S. military service.*

To the untrained eye, the shorter and far more slender AH-1 HueyCobra looks nothing like its parent, the fat-bodied, lumbering UH-1 Huey. In 1965, Bell Helicopter began to develop a specific Huey variation to serve as an armed helicopter to escort slow, unarmed or lightly armed transports and medevac choppers. Today, the AH-1W SuperCobra is a "do anything, go anywhere" combat helicopter that can fly escort missions or bust tanks.

The HueyCobra first flew in September 1965. Basically, the new helicopter retained the engine, transmission, and other major parts of the Huey, but the bulky fuselage was replaced with a new, thin-profile fuselage. Stub wings were added to ease the load on the main rotor and serve as attaching points for additional weapons. The narrow fuselage dictated a tandem cockpit seating arrangement, and the pilot was placed behind and above the copilot/weapons operator.

A turret was mounted under the nose of the fuselage to carry miniguns, rapid firing cannons, or grenade launchers, which are controlled by the copilot/weapons operator. When the copilot/weapons operator releases the weapon controls, the turret resumes a locked fore and aft position and the pilot can fire the weapons while flying the helicopter. Aiming in this case is done by turning the helicopter. The copilot/weapons operator can also fly the helicopter.

The initial model designation of the HueyCobra was AH-1G. The AH-1G was powered by a Lycoming T53-L-13 turboshaft engine producing 1,100 horsepower. The United States Army acquired the majority of the AH-1Gs produced, but Israel and the Spanish Navy ordered six and eight, respectively. The United States Marine Corps ordered a twin engine version, the AH-1J SeaCobra. Two Pratt & Whitney Canada T400-CP-400 twin turboshaft engines coupled to a single transmission provided 1,100 horsepower for the SeaCobra, as well as the insurance of an extra engine for over-the-water emergencies.

Soon, however, the Army wanted an attack helicopter powerful enough to cope with the growing threat of Soviet and Warsaw Pact tanks. The TOW missile provided the Army with a guided missile potent enough to destroy any Soviet main battle tank. The first HueyCobra model to be fitted with the TOW was the AH-1Q, which was intended as an interim solution until the modernized HueyCobra, the AH-1S, could be developed.

The modernized versions of the HueyCobra were delivered in three phases. The first AH-1S, which entered Army service in March 1977, had a flat plate canopy, new and more extensive electronics, and the up-rated Lycoming T53-L-703 1,800 horsepower turboshaft engine. The second phase included a new universal turret mounting either a 20 millimeter or 30mm gun. The third phase, the "modernized" AH-1S, had new composite rotor blades, a new fire control system that included a laser range finder, an improved navigation system, and an infrared jammer. All versions of the AH-1S are capable of firing the TOW missile.

The most recent enhancement for the HueyCobra is the C-NITE project, which provides the HueyCobra with the ability to kill tanks at night. The C-NITE sight uses the tank thermal imager developed for the M-1 Abrams Main Battle Tank and the TOW 2 system video thermal tracker from the Bradley Armored Fighting Vehicle.

Other versions of the HueyCobra include the United States Marines' AH-1T SeaCobra and AH-1W SuperCobra. The AH-1T, which carries a more powerful Pratt & Whitney Canada T400-WV-402, is an up-rated version of the twin-engine AH-1J. The AH-1W SuperCobra "Whiskey," originally called the AH-1T+, is powered by twin General Electric T700-GE-401 turboshaft engines producing 3,250 horsepower. All AH-1T SeaCobras in the Marine Corps inventory have now been up-rated to the AH-1W configuration.

BELL AH-1S HUEYCOBRA

Main rotor diameter:	44 ft.
Tail rotor diameter:	8 ft., 6 in.
Length:	44 ft., 7 in.
Width:	3 ft., 3 in.
Height:	13 ft., 5 in.
Weight (maximum take-off):	10,000 lbs.
Maximum altitude:	12,200 ft.
Top speed:	141 mph
Maximum range:	315 miles
Date of service:	1966

Above: *This AH-1 HueyCobra is loaded with TOW antitank missiles mounted under its stub wings.* Left: *Helicopter gunships, such as this AH-1 HueyCobra, operate in close conjunction with ground forces.* Bottom, left: *The M230 30mm chain gun, which fires shells tipped with depleted uranium, is clearly visible on this Marine Corps AH-1W SuperCobra.* Bottom, right: *The AH-1T Improved SeaCobra is a twin-engine version of the original AH-1 built for the Marine Corps.*

An AH-1 HueyCobra gunship (foreground) flies in tandem with an OH-58 Kiowa (background).

530M Defender

(McDONNELL DOUGLAS MODEL 500M)

The wasp-like Defender resulted from the United States Army's Light Observation Helicopter (LOH) competition in the early 1960s. The LOH was expected to fly medical evacuation, close support, photo reconnaissance, light transport, and observation duties. Hughes Helicopter's entry won the competition in May 1965.

Designated the OH-6A, this small helicopter was extremely fast and agile as well as durable—one was shot down five times in South Vietnam and repaired each time—but far more costly to build than anticipated. The OH-6As developed a fine service record in South Vietnam, where they were called "Loaches," derived from the acronym, LOH.

After the military contract ended, Hughes Helicopter—which became a subsidiary of McDonnell Douglas in 1984—continued to build the OH-6A under the designation Model 500 for civilian use as a corporate helicopter. To expand its market, Hughes developed an armed military model called the Model 500M. It used the same Allison T63-A-5A turboshaft engine as the earlier OH-6A. An up-rated version of the 500M, the 500M Defender (500MD), has been configured to carry the TOW wire-guided missile.

The original OH-6A was the first production light helicopter to use a gas turbine engine. The Allison T63-A-5A engine gave the small helicopter such extraordinary performance that it set 23 world records. The 530MD series, an up-rated version of the 500MD series, uses a more powerful 420 horsepower Allison 250-C-20B turboshaft engine.

The original OH-6A Cayuse employed a four-bladed main rotor 26 feet four inches in diameter and a single, twin-bladed tail rotor mounted at the end of the tail boom. A vertical, down-pointing stabilizer helped offset engine torque (the tendency of a helicopter to spin out of control, caused by the turning of the main rotor).

The helicopters in the 500/530 series can be differentiated from the original OH-6A by the five-bladed main rotor and the tail rotor mounted inside a T-shaped stabilizer.

The Scout Defender carries a wide variety of armament, including 2.75-inch rockets, a 7.62 millimeter NATO minigun, and a 40mm grenade launcher or a 7.62mm chain gun. The 500MD/TOW Defender is an antitank version of the Scout Defender and comes armed with four TOW air-to-ground missiles mounted in two pods. The TOW Defender can be easily identified by the TOW pods on outriggers at the rear of the cabin and by the turret, which houses the TOW sight, slung under the nose. The 500MD/ASW Defender is equipped for antisubmarine work. The 530MF Defender is an assault, support, and anti-armor helicopter, but it can also perform scouting, day/night surveillance, utility, and cargo-lift missions.

The 530MG Defender is the latest version to be offered in this well-tested series. It is powered by the Allison 250-C30 turboshaft engine producing 650 horsepower. The 530MG Defender can carry 2.75-inch rockets, TOW missiles, 7.62mm and .50 caliber machine guns, Stingers, and the 7.62mm McDonnell Douglas chain gun. Based on the larger, more powerful civilian MD 530F Lifter, the 530MG integrates much of the technology that will appear in the United States Army's Light Helicopter Experimental (LHX) program, which is designed to produce a new light, all-purpose helicopter by the mid-1990s. With further cuts in the United States military budget possible, it is conceivable that the 530MG Defender could be substituted for the multibillion dollar LHX program.

Above: *The 530MG Defender is an up-rated version of the original OH-6 Cayuse, which was better known as the Loach during the Vietnam War.*

Left: *The 530MG Defender can carry a wide variety of armament (outermost to center): 12-tube 2.75-inch rocket launcher, twin 7.62 machine gun pod, .50 caliber machine gun pod, seven-tube 2.75-inch rocket launcher, and twin Stinger antiaircraft rocket launcher.* Center, left: *This Defender is equipped with two twin TOW missile launchers.* Center, right: *The maneuverability of the 530MG makes it ideal for close support of ground troops or for the anti-armor role.* Bottom: *The Defender's engine produces 650 horsepower.*

McDONNELL DOUGLAS 530MG DEFENDER

Main rotor diameter:	27 ft., 4 in.
Tail rotor diameter:	4 ft., 9 in.
Length:	25 ft.
Width:	6 ft., 4.75 in.
Height:	8 ft., 8 in.
Weight (maximum take-off):	3,000 lbs.
Maximum altitude:	16,000 ft.
Top speed:	137 mph
Maximum range:	207 miles
Date of service:	1968

Like its predecessor, the OH-6, the 530MG Defender is an extremely agile and fast helicopter.

AH-64A Apache

The AH-64A Apache grew out of the recognition following the Vietnam War that the United States Army needed a helicopter specifically designed for the attack role. After extensive evaluation of several designs, the YAH-64 prototype from Hughes Helicopter, which became McDonnell Douglas Helicopter in 1984, was chosen in 1976. The first production Apache was rolled out on September 30, 1983, and the first delivery to the Army was made January 26 of the following year.

To carry out its anti-armor role, the Apache is equipped with the McDonnell Douglas M230 30 millimeter chain gun and up to 16 laser-guided Hellfire antitank missiles, which have a range of more than 3.7 miles and can penetrate the armor of any known main battle tank. The Apache can also provide suppressive fire against concentrations of light armored vehicles and troops with either the chain gun or 2.75-inch folding-fin aerial rockets.

The Apache is also being tested in the air-to-air role and has been approved to fire the Stinger antiaircraft missile. Its M230 30mm chain gun can be used against other helicopters and fixed wing aircraft.

The Apache, while carrying a load of eight Hellfire missiles, 320 rounds of 30mm ammunition, and fuel for 1.83 hours, can climb at the rate of 1,450 feet per minute on what is known as the Army Standard Hot Day—90 degrees Fahrenheit at 4,000 feet. The aircraft can also climb at a rate greater than 3,000 feet per minute in the cold, more humid weather conditions expected to be encountered in central and western Europe—faster than most jet airliners.

The Apache was designed to be crashworthy. The fixed landing gear can absorb a straight-down impact at 20 feet per second, and the airframe is designed to collapse in on itself, giving the crew a 95 percent probability of walking away from a crash at up to 42 feet per second. The armored crew seats also absorb impact energy while the canopy protects the crew from the rotor blades.

Above: *The prototype of the AH-64 Apache made its first flight in September 1975.*

The two General Electric T700-701 turboshaft engines provide 1,694 horsepower each and drive the rotor system through individual gear boxes and transmissions mounted in the nose. The engines are mounted 6.6 feet apart to minimize the chance of enemy fire damaging both engines at the same time.

The exhaust system is divided into two subsystems. The main exhaust nozzle is immediately followed by three secondary nozzles per engine in which engine cooling air and external air, drawn in through auxiliary inlets, are mixed with the exhaust to reduce the exhaust temperature from 1,065 to 580 degrees. This reduces the engine's infrared signature below the level detectable by current heat-seeking guided missiles.

The Apache's main rotor has four blades composed of stainless steel spars and glass fiber tubes. They can cut through tree branches up to two inches in diameter or withstand .50 caliber machine gun or 23mm high-explosive shell strikes. The Apache has a wire strike protection system to sever power or other lines during low-level flights or

McDONNELL DOUGLAS AH-64A APACHE

Main rotor diameter:	48 ft.
Tail rotor diameter:	9 ft., 2 in.
Length:	48 ft., 2 in.
Width:	10 ft., 6 in.
Height:	12 ft., 7 in.
Weight (maximum take-off):	21,000 lbs.
Maximum altitude:	21,000 ft.
Top speed:	184 mph
Maximum range:	300 miles
Date of service:	1984

landings. Wire strikes are a major cause of helicopter crashes.

The Apache has two stub wings that provide additional lift and serve as attaching points for external fuel tanks or external pylons to carry Hellfire or 2.75-inch rockets. The tail surfaces consist of a fixed vertical stabilizer and a horizontal stabilizer—dubbed a stabilator. The stabilator is mounted aft of the vertical stabilizer and moves as one piece.

Fuel cells are located forward and aft of the ammunition bay. They are self-sealing against .50 caliber rounds and can absorb the impact of rounds up to 23mm. Against 14.5mm armor-piercing rounds, the cells, which are further protected by foam and backing boards, will self-seal to provide a 30-minute fuel supply. Nitrogen gas purging prevents fire in the event of incendiary-round penetration. With external tanks fitted for extended ranges, the Apache is fully capable of trans-Atlantic flight.

Armor made of boron carbide bonded to Kevlar protects the Apache crew and vital systems. Blast shields, which protect against 23mm or smaller high-explosive incendiary ammunition, separate the pilot and copilot/weapons operator from each other; thus, both crew members will not be knocked out by a single round. Armored seats and airframe armor can withstand rounds up to .50 caliber of armor-piercing incendiary shot.

The AH-64A Apache will be the Army's main battle tank killer well into the 1990s. The helicopter is being distributed throughout the Army, the National Guard, and the Army Reserves.

Top, left: *The AH-64A Apache, while carrying a heavy combat load, can climb at the rate of 1,450 feet per minute.* Top, right: *The Apache is equipped with a 30mm chain gun and up to 16 Hellfire missiles.* Bottom: *The Apache's armament includes Hellfire missiles (on wing pylons) and 2.75-inch (red) and 5-inch (blue) rockets.*

The AH-64A Apache is armored against small arms fire as well as larger caliber infantry weapons. The Apache's blades can withstand strikes by 20mm projectiles.

8

CRUISE MISSILES

At its most basic, the cruise missile is an unmanned aircraft, steered by either remote control or a self-contained guidance unit. The first cruise missiles appeared during World War II.

The first American cruise missile project was codenamed Operation Aphrodite. Its objective was to destroy heavily armored and protected Nazi submarine pens. Aging B-17 and B-24 aircraft were filled with explosives and flown to the vicinity of the target. After the crew bailed out, a pilot in a following plane used remote controls and a television camera to steer the aircraft during the remainder of the flight until it crashed into the target.

Nazi Germany developed a far more elaborate unmanned aircraft. The Luftwaffe's V-1 was powered by a small jet engine that gave it a top speed of almost 500 miles per hour. The V-1 was launched from a sloping ramp and carried an explosive charge in its nose. Its range was just enough to carry it from the coast of France across the English Channel to London.

After World War II, the United States and the Soviet Union continued to develop what came to be called the cruise missile. While the U.S. Navy concentrated on short-range missiles for shore bombardment and antiship use, the U.S. Air Force developed long-range missiles able to carry nuclear warheads.

The first American missile with intercontinental range was the SM-62A Snark cruise missile, first deployed in 1957. The Snark was to be followed by the SM-64 Navajo and the MX-774, but both were canceled. Instead, resources were devoted to rocket-propelled ballistic missiles, which were far less vulnerable to countermeasures.

For a short time, it seemed that land-based ICBMs might eclipse the cruise missile. But work was progressing on propulsion units and guidance systems. When President Jimmy Carter canceled the original B-1 bomber program, part of the reason was that the B-1 had not been designed to carry the AGM-86 cruise missile.

Today, the Strategic Air Command's long-range bombers all carry air-launched cruise missiles. The missiles are equipped with electronic countermeasures to defeat enemy search radars. The bombers can be hundreds of miles from their targets and launch their cruise missiles in relative safety. The cruise missile will make for a safer mission for crew members as well as extend by a decade the life of the Air Force's B-52G/H models.

Opposite: *The AGM-86B is a nuclear-tipped cruise missile carried by the B-52 and B-1B strategic bombers.* Top, left: *The AGM-86B cruise missile is a standoff weapon; the bombers can fire the missiles while still well out of range of enemy air defenses.* Top, right: *The AGM-86B has a range of more than 1,500 miles.* Center, left: *The AGM-86B is powered by a small, 600-pound-thrust turbofan engine.* Center, right: *The small size and radar profile of the AGM-86B make it difficult for enemy air defenses to spot.* Right: *A mock-up of a launch control station for the AGM-86B cruise missile.*

AGM-86B Air-Launched Cruise Missile

The AGM-86B is a cruise missile launched from B-52G and B-52H Stratofortress bombers and FB-111 Aardvark bombers. With the AGM-86B air-launched cruise missile (ALCM), these bombers can stand off from their target and send large numbers of cruise missiles toward that target. Since each cruise missile carries a nuclear warhead, each missile must be countered. Some missiles are bound to get through simply by overwhelming the enemy's air defenses.

The AGM-86B was originally designed to be a long-range decoy that would replace the Quail. But in the early 1960s, it became a potential strategic weapon when small nuclear warheads were developed. In the early 1970s, the Air Force redirected the project as an air-launched cruise missile.

President Jimmy Carter backed the AGM-86B during his administration. President Carter suggested that once the cruise missile was deployed, the B-1 bomber then under development would no longer be needed. The Carter administration believed the combination of long-range B-52 bombers, flying low to penetrate initial Soviet air-defense radars, and the AGM-86B, which could be launched as far as 1,500 miles away from its target, could effectively substitute for the new manned bomber.

To fit three at a time on either an external pylon or a rotary launcher mounted in the bomb bay of the B-52H, the AGM-86B has folding wings, tail, and air inlet. The missiles are powered by a single F107-WR-100 turbofan engine developed by Williams International Corporation. The engine produces 600 pounds of thrust to drive the missile at speeds of 500 mile per hour. The missile is guided by the P1000 inertial guidance system and the 4516C computer, both developed by Litton Industries. The AGM-86B carries the W80-1 nuclear warhead.

The first configuration, AGM-86A, began flight tests on March 5, 1976. Several of the first flights were failures, but by mid-1977, all bugs had been worked out and testing was complete. Originally, the AGM-86A was to compete against the Tomahawk cruise missile, but a range greater than the Tomahawk's was desired. The answer lay in stretching the AGM-86A to add extra fuel capacity. The AGM-86B was the result. Its fuselage is 30 percent longer than the A version, and its range is double the A model's range.

Production ended in October 1986 after 1,715 missiles were produced. A total of 12 missiles—four pods of three missiles each slung under the wings—are carried on 98 modified B-52Gs. The B-52H is also being converted to carry 12 AGM-86Bs. The H models will be further modified to carry a rotary launcher that will hold eight more cruise missiles in their bomb bays. Decisions are pending on whether to fit the B-1B bomber with the AGM-86B. If the B-1B is so armed, 12 would be carried on stations under the fuselage and eight in a rotary launcher in the bomb bay.

Below: *The AGM-86B cruise missile has a wingspan of 12 feet. The wings remain folded until the missile is launched.*

AGM-86B AIR-LAUNCHED CRUISE MISSILE

Wingspan:	12 ft.
Length:	20 ft., 9 in.
Diameter:	2 ft., 2 in.
Weight:	3,200 lbs.
Engine:	William International F107-WR-100 turbofan
Engine thrust:	600 lbs.
Speed:	500 mph
Maximum range:	1,500 miles
Date of service:	1981

Left, top: *More than 1,700 AGM-86B missiles have been produced.* Left, center: *Eight AGM-86B cruise missiles can be carried on special rotary launchers inside the bomb bay of the B-52H.* Left, bottom: *The B-52G and B-52H strategic bombers that can deliver between 12 and 20 AGM-86B nuclear-tipped cruise missiles form a strong deterrent to nuclear war.* Above: *AGM-86B missiles are mounted three at a time on special wing pylons on the B-52G and B-52H.*

Even with the B1-B bomber now completely operational, the 36-year-old B-52 equipped with the AGM-86B cruise missile remains a potent weapon in the American defensive arsenal.

U.S. LAND POWER

The M-1 Abrams Main Battle Tank is one of the most powerful tanks ever fielded.

U.S. LAND POWER

THE IMPORTANCE OF LAND POWER FORCES

On June 14, 1775, the Continental Congress voted to establish an army to be raised from the individual member colonies, but to be paid and equipped by Congress. The small Continental Army, as it came to be known, was to be supplemented by militias raised by each of the individual colonies, but those militias were to be subordinate to the Federal Army and its commanders. This organization set a pattern that has endured to the present day.

The United States Navy was approved by the Continental Congress on October 13, 1775. A month later, on November 10, the Marine Corps was established with two battalions. By 1917, the Marine Corps had grown sufficiently and its area of operations had been so extended that it was provided with its own air arm, field artillery, and other combat support elements.

America's land combat forces—the Army and the Marine Corps—have been engaged in nine major wars and 13 international incidents during the nation's more than 200-year history. With three exceptions, the United States has prevailed in every war or incident. In Korea and Vietnam, U.S. forces withdrew after a negotiated armistice. In Lebanon in 1982, the multinational peacekeeping force withdrew without prevailing or reaching a negotiated truce.

Threats to the United States, its interests abroad, and its allies and friends have changed in the years since the nation's inception. Today, the United States faces threats from nations wishing to destroy the U.S. because of differences in political systems or religious beliefs. There are also nations that wish to reduce or destroy the U.S. because of its friendship and support of other nations. And still other nations wish to gain military or economic power at the expense of the U.S. As a result, the United States faces a variety of threats ranging from nuclear war to terrorism. The combat forces of the United States have evolved to meet this wide range of threats.

Today, the United States' land power component totals 1,731,854 men and women. These ground forces are stationed throughout the world in allied and friendly nations in support of combined interests and national borders.

The U.S. infantry soldier is the backbone of the United States' military organization. The infantry soldier takes and holds ground in the face of enemy opposition. The air force may clear the way, may hold the enemy's reinforcements well to the rear, and may destroy the enemy's capability to produce weapons of war, but the infantry soldier with a rifle is at the sharp end. It is this soldier, eating and sleeping in the mud, enduring fatigue and fear, who decides whether a battle is won or lost.

The infantry soldier of the United States is equipped with and supported by the most modern weapons—from the M9 Beretta sidearm to the M-1 Abrams tank—possessed by any military organization in the world. Today, one American soldier can carry the firepower equivalent of an entire World War II platoon. A quarter of a century ago, much of this amazing array of weaponry would have sounded like the inventions of science fiction writers.

THE ORGANIZATION OF U.S. LAND POWER FORCES

The land combat forces of the U.S. Army are divided into five major commands: U.S. Army Forces, Europe; U.S. Army Forces, Korea; U.S. Army Western Command, located in Hawaii and responsible for the Pacific Rim; Forces Command, which is

Opposite, top: *The M198 155mm Howitzer is the mainstay of the Army's towed artillery pieces.* Opposite, bottom: *The HMMWV vehicle has replaced the jeep, MULE, and light truck in U.S. military service.* Left: *The Multiple Launch Rocket System can devastate an area the size of three football fields in less than a minute.* Bottom, left: *The Light Assault Vehicle 25 is the Marine Corps' newest armored personnel carrier.* Bottom, right: *The M60 machine gun is an outgrowth of the German MG42 design.*

headquartered and garrisoned in the United States and which provides reserve forces for the three forward commands; and 1st Special Operations Command, which includes such special forces as Air Force Special Warfare and the Green Berets. These five combat commands are supported by special services ranging from weapons development to health maintenance.

Army combat forces are organized in a pyramid structure. At the bottom is the infantry *squad*, which has between nine and 12 soldiers and is commanded by a sergeant. The next level up is the *platoon*, with between 31 and 50 troops. Normally, the platoon is made up of three squads of infantry and is typically commanded by a lieutenant. Next is the *company*, usually commanded by a captain and consisting of two or more platoons/ sections plus headquarters personnel. The *battalion*, the basic maneuver group of the Army, contains three to five companies and includes headquarters personnel. Battalions are commanded by a lieutenant colonel or colonel. The *brigade* is a flexible unit that changes to meet the threat of the moment. The brigade contains two or more combat battalions and is normally commanded by a brigadier general. *Divisions* are the largest units trained to fight as a combined arms team. A division can contain from as few as two to as many as six brigades—more if circumstances warrant. Divisions are commanded by a major general. Divisions are grouped into *corps*—the American equivalent to Soviet armies. Corps are composed of the units needed to meet a specific threat; therefore, no two corps are ever alike. A corps usually contains two to five combat divisions. The corps, seldom smaller than 60,000 soldiers, is commanded by a lieutenant general.

The Marine Corps maintains three active divisions and one reserve

Left: *The M60 Main Battle Tank carries a 105mm main gun.* Bottom, left: *The Stinger antiaircraft weapon has proved to be extremely capable against enemy helicopters and low-flying aircraft.* Bottom, right: *The Mk 19 40mm grenade launcher is effective against lightly armored vehicles and enemy bunkers.*

combat division to meet its operational responsibility under the National Security Act of "providing rapidly deployable forces for contingency missions in support of national strategy." In addition to the reserve division, an air wing and a service support group are also maintained in reserve. The organizational structure of the Marine Corps is similar to but more flexible than that of the Army.

Another component of U.S. land forces is made up of the U.S. Army National Guard and the Army and Marine Corps Reserves—collectively referred to as the Reserve Component. The National Guard supplies 50 percent of all U.S. combat forces, while the Reserves provide 70 percent of all combat support units. In 1941, the National Guard was expected to mobilize, train, and deploy to their overseas positions within six months. By the end of the Vietnam War, the time allowance had been reduced to as little as three months. Today, the Guard and Reserve are expected to maintain a readiness capability equal to the active-duty military.

The various components of the Army and Marine Corps land combat force (both active and Reserve/National Guard) can be distinguished by a numbering system devised in 1916. Divisions numbered 1 through 25 are active-duty Army. Divisions numbered 26 through 75 are National Guard. Units numbered 76 and higher belong to the Reserves. Regiments numbered 1 through 99 are active-duty Army. From 100 through 300 are National Guard, and 301 and higher are Reserve. Thus, the 40th Infantry Division (Mechanized) is a California National Guard unit, and the 278th Armored Cavalry Regiment belongs to the Tennessee National Guard.

Until the late 1930s, United States ground combat forces were categorized as infantry, artillery, or cavalry. Since then, each has

Top, left: *The M16 rifle, despite media criticism, may be the best shoulder arm ever issued to American troops.* Top, right: *The M47 Dragon is a soldier-portable antitank weapon capable of dealing with many of today's main battle tanks.* Left: *The M-1 Abrams Main Battle Tank is equipped with special armor that is a mix of steel and ceramic.*

developed numerous sub-specialties. Currently, the Army divides its ground combat forces into heavy, light, airborne, and special operations forces.

Heavy forces are essentially mechanized infantry. The task of heavy infantry is to meet and defeat the enemy with an overwhelming concentration of firepower. Light infantry, which includes ground and airborne troops, are essentially unarmored. They are expected to move quickly and in force to take advantage of sudden enemy weaknesses. Airborne forces are moved primarily by aircraft. Airborne units are lightly equipped and function with a minimum of armor support. Their task is to capture key objectives and hold them until relieved by light or heavy infantry forces. Airborne troops are also used for strikes deep in the enemy's rear. Special operations forces (SOF) serve in the reconnaissance, guerrilla, counter-guerrilla, and strike roles. Their job is to disrupt command and communications facilities, logistics lines and junctions, transportation nets, airfields, ports, and other areas that support the enemy's conventional operations. Since 1986, SOF forces have been under the command and control of the Department of Defense rather than any single service.

A new component—the Rapid Deployment Force (RDF)—was conceived in 1979. This force is organized and equipped to move rapidly to trouble spots anywhere in the world outside of Europe. Troops, equipment, and supplies are available for rapid deployment without actually stationing large numbers of troops in a troubled area. Specific units from the Army, Marine Corps, Air Force, and Navy are designated as part of the RDF. The four services continue their normal training and deployment activities, but are always on call should it be necessary to activate the RDF.

INFANTRY WEAPONS

No matter how technologically sophisticated an army becomes, it still depends on the individual infantry soldier and his personal weapons to take and hold ground. Modern technological advances in small arms have increased the infantry soldier's firepower, improved his shooting accuracy, and minimized ammunition waste. But it wasn't always this way.

In the early 1700s, Europe was convulsed by the War of the Spanish Succession (1701–14). The flintlock musket, which used a simple U-shaped spring to drive the cock holding the flint, was adopted by the French and British armies, and quickly spread to the New World. The flintlock smoothbore musket, with minor improvements, remained the standard American military weapon until the adoption of the percussion musket in 1840. During the next century, various rifles representing several technological advances were used by the U.S. Army. Among these were the Springfield rifled musket of the Civil War, the Krag bolt action rifle, the Model 1903 Springfield, and the M1 Garand. The M1 remained in service into the 1960s.

In 1964, Eugene Stoner, an employee of the Armalite Corporation of Costa Mesa, California, developed a new, lightweight battle rifle that fired a small-caliber cartridge. The new rifle, the M16A1, received its baptism of fire in the Vietnam War, and is now the main battle weapon of the military forces of the United States. The M16 can almost be said to mark the introduction of the host of high-technology weapons that followed. In each instance, the emphasis was on volume fire power, light weight, and rugged construction.

Another type of rifle—the sniper—has also been developed. During the Civil War, several militia and volunteer units of sharpshooters using rifles were organized on both sides. Sharpshooters were given the task of picking off enemy artillery crews and disrupting morale and communications. World War II saw increased emphasis placed on sniping. But rearming the United States after nearly two decades of neglect left little time or money to spare for this esoteric military field. The Vietnam conflict demonstrated the need for an effective sniper rifle. As a result, the Army Marksmanship Unit developed both the rifle, the M21, and the telescopic sight, the ART II. This rifle/sight combination was the standard Army sniper rifle from 1968 to 1985.

Machine guns are an extremely effective infantry weapon. The first practical rapid-fire weapon was the Gatling Gun, which saw limited action during the Civil War. While not a true machine gun, it helped prove the validity of rapid firepower from a single weapon. But the United States military came to appreciate the Gatling Gun only slowly. When the United States entered World War I in 1917, less than 1,200 machine guns were in the entire U.S. Army inventory. The shattering experiences of all participants in World War I convinced the reluctant U.S. Army that the machine gun was a viable weapon, and several machine guns were developed. John Browning developed the Browning Automatic Rifle (BAR) and the .30-06 Model 1917 Heavy Machine Gun. The BAR was perhaps the most widely used of all American light automatic weapons, seeing service in every war in which Americans have participated, from World War I to Vietnam. U.S. land combat forces in World War II were mostly equipped with machine guns that had been designed during the previous war. When World War II ended, military authorities clearly saw that a new machine gun was needed to replace the older Browning machine gun. Extensive studies resulted in the M60 series. Today, the M60E1 remains the most widely used automatic weapon in both the Army and the Marine Corps. Since the end of the Vietnam War, the U.S. Army and Marine Corps have sought a lighter machine gun of smaller caliber. They found it in the M249 Squad Automatic Weapon.

The land combat forces of the United States possess the best personal weaponry in the world. In addition to rifles and machine guns, the American infantry soldier is supported by a variety of new sidearms, grenade launchers, and mortars. Today's American infantry soldier is far better trained and equipped to survive on a far more hostile battlefield than his predecessors of World War II or Korea.

Opposite: *The M16 is a selective-fire battle rifle.* Top: *The Mk 19 fires 40mm grenades that can deal with lightly armored vehicles.* Center, left: *The SMAW is a Marine Corps shoulder-launched rocket that can destroy enemy bunkers or armored vehicles.* Center, right: *The M249 Squad Automatic Weapon is lighter than the M60 machine gun, and the gunner can carry more ammunition.* Bottom: *The M60 General Purpose Machine Gun was based on Germany's World War II MG42 machine gun design.*

Beretta Double Action, 9mm Sidearm

Above: *The M9 Beretta 9mm pistol was adopted as the sidearm of the U.S. military in 1985.*

Before 1985, the standard-issue military service pistol of the United States was the semiautomatic Government Model 1911, designed by John Browning and manufactured by Colt Firearms. The pistol served with distinction for more than 70 years.

After a series of pistol trials in the early 1980s ordered by Congress, the Model 92F 9 millimeter pistol, manufactured by the Italian firm of Beretta, was selected in April 1985 as the replacement for the Model 1911 .45 caliber pistol. The new pistol, designated the M9, is a double action, semiautomatic pistol with a detachable box magazine that holds 15 rounds of 9mm Parabellum ammunition. In striking power, the 9mm cartridge is slightly inferior to the .45 caliber round, but the M9's smaller-diameter bullet has greater penetrating ability, especially through personal armor.

The Beretta Model 92's frame is made of an aluminum alloy; the slide and barrel are made of steel. This pistol has an improved safety over the twin safety of the Model 1911: The firing pin isn't struck directly by the hammer, but by a sliding insert interposed between the hammer and the firing pin. When the safety is applied, the firing pin is automatically locked and the insert is rolled out of possible contact with the hammer. After the safety is pushed to the off position, a single pull on the trigger cocks and fires the weapon. The ambidextrous safety lever can be manipulated by right- or left-handed shooters.

The rear sight, like the front sight, is marked on either side of the sighting notch with luminous material that glows in the dark. In low-light situations, the shooter can center the sights simply by aligning the three dots.

The Beretta design employs a barrel lockup system devised by John Browning for his Model 1935 High Power Pistol. When the pistol is in battery—when a cartridge is chambered—the barrel and slide are locked together by a spring-driven wedge. When the cartridge is fired, the recoil pushes the slide and barrel back. The barrel is stopped when the wedge, driven by its spring, drops into a recess in the barrel. The slide continues to travel backward until the downward projection at the front of the slide stops against the front of the frame. The fired case, gripped by an extractor claw mounted in the top of the frame, strikes a projecting ejector rod mounted on the frame's left side and is kicked out. As the slide comes to a stop, the hammer is pushed to the full-cock position and the recoil spring is compressed. The recoil spring now drives the slide forward, stripping the next cartridge from the magazine and pushing it into the chamber. The barrel continues forward until it is once again locked together with the slide—in battery—ready to be fired again.

The Beretta M9 survived extremely tough trials in three separate series of tests against the best pistols the United States and several European countries could produce, including the venerable Model 1911. The Beretta M9 will continue in service with U.S. armed forces well into the next century.

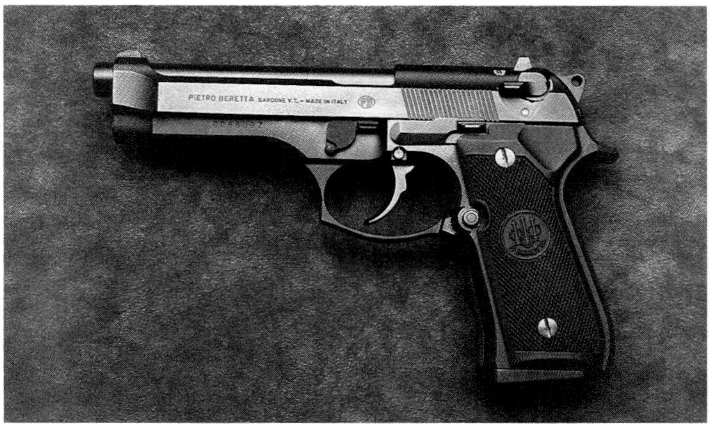

M9 BERETTA DOUBLE ACTION, 9mm SIDEARM

Caliber:	9 x 9mm NATO
Length:	
Overall:	8.5 in.
Barrel:	4.87 in.
Weight:	2.19 lbs.
Magazine capacity:	15 rounds
Muzzle velocity:	1,080 fps
Date of service:	1985

Top: *The M9 pistol (right) holds fifteen rounds and is easier to handle than the old Government M1911A1 .45 caliber pistol (left).* Bottom, left: *The Beretta will serve with U.S. armed forces well into the next century.* Bottom, right: *The M9 pistol breaks down into component parts for easy field maintenance.*

M16A2 Rifle

The U.S. Army began development of a new battle rifle in 1957 due to dissatisfaction with the then current-issue M14, a redesigned M1 Garand used in World War II and Korea. The tank had returned mobility to the battlefield and most firefights in modern warfare took place at distances between 200 and 300 yards. The current M16 cartridge (M855) is accurate to 460 yards.

The M16 rifle is a gas-operated, rotary bolt, self-loading rifle that uses a box magazine holding 20 rounds. A 30-round magazine is also available. Above the receiver is a handle that doubles as the sight base. The handle makes it easy for the infantryman to carry the rifle. The military version of the rifle has a three-position switch on the left side of the receiver. When turned toward the muzzle, the rifle is on "safe"; straight up provides semiautomatic fire; when turned toward the buttstock, automatic fire.

In the early 1980s, the U.S. Marine Corps became dissatisfied with the M16's performance. The Marines felt that the gun did not offer the desired penetration or accuracy. Other services concurred and the Marines began a product improvement program. In 1986, the M16A2 rifle was accepted. The A2 version fired a new NATO-standard 5.56 cartridge designated the M855, with a heavier bullet for increased accuracy. The bullet included a steel penetrator inside the lead and copper jacket to slice through light vehicles and body armor.

The M16A2 was given an upgraded barrel designed to fire new ammunition with greater accuracy. The rifling was changed from one twist in 12 inches to one twist in seven inches. This caused the bullet to spin faster as it traveled down the barrel, increasing its stability in flight and, therefore, its accuracy. The fully automatic capability was replaced by a three-round burst action—three shots for every pull of the trigger.

To fire the M16, a loaded magazine is inserted into the magazine-well located beneath the receiver. The charging handle is pulled to the rear and released to load a round from the magazine into the chamber. The shooter then turns the safety switch to the semiautomatic or automatic mode and pulls the trigger.

The M16 is scheduled to be replaced in the mid- to late 1990s by the Advanced Combat Rifle, under the Army's Infantry School Small Arms Strategy, Phase II.

Above: *These soldiers tote M16 rifles while on patrol in South Vietnam in 1967.*

M16A2 RIFLE

Caliber:	5.56 x 45mm NATO (.223)
Length:	
Overall:	39 in.
Barrel:	20 in.
Weight:	6.6 lbs.
Rate of fire:	700 to 900 rpm in three-round bursts
Muzzle velocity:	3,250 fps
Date of service:	1967

Left, top: *This soldier holds an M16A1 rifle equipped with a blank firing device (red box) and a laser projector mounted atop the barrel. He is also wearing laser receivers on his harness.* Left, bottom: *This M16A1 rifle has been equipped with the M203 Grenade Launcher mounted under the barrel.* Right, top: *The M16A1 was the U.S. Army and Marine Corps basic battle rifle during the Vietnam War.* Right, bottom: *The M16 fires the 5.56 x 45mm cartridge.*

M21, M24, and M40A1 Sniper Rifles

Above: *The M40A1 is the Marine Corps' basic sniper weapon.*

The U.S. Army has a tradition of marksmanship dating from the Revolutionary War, but it is only since 1973 that it has possessed a rifle capable of any real degree of accuracy beyond 100 yards.

The Vietnam War—as no previous war had—demonstrated the need for an effective sniper rifle. The Army's Marksmanship Unit developed the M21 rifle, fitted with the ART II telescopic sight designed by Lieutenant James Leatherwood. The M21 rifle was simply an M14 service rifle with improved accuracy created by placing a fiberglass bed in the wooden stock to hold the action. The M21 was the standard Army sniper rifle from 1968 to 1985. It was a rugged and reliable weapon and quite accurate up to about 900 yards.

In 1985, the Army's Special Operations Target Interdiction Committee defined a new sniper rifle and issued a proposal request for its development and manufacture. The new rifle had to be easy to shoot and light enough to be carried by airborne and air mobile troops. Further, it would have to be accurate enough to engage targets at distances greater than 1,100 yards. The rifle also had to be easily converted from the standard 7.62 caliber NATO (.308) to .300 Magnum.

The M24 is based on the Remington Model 700 sporting rifle—the same model adopted by the U.S. Marines for their M40 and M40A1 sniper rifles—and holds five rounds in its magazine. The M24 rifle has an adjustable butt plate that allows the shooter to fit the stock to his reach. The stock is made of carbon-fiber plastic. A ten-power variable-telescopic sight with a built-in bullet drop compensator has been developed for the rifle. Once the scope has been "zeroed" for a specific distance, the operator has only to dial in his estimate of the new range and the optics adjust accordingly. The M24 was designed with the needs of special operations forces in mind and is also issued to infantry units.

The Marine Corps recognized the inherent accuracy of the Remington Model 700 sporting rifle at the start of the Vietnam War. Their first postwar sniper rifle was the M40, which used the Remington bolt action coupled to a heavy barrel for increased accuracy. In the mid-1970s, the rifle was refined to increase accuracy and ruggedness. New stainless steel barrels were procured and mated to the Remington actions, then bedded into a fiberglass stock. Known as the M40A1, the weapon is extremely accurate to about 1,000 yards and remains the Marine Corps' standard sniper rifle.

M21, M24, AND M40A1 SNIPER RIFLES

Caliber:	
M21/M24/M40A1:	7.62 NATO
M24:	Winchester .300 Magnum
Length:	
Overall:	
M21:	44.14 in.
M24:	Not available
M40A1:	43.5 in.
Barrel:	
M21:	22 in.
M24:	Not available
M40A1:	24 in.
Weight:	
M21:	10.1 lbs.
M24:	Not available
M40A1:	8.8 lbs.
Muzzle velocity:	
7.62 NATO:	2,550 fps
.300 Winchester:	3,400 fps
Date of service:	
M21:	1968
M24:	1988
M40A1:	1977

Left, top: *The U.S. Army's standard sniper rifle from 1968 to 1985 was the M21.* Left, bottom: *The Army's newest sniper rifle is the M24, shown here with an AN/PVS-4 Starlight Night Sight. The spotter to the sniper's right is using a hand-held laser range finder.* Right, top: *The Marine Corps uses a ten-power telescopic sight on their M40A1 Sniper Rifle.* Right, center: *This Marine Corps sniper wraps his head with a special veil that breaks up his outline into shapes unfamiliar to the eye.* Right, bottom: *The M24 Sniper Rifle has an adjustable butt plate.*

M249 5.56mm Squad Automatic Weapon

Ever since Hiram Maxim developed his machine gun in 1885, military planners have been looking for ways to provide the infantry squad with improved automatic firepower without the penalty of weapon and ammunition weight. The U.S. Army and Marine Corps believe they have realized this goal in the new M249 Squad Automatic Weapon.

Developed by the famous Belgian arms firm, Fabriqué Nationale, and christened the MINIMI, the M249 was adopted into U.S. service in 1982 over four other contenders. The Squad Automatic Weapon (SAW) was first issued to the 82nd Airborne Division in 1984. The SAW is designed to replace one M16 rifle in each infantry squad fire team. The M249 is the first such special-purpose automatic weapon to be issued to an infantry squad since the Browning Automatic Rifle was withdrawn from service in the 1960s.

The M249 is a gas-operated automatic weapon. This means it functions entirely by the energy developed when a cartridge is fired. The initial energy developed to detonate the first cartridge is provided when the gunner cocks the weapon, compressing the bolt spring. After the cartridge ignites, gas bled from the barrel is channeled through a stainless steel tube acting against the face of the bolt, causing it to move back in its track and unlock from the breech walls. The compressed spring then drives the bolt forward, stripping a new round from the linked belt, or magazine, and inserting it into the chamber.

As a result of its design features, the M249 has proved far more reliable than any other automatic weapon firing the high-pressure 5.56mm NATO round. Normal cyclic rate is 725 rounds per minute. The original M249 had an adjustable gas regulator that allowed the gunner to compensate for inclement weather and lack of cleaning; the regulator was eliminated later in the weapon's production.

The M249 is fired from a metal bipod attached to the weapon's fore end, which can be folded aft along the barrel. Equipped with a quick release, the barrel can be changed in less than ten seconds. The barrel assembly includes a carrying handle, front sight, and gas regulator.

Ammunition is linked together in 200-round box containers attached directly to the weapon, or the linked ammunition can be fired without the box. The M249 can also be fired using standard M16 30- and 20-round magazines. A gunner normally carries two more 200-round containers—a total of 600 rounds. Other members of the squad carry additional containers as needed.

The M249 has recently been modified. Besides the elimination of the adjustable gas regulator, the weapon has been fitted with a new hydropneumatic buffer system that offers improved absorption of recoil. To house it, the tubular metal buttstock was replaced with a solid one made of foam-filled plastic; this redesigned buttstock is similar to that found on the new M16A2 rifle. A folding handle and barrel shield have been added to the M249's barrel.

The M249 MINIMI squad automatic has been fully integrated into the land combat forces of the United States. The weapon's buffering system and straight-line design make the M249 more accurate than every other U.S. machine gun in service. What's more, the M249's lightweight design makes it possible for the gunner to fire it accurately from the hip, a feat almost impossible with the heavier, larger-caliber M60E1 machine gun.

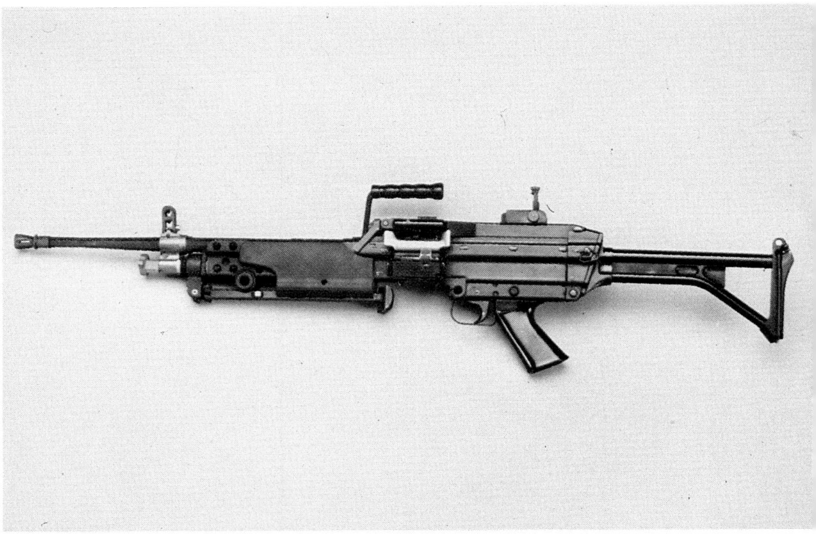

Top: *The M249 Squad Automatic Weapon (SAW) fires the same 5.56 x 45mm ammunition as the M16 rifle.* Bottom: *U.S. Army tests show that M249 SAW is far more reliable in combat operations than any other design tested.*

Left, top: *Each Army squad will be equipped with one M249 SAW.* Left, bottom: *The low profile, light weight, accuracy, and reliability of the SAW gives the combat soldier a real advantage.* Above: *The M249 SAW weighs only 15 pounds, much lighter than the M60 General Purpose Machine Gun.*

M249 5.56mm SQUAD AUTOMATIC WEAPON

Caliber:	5.56 x 45mm NATO
Length:	
Overall:	39.4 in.
Barrel:	18.5 in.
Weight:	22.1 lbs. with 200 rounds of ammunition
Rate of fire:	725 rpm
Muzzle velocity:	3,250 fps
Date of service:	1982

M60 General Purpose Machine Gun

U.S. Army troops faced German infantry for the first time in World War II at the Kasserine Pass in Tunisia, North Africa. There, in early 1943, green, untried American soldiers were soundly defeated by hardened Wehrmacht professionals. One of the weapons the German soldiers used to devastating effect was the new Machine Gun Model of 1942, or MG42. The U.S. Army's Ordnance Department began studies in late 1943 to develop a new American machine gun. The result, 14 years later, was the M60 General Purpose Machine Gun.

The M60's designers borrowed heavily from the MG42 and the German Fallschirmjäger Gewehr (FG) 42 automatic rifle. This melding of attributes produced the first prototype of the new American machine gun, called the T44. Subsequent testing and modifications produced the T52 prototype, followed by the T161 series. Other systems were borrowed and incorporated after suitable improvements; a dependable gas-driven bolt was adapted from the Lewis gun of World War I, and a quick-change barrel that allowed sustained fire was taken from the Czechoslovakian ZB26 machine gun. Finally, in 1957, the new machine gun was accepted, and production contracts went to the Saeco Division of Maremont Industries.

The M60 machine gun is a gas-operated automatic weapon. The gun and its ammunition have been standardized by NATO. The M60 has also been modified for use in tanks and armored personnel carriers. The land-vehicle version has a barrel extension and evacuator tube that vent the propellant fumes to the outside of the vehicle. The M60 is used throughout the U.S. armed forces and by many allied nations as well; the gun has seen intensive service with U.S. forces in Vietnam, Lebanon, and Grenada.

The M60C and M60D models arm helicopters. The M60C version does not have the gun's standard stock; it is charged and fired electrically. The M60D is configured for use by door gunners. In this variant, the buttstock is replaced by two spadehandle grips, with the trigger mounted in between.

The M60 machine gun is a versatile, reliable piece of ordnance that will remain in service with U.S., NATO, and allied forces well into the next century.

M60 GENERAL PURPOSE MACHINE GUN	
Caliber:	7.62 × 51mm NATO
Length:	
Overall:	42 in.
Barrel:	22 in.
Weight:	23.05 lbs.
Rate of fire:	550 rpm
Muzzle velocity:	2,800 fps
Date of service:	1957

Opposite, top: *This M60 has been modified to the M60D for use as a helicopter door gun.* Opposite, bottom: *The M60 provided the infantry with a general purpose machine gun that was more effective than the Browning Automatic Rifle or the Browning Light Machine Gun.* Top: *The M60 General Purpose Machine Gun can be fired from a separate tripod (as show here), from the bipod folded under the barrel, or from a sling over the gunner's shoulder.* Bottom, left: *The M60 has an effective range of 1,000 yards.* Bottom, right: *Ammunition for the M60 is fed into the breech from a linked ammunition belt.*

Mark 19-3 40mm Automatic Grenade Launcher

Grenades have been in use almost since the invention of gunpowder. Early grenades were simple canisters filled with scrap metal and containing a bursting charge of gunpowder. They were thrown by hand, by sling, or launched by catapult. By World War I, the grenade was a relatively sophisticated weapon in the hands of infantry soldiers. The Mills Bomb, developed by the British, had a segmented iron container that fractured into dozens of fragments. Germany developed the familiar "potato masher" grenade, an iron canister filled with shot surrounding a bursting charge. The grenade's long handle provided extra leverage when thrown.

Weapons designers began looking for a way to launch grenades to even greater distances. Attachments were developed for rifles using the gases from a blank cartridge to propel the grenade, but accuracy was quite poor.

After World War II, United States ordnance designers developed the high-low power grenade cartridge. Inside the metal base of the plastic shell is a brass cup with a series of holes. The cup contains a propelling compound ignited by a primer. When the pressure of the expanding gases reaches 35,000 pounds per square inch, the vent holes rupture and the gases blast outward into the "low pressure chamber," where their pressure is reduced to 3,000 pounds per square inch. The projectile is launched at a velocity of 250 feet per second. Most grenades of this type are 1.57 inches in diameter and are spun at the rate of 37,000 revolutions per minute to stabilize them and arm their centrifugal-type fuse.

The first weapon designed to use the new grenade was the M79 Grenade Launcher, which looked like an oversized, single-barrel shotgun. The M203 Grenade Launcher, an attachment for the M16A1 rifle, followed. The success of these two grenade launchers led the Navy to develop the Mark 19, modification 3 Automatic Grenade Launcher in 1981, which is now used by the U.S. Army and Marine Corps.

Resembling a short-barreled, tripod-mounted heavy machine gun, the Mark 19-3 is designed to be used in both offensive and defensive situations against personnel and lightly armored vehicles. The Mark 19-3 has an effective rate of fire of 325 to 375 rounds per minute. However, due to the length limitations of the ammunition belts, an actual rate of 35 to 60 rounds per minute is more usual. The effective range of the 40mm grenades fired by the Mark 19 is 1,749.8 yards.

Several types of grenades can be fired. The antipersonnel grenade has a lethal range of 16.4 feet. The antitank grenade can penetrate two inches of armor at its maximum range of 2,405.9 yards. Three types of grenades are fired by the Mark 19-3: the M383 High Explosive; the M430 High Explosive Dual Purpose; and the M385 Practice Grenade, which contains a bright orange powder to mark the impact point.

The Mark 19-3 can be used by infantry troops as a defense point or as an offensive weapon. It is sometimes mounted on the M151 quarter-ton truck, the M113 Armored Personnel Carrier, or the High Mobility, Multipurpose Wheeled Vehicle (HMMWV).

Following adoption by the Navy in 1981, the Mark 19-3 was purchased by the Army for delivery in mid-1985. The Marines are purchasing enough Mark 19-3s to provide each Marine infantry battalion with 12 launchers.

Below: *The Mk 19-3 40mm Automatic Grenade Launcher has an effective range of just under one mile.*

MARK 19-3 40mm AUTOMATIC GRENADE LAUNCHER	
Caliber:	40 × 53mm
Length:	
Overall:	40.45 in.
Barrel:	16.5 in.
Weight:	76 lbs.
Rate of fire:	375 rpm (nominal)
Muzzle velocity:	
M383:	790 fps
M430:	1,200 fps
Date of service:	1981

Top, left: *The Mk 19-3 Grenade Launcher has been mounted on a variety of ground vehicles, both armored and unarmored, and on helicopters.* Top, right: *The Mk 19-3's grenades are fired at the rate of 350 rounds per minute.* Bottom, left: *The Mk 19-3 Automatic Grenade Launcher weighs 76 pounds.* Bottom, right: *Ammunition for the Mk 19-3 includes high-explosive, antipersonnel, and armor-piercing grenades.*

M29A1 81mm Mortar

Simplicity and light weight combine to make the M29A1 mortar an ideal infantry weapon. It is portable and delivers a tremendous amount of concentrated firepower in a short period of time against both narrow and wide areas. The M29A1 is capable of a maximum rate of fire of up to 30 rounds per minute for the first minute, then up to 12 rounds for each additional minute. Effective range is nearly three miles. The unit breaks down into three major components—baseplate, bipod, and barrel—making it extremely easy to transport. Total weight is 115 pounds, and each section can be carried by an individual soldier.

The mortar barrel is grooved on the outside, like a piece of corrugated piping, and smoothbore on its inside. The external grooving aids in the barrel's cooling and increases reliability, particularly when the mortar is called upon to provide sustained fire. The mortar can be set up from its basic components in just a few minutes. Because the unit can stand free on level or uneven ground, preparation is minimal. Once sighted in by the gunner, who is part of the standard five-member crew, the M29A1 can begin lobbing rounds at an enemy's position in a matter of minutes, and continue firing a host of different types of rounds that may be needed for different types of targets.

While accuracy is not as good as with the more modern "smart" weapons, the M29A1 is nonetheless a devastating part of the modern ground forces arsenal. It can fire high-explosive (HE) rounds to 5,140 yards, and can easily take out enemy troop concentrations and light vehicle/truck convoys. When a mortar team spots a convoy of heavy armor, the team can use white phosphorus smoke rounds to mark the position so that heavy artillery or air power can be called in to finish the job. White phosphorus rounds are also used to cover advancing friendly forces.

At night, when not called upon to deliver HE rounds against enemy positions from a firebase, the M29A1 is capable of firing a variety of illumination bombs. These rounds are fired to a height of approximately 600 yards at ranges of more than 3,200 yards. The rounds will illuminate a 1,200-yard area for approximately 60 seconds.

When the M29A1 has to be moved quickly, it can be mounted in the rear section of an M225A2, a modified M113 Armored Personnel Carrier. The mortar is mounted on the vehicle's floor on a turntable platform that enables the weapon to rotate quickly in a 360-degree circle. So set up, the mortar can quickly pick a target, fire, rotate to a new target, and fire again. The M225A2 vehicle can normally carry up to 115 rounds of M29A1 ammunition.

While its technology may not be fancy, the M29A1 can deliver devastating firepower. Technological breakthroughs are not anticipated in terms of mortar designs, but new ammunitions continue to improve the effectiveness of this medium mortar. The M29A1 remains in production today.

Above: *The M29A1 Mortar consists of the barrel, the bipod mount, and the heavy steel baseplate.*

M29A1 81mm MORTAR	
Caliber:	81mm
Barrel length:	51.2 in.
Weight:	
Overall (with sight):	115 lbs.
Barrel:	28 lbs.
Baseplate:	25 lbs.
Bipod:	40 lbs.
Rate of fire:	
Maximum:	30 rpm for one minute
Sustained:	4 to 12 rpm
Muzzle velocity:	970 fps
Range:	5,140 yds.
Elevation:	+40 degrees to +85 degrees
Date of service:	1981

Above: *The M29A1 81mm Mortar is fired by dropping a mortar bomb into the muzzle. A percussion cartridge ignites the main propelling charge.* Left: *The M29A1 Mortar is aimed by raising or lowering the elevation of the launching tube.*

M252 81mm Mortar

Revolutionary in terms of design compared with the older M29A1 mortar system that remains in use by U.S. forces, the new British-designed M252 81mm mortar offers some revolutionary firepower capabilities, thanks to a host of new technological ammunition packages.

Many are calling the new system a "magnumized" mortar because of its capability to fire faster, longer-ranged, and more potent mortar rounds. In service since 1987, the M252 can handle the higher chamber pressures currently being produced by successive generations of improved munitions. Such improved ammunition includes the British High Explosive round that is 30 percent more lethal than the current U.S. rounds, a new Illumination Bomb that is 160 percent brighter than older rounds, and a White Phosphorous smoke round that is 500 percent more effective than its predecessor.

Like the M29A1 mortar, the M252 breaks down into three major components: baseplate, bipod, and barrel. This unit weighs appreciably less than the M29A1, topping the scales at 87 pounds. The M252 can be transported by three infantry soldiers and set up quickly to begin firing on enemy targets. The barrel has a smoothbore interior and thin, concentrated cooling threads along three-fifths of the exterior; the threads allow quick dissipation of heat. On top, the M252 has a muzzle-blast device that reduces blast pressure impact on the operating crew and cuts down on muzzle flash that could reveal the mortar's concealed position.

The mortar can deliver up to 33 rounds per minute for up to one minute of high-volume rapid fire; it can fire up to 16 rounds on a sustained basis. This means the M252 not only packs more power in the types of munitions it fires but it can keep lobbing shells onto enemy positions for a much greater period of time without overheating or jamming.

One of the future roles of the M252 will be to fire the new generation of mortar ammunition known as "Merlin," —the first terminally guided, "fire-and-forget" mortar projectile capable of finding and knocking out enemy armor. Once fired, the Merlin projectile deploys stabilizing fins and control canards that work in concert with a nose-mounted radar seeker system to detect the presence of a target. The projectile can steer itself to the top of its target, a tank or other armored vehicle. The shaped charge located in the rear of the projectile is said to be capable of piercing the topside armor of any tank now in production.

Lighter weight, higher firing rates, and a host of current and advanced munitions make the M252 the mortar of the future. In total, the U.S. Army will procure nearly 1,100 systems, with an additional 800 going to the Marine Corps.

Below: *The M252 81mm Mortar is lighter than the M29A1 Mortar by some 25 to 30 pounds.*

Left: *The British-designed M252 entered serviced with U.S. forces in 1987.* Below: *The M252 Mortar will play an important role in any conflict in Central Europe.*

M252 81mm MORTAR	
Caliber:	81mm
Barrel length:	50.14 in.
Weight:	
Overall (with sight):	87 lbs.
Barrel:	28 lbs.
Baseplate:	26 lbs.
Bipod:	27 lbs.
Rate of fire:	
Maximum:	33 rpm for one minute
Sustained:	16 rpm
Muzzle velocity:	974 fps
Range:	5,650 yds.
Elevation:	+40 degrees to +85 degrees
Date of service:	1987

Shoulder-Launched, Multipurpose Assault Weapon

The Shoulder-Launched, Multipurpose Assault Weapon (SMAW) is a light rocket launcher that resembles the World War II bazooka. The resemblance is strictly superficial, however, for the SMAW is a far more capable weapon.

In the late 1970s, both the U.S. Army and Marine Corps had identified a need for a more powerful rocket and launcher system to replace the older Light Armor Weapon (LAW) that had proved its worth in Vietnam. A joint services program was initiated. The Army later dropped out to develop its own one-man rocket launcher, and the Marines went on to develop the SMAW.

Program parameters called for a cost-effective weapon to be developed as quickly as possible from off-the-shelf components. The rocket launcher system, developed by Israeli Military Industries as the B300, was combined with the McDonnell Douglas B300 missile launcher and a new 3.27-inch warhead and fusing system developed by the Naval Surface Weapons Center at Dahlgren, Virginia.

By November 1984, the new SMAW system was operational in the U.S. Marine Corps. The complete, assembled system is 54 inches long, and is reusable. The rocket, when contained in its packaging, has a shelf life of ten years.

The SMAW's unique sighting system consists of a British Enfield rifle barrel and breech into which the operator inserts a special 9mm rifle cartridge that duplicates exactly the ballistics of the rocket. After estimating the range to the target, the operator sets the sight by turning the range-finder drum. Then, using a built-in rifle telescopic sight, the operator sights the target, fires the rifle, and watches for the impact of the 9mm round. Maintaining the original point of aim, the operator adjusts the telescopic sight until the cross hairs are on the point of impact. The SMAW is now sighted-in. If circumstances permit, the operator can fire additional spotting rounds for confirmation. He then attaches a rocket, still in its transport/storage package, and launches it at the target. The rocket travels at 722 feet per second.

SMAW's primary use is against fixed targets. What appears to be a cumbersome sighting system is, in fact, straightforward. Since bunkers are not mobile, the gunner, who is usually under cover, has time to ascertain his aim. The SMAW's secondary use is against tanks, and for this type of target, iron, or "open," non-optical sights are used.

Two warheads have been developed for the SMAW. The first contains a high-explosive charge that detonates either on impact or after a short delay. The second warhead is designated High Explosive Anti-Armor (HEAA) and carries a shaped-charge explosive. A long, slender nose carries the fuse. When the fuse strikes the target, it fires the main charge, which is not yet in contact with the target. The explosion of the main charge is directed at a cone-shaped disk of metal, turning it instantly into an extremely hot jet of gas capable of penetrating armor. The HEAA warhead can penetrate as much as 2.36 inches of armor angled at 70 percent from vertical.

Other SMAW warheads under development are illumination and flame rounds, and a fuel-air warhead. The latter sprays aviation gasoline or a similar combustible fuel into the air when it strikes the target. The resulting fuel-air mixture is then detonated, causing a severe concussion in the immediate area.

Above: *The Shoulder-Launched Multipurpose Assault Weapon was developed by McDonnell Douglas Astronautics for the U.S. Marine Corps.*

Above: *The SMAW is effective against steel reinforced concrete bunkers and other similar structures.*

SHOULDER-LAUNCHED, MULTIPURPOSE ASSAULT WEAPON

Caliber:	3.26 in.
Length:	
Launcher:	54 in.
Rocket:	29.5 in.
Weight:	
Launcher:	16.5 lbs.
Rocket:	12.9 lbs.
Muzzle velocity:	722 fps
Range:	1,640 ft.
Date of service:	1984

FIRE SUPPORT (ARTILLERY)

Artillery has developed from awkward, ponderous bombards throwing stone shot a few hundred yards against castle walls to sophisticated mechanisms of steel and aluminum that can fire a variety of ammunition to distances of 18 miles and more.

When the United States gained its independence, three types of artillery were in use: the cannon, the howitzer, and the mortar. The howitzer was relatively short in relation to its bore diameter. Howitzers fired shots at a greater elevation than cannons against fortified positions and buildings. The cannon, with its low trajectory, was used against infantry. The mortar was often little more than one to three times long as its bore diameter, firing its shells at a steep angle to clear obstructions before dropping over walls.

During the War of 1812, the six-pounder (referring to the weight of the shot) iron cannon was the predominant model. In the Mexican War of 1846–48, at least 24 types of artillery were used. By 1860, the breech-loading cannon had been introduced, but except for stationary coastal and siege guns, it was not widely used because it was heavy and cumbersome. The new rifled guns developed between 1850 and 1860 proved more popular. The main standby of the artillery units of both sides in the Civil War remained the six- and 12-pound smoothbore Napoleons.

By the beginning of the Spanish-American War in 1898, the U.S. Army was equipped with smokeless, quick-firing cannons and well-versed in using them in the indirect firing mode. Accurate maps and scouting parties provided target data. Forward and balloon-borne observers, communicating by telephone, telegraph, heliograph, and signal flag, corrected aim.

At the outset of World War I in 1914, it was immediately apparent that artillery had become a bigger factor in warfare than anyone had expected. The new quick-firing artillery drove soldiers of both sides into trenches and, with the help of the machine gun, kept them there. The new artillery guns were larger and more mobile than their predecessors. Railroads and motor trucks supplied them with far more shells than had been possible in the days of horse-drawn wagons. In 1918 alone, more than 152,000,000 shells were fired by the Allies. During World War II, the U.S. Army fielded the 105 millimeter M2 howitzer and the 155mm M1 as its standard artillery weapons. The Army also developed a 240mm howitzer and an 8-inch cannon.

Artillery development in the United States since 1945 has been directed largely toward improving 105mm and 155mm guns that are quite similar to those used in World War II except for weight and range. The United States has also worked to develop faster and more rugged self-propelled guns. Today, the U.S. Army and Marine ground forces are equipped with five towed artillery pieces—three 105mm and two 155mm units—and two self-propelled units—one 155mm and one 8-inch 203mm.

Towed artillery pieces require a tracked mover or a wheeled truck to carry them to and from their firing positions. Self-propelled artillery pieces have a cannon tube and breech assembly permanently mounted on a tracked vehicle. The advantages of the self-propelled gun are obvious. The number of soldiers needed to service a self-propelled artillery piece is reduced by the crew of the towing vehicle. Self-propelled guns are also more responsive to the needs of a ground commander since the guns can be placed in position or quickly moved to a new position. And these guns can change position at a moment's notice to avoid enemy counterbattery fire.

A third type of artillery—the rocket—made its appearance early in World War II. Since the war, the rocket has been developed to a very high degree of sophistication. Two types of multiple launch rockets and the longer-ranged Lance guided missile have extended the range of the artillery branch up to a distance of 75 miles.

Opposite: *The Multiple Launch Rocket System carries a crew of three. The system employs the "shoot and scoot" method to decrease its vulnerability to enemy counterbattery fire.* Top: *The Lance Battlefield Support Missile is a corps-level weapon designed to be fired against enemy airfields; missile-launching sites; and communications, command, and transportation centers.* Left: *The M110A2 self-propelled artillery piece fires a 203mm shell.* Above: *This M114 155mm Towed Howitzer (foreground) is in full recoil.*

M101A1 105mm Towed Howitzer

The M101A1 Howitzer is the oldest artillery piece still in active service with the U.S. Army and Marine Corps. This powerful weapon first entered service in 1934 and was in near continuous production from 1939 to 1953. It is termed a "towed" howitzer because it must be towed to its firing position.

Originally designed in 1919 as the Model 1920 105mm Howitzer, it underwent a series of refinements and upgrades until it was standardized as the Model 1925E, and its carriage as the Model 1925E1. In 1934, this gun was further upgraded to fire fixed ammunition, becoming the M2. When modified in 1940 for mounting on a specially designed split-trail carriage (the part of the gun carriage that rests on the ground when the piece is unlimbered), the M2 became the M2A1. By the time production ended in 1953, approximately 10,202 had been built.

After World War II, the M2 was redesignated to its current nomenclature: Howitzer, Light, Towed: 105mm, M101 and M101A1. The complete artillery piece consists of the Cannon M2A1 or M2A2, the Carriage M2A1, and a recoil system, which can be the M2A1, M2A3, M2A4, or M2A5. The differing designations refer to various design features unique to each model.

The M101 and M101A1 both employ a single-axle, split-trail carriage. The trail is the long balancing and towing piece on the carriage. The trail is divided in two so that the two pieces can be pulled apart to form a "V" to provide stability.

When the M101 is fired, recoil is absorbed by hydraulic shock absorbers similar to those used in automobiles. Attached to the carriage are two sheet-steel shields designed to protect the gun crew from small arms fire or shrapnel from counterbattery fire. The barrel can be raised and lowered by an elevating mechanism. The fire control system consists of a three-power telescope that provides a 13-degree field of view and a four-power panoramic telescope that provides a ten-degree field of view. The M101 series fires semi-fixed ammunition—a warhead separate from the propelling charge—that includes high-explosive, smoke, flare, rocket-assisted, tracer, and leaflet dispensing projectiles.

Because of its simplicity, the M101 and M101A1 series of howitzers can be unhooked from their tow vehicle, loaded, aimed, and fired within three minutes by a trained battery crew. The M101 series has proved so reliable that, as old as it is, more than 400 are still in U.S. military service.

Below: *The 105mm M101A1 Howitzer is one of the oldest towed artillery pieces still in service with U.S. military forces.*

M101A1 105mm TOWED HOWITZER	
Caliber:	105mm
Length:	
Overall:	19 ft., 7.8 in.
Barrel:	8 ft., 5.3 in.
Width:	12 ft. (firing)
Weight:	
M101:	4,475.3 lbs.
M101A1:	4,977.9 lbs.
Recoil system:	Hydropneumatic
Carriage:	Split-trail
Rate of fire:	
Maximum:	Ten rounds per minute for 3 minutes
Sustained:	Three rounds per minute
Range (conventional ammunition):	12,314 yds.
Date of service:	1934

M114 155mm Towed Howitzer

The M114, like the M101, has its roots in World War I. The M114 is based on the M1918 155 millimeter Howitzer, which in turn was based on the French Schneider-built M1917. The M1918 was equipped with a split-trail carriage similar to that used on the M101 series in the late 1930s; the M1918 was standardized in April 1941 as the 155mm Howitzer M1. After the war, the gun was redesignated the Howitzer, Medium, Towed: 155mm, M114. The M114A1 is nearly identical to the M114 except for slight modifications to the carriage.

The M114 designation applies to the entire cannon tube assembly (barrel, breech, and breech mechanism) and the M1A1 or M1A2 carriage. The carriage is equipped with three axles. The trail axle carries two tires; the other two axles, which are under the carriage proper, carry four tires each. Each wheel has hand brakes, and the carriage is equipped with air brakes, which are operated from the towing vehicle.

The barrel is elevated by spring-actuators, or "equilibrators," and the recoil system is hydropneumatic. The carriage is divided into two parts. The cannon tube, recoil system, shields, elevating and traversing mechanism, and the aiming telescope are mounted on the top carriage. The bottom carriage supports the top carriage. The towing vehicle is the M5 five-ton (6 × 6) high-speed tractor.

The M114 fires a range of ammunition similar to that of the 105mm series. The U.S. Army has nearly completed retrofitting all M114A1s with the longer 20-foot barrel used on the M198. The retrofitted guns are designated M114A2 and will be deployed to Reserve units. A total of more than 4,800 M114 Howitzers have been built.

Above: *The M114A2 155mm Howitzer was originally designed and fielded as the M1. It is now being replaced in U.S. military service by the M198 155mm Towed Howitzer.*

M114 155mm TOWED HOWITZER	
Caliber:	155mm
Length:	
Overall:	24 ft.
Barrel:	
M114:	8 ft., 5.3 in.
M114A1:	12 ft., 4.7 in.
M114A2:	20 ft.
Width:	8 ft. (traveling)
Weight:	12,786 lbs.
Recoil system:	Hydropneumatic
Carriage:	Split-trail
Rate of fire:	
Maximum:	Two rounds per 1/2 minute Eight rounds per 4 minutes Sixteen rounds per 10 minutes
Sustained:	One round per minute
Range (conventional ammunition):	15,966 yds.
Date of service:	1941

M102 105mm Towed Howitzer

The M102 Howitzer is a lighter—nearly three-quarters of a ton—version of the M101 series; the lighter weight makes it easier to maneuver about the battlefield. The M102 was standardized in 1956 and entered service the following year. Because of its lighter weight, the M102 replaced the older M101A1 in air transportable divisions.

Experience gained with the M102 under actual battle conditions in South Vietnam led to further modifications. Modifications included those necessary to lighten the howitzer still further for airborne service. Today, the M102 is the primary-issue artillery piece of U.S. Army airborne and air mobile divisions.

To achieve the required weight reduction, aluminum is used throughout the carriage. Instead of a split-trail, the M102 uses a box-trail, which consists of two aluminum box-girders fastened together with a transverse girder. When the howitzer is to be fired, a circular base plate attached to the single axle is lowered to the ground and staked in place. The gun is then jacked up until the wheels are off the ground. A roller at the end of the trail allows the gun to be turned 360 degrees for aiming.

The M102's fire control system consists of a quadrant, a panoramic telescope, and an elbow telescope. For low-light or night firing situations, all reticles are illuminated by tritium sources. Like the M101, the M102 is normally towed by the five-ton M5 (6 x 6) high-speed tractor or the M561 Gama Goat, or it is slung beneath the CH-47 Chinook transport helicopter. The M102, as with the M101, is normally deployed in battalions containing three batteries of six guns each.

The M102's barrel is about two and a half feet longer than the M101's, giving projectiles a slightly greater muzzle velocity that translates into 262 yards of greater range. Rocket-assisted projectiles can reach 16,404 yards. The M102 fires the same variety of ammunition as the M101 series. More than 1,200 M102s have been produced for the United States Army and Marine Corps.

Below: *The M102 105mm Towed Howitzer was specially designed for use by airborne and air mobile forces.*

M102 105mm TOWED HOWITZER

Caliber:	105mm
Length:	
Barrel:	11 ft., 1 in.
Overall:	17 ft.
Width:	6 ft., 5.3 in.
Weight:	3,298 lbs.
Recoil system:	Hydropneumatic
Carriage:	Box-trail
Rate of fire:	
Maximum:	Ten rounds per minute for 3 minutes
Sustained:	Three rounds per minute
Range (conventional ammunition):	12,576 yds.
Date of service:	1957

Above: *The M102 105mm Howitzer was used extensively by U.S. and South Vietnamese military forces during the Vietnam War.* Left: *Three levels of infantry firepower are seen in recent exercises: the M16A1 rifle (foreground), the M72A2 Light Antitank Weapon (center), and the M102 artillery piece (background).*

M198 155mm Towed Howitzer

The M198 Howitzer was designed to replace the less capable M114. Development work began in 1968 at the Rock Island Arsenal with the objective of increasing the gun's range while keeping weight within acceptable limits. Firing trials took place in 1970, and the first production prototypes were delivered in 1972. In 1978, the new gun was standardized as the M198 Howitzer, and the first production guns were delivered in July of that year. Total production of approximately 1,800 units was completed by 1982. The U.S. Army and Marine Corps absorbed 1,400 units.

In the mid-1980s, the U.S. Army decided to standardize its artillery on the 155 millimeter caliber. Except for those guns in use by direct-fire battalions supporting light infantry, airborne, and air assault divisions, all artillery pieces would be 155mm. The M198 will be the U.S. Army and Marine Corps standard towed field artillery piece for the foreseeable future.

To obtain increased range over the M114, the weight of the gun and carriage had to be increased by more than 3,000 pounds. Despite the extra weight, the M198 can still be lifted by the CH-47 and CH-53D helicopters, prime movers respectively of the Army and Marine Corps. The M939 five-ton truck is the weapon's other prime mover.

The M198 and its recoil mechanism are mounted on a split-trail carriage. The carriage wheels are mounted on a two-position suspension system so that the wheels can be lifted up and out of contact with the ground by a hand-operated hydraulic pump. In the firing position, the M198 sits solidly on its firing platform without having to be anchored, and its long trails are opened into a wide "V." The cannon itself is transported either with the barrel forward or rotated to rest aft along the trails.

The M198 has a two-part carriage similar to that used by the M114. It also employs a hydropneumatic recoil system, and the gun tube is fitted with a screw-on, double-baffle muzzle brake (a device that retards a gun's "kick"). The aiming system comprises a four-power panoramic telescope with a ten-degree field of view, two elevation quadrants, and an elbow telescope with eight-power magnification and a six-degree field of view. The barrel can be elevated by hand to an angle of 71 degrees for firing at close range, and it can be depressed to five degrees below centerline for transporting or for point-blank firing.

The M198 fires a full range of U.S. separate-loading (projectile and charge separate) 155mm ammunition. A trained crew of 11 needs less than five minutes to ready the M198 for firing. The M198 has a range of 32,808 yards with the M549 High Explosive Rocket-Assisted projectile, and first-round hits are within 109 yards of the target. The barrel of the M198 is equipped with a thermal-sensing device that warns the crew when the tube is too hot to fire. This feature allows the crew to exceed the recommended rate of fire in certain situations.

Above: *The M198 Howitzer has a range of approximately 18 miles when firing conventional ammunition.* Opposite, top: *The M198 Howitzer can be air-delivered by the CH-53D Sea Stallion (right) or the CH-47 Chinook (upper left).* Opposite, bottom: *The M198 155mm Howitzer is usually fielded in battalions of three batteries, each battery with six guns.*

M198 155mm TOWED HOWITZER

Caliber:	155mm
Length:	
Barrel:	20 ft.
Overall:	40 ft., 5.8 in. (traveling)
Width:	
Traveling:	9.16 ft.
Firing:	28 ft.
Weight:	15,791.4 lbs.
Recoil system:	Hydropneumatic
Carriage:	Split-trail
Rate of fire:	
Maximum:	Four rounds per minute for 3 minutes
Sustained:	Two rounds per minute
Range (conventional ammunition):	24,059 yds.
Date of service:	1978

M119 105mm Towed Howitzer

Light infantry divisions (LID) pack all their equipment and fire-support on their backs or in their transport aircraft. The LID's role requires a number of new pieces of equipment, with transportability in mind. One requirement is a light field artillery piece that can be air-dropped from all existing U.S. Air Force cargo aircraft, carried by the U.S. Army's Black Hawk helicopter, or towed by the High Mobility, Multipurpose Wheeled Vehicle (HMMWV) light utility vehicle.

In the mid-1960s, the British Army developed a requirement for a new light artillery piece to replace their existing 105mm pack howitzer. The Royal Armament Research and Development Establishment (RARDE) went to work on a design for a new lightweight gun. By 1973, RARDE had tested several successful prototypes. Production began in 1974 at the Royal Ordnance works in Nottingham, England. The new lightweight gun earned an excellent combat record during the Falkland Islands War in 1982, which prompted the U.S. Army to lease six guns for evaluation in 1984. In 1985, 14 additional guns were leased and sent to the 9th Infantry Division at Fort Lewis, Washington, for rigorous testing.

In 1986, the Army purchased the first of a projected 542 of the new guns, which has been designated in U.S. service as the M119 Light Gun. The entire evaluation and procurement process took just 19 months under the new nondevelopmental item (NDI) procurement process, which allows the military to buy "off-the-shelf" items as needed. Starting in 1989, the M119 began replacing the remaining M101A1 and M102 howitzers being used in direct-support artillery battalions for LIDs, airborne divisions, and air mobile divisions.

Lightweight at just 4,100 pounds, the M119 makes extensive use of high-strength aluminum alloys. The trail is made from high-strength, corrosion-resistant steel. The bow-shaped trail allows the breech-operator and loader to remain inside, maintaining a high rate of fire. The platform upon which the gun rests is constructed of lightweight steel, providing a firm base. The operator sits in a saddle on the left trail, where he uses a direct- and indirect-sighting system. All sight reticles use tritium illumination for low-light or night firing. The M119's barrel is elevated by a handwheel; the gun can be towed with its barrel in the firing position or, for stowage along the trail, with the barrel turned 180 degrees.

The M119 fires all U.S.-standard 105mm ammunition. Development work on a rocket-assisted projectile and conventional, improved munitions is currently in progress. It is expected that the new ammunition will extend the gun's range by 6,014 yards.

Below: *The M119 Howitzer is an American modification of the British-designed L7 105mm Towed Howitzer. The M119 will be used by airborne, air mobile, and light infantry forces.*

M119 105mm TOWED HOWITZER	
Caliber:	105mm
Length:	
Barrel:	10.38 ft.
Overall:	21.75 ft.
Width:	5.83 ft.
Weight:	4,100 lbs.
Recoil system:	Hydropneumatic
Carriage:	Split-trail
Rate of fire:	
Maximum:	Eight rounds per minute Six rounds per minute for 3 minutes
Sustained:	Three rounds per minute
Range: (conventional ammunition):	15,310 yds.
Date of service:	1989

M109 155mm Self-propelled Howitzer

By 1952, well into the Korean War, it became obvious that there was serious need for a new self-propelled 155mm howitzer to replace the World War II-vintage M44 and the postwar M107, neither of which were air-transportable. In July 1963, after extensive development and testing, the new gun was accepted as the Howitzer, Medium, Self-propelled: 155mm, M109.

Originally a short-barreled howitzer, a longer gun tube (M185) with a fume extractor (a system that draws propellant fumes out of a gun's barrel) and a large muzzle brake were installed. This version was reclassified as the M109A1. The M109A2 is the M109A1 with improvements to armor, maintainability, and reliability. The M109A3 is the M109A1 modified in Army depots. The M109A2 and the M109A3 have replaced the M109A1 in Army and Marine Corps active service. Both of these turreted, long-tube vehicles are fully tracked, diesel-powered, and aluminum armored. Both are air-transportable in the U.S. Air Force's C-141 Starlifter or C-5 Galaxy. They possess all-weather capability and are quite agile.

The M109 Self-propelled 155mm Howitzer is the standard direct support artillery weapon in armored and mechanized infantry units. It carries a crew of six: commander, gunner, driver, and three ammunition handlers. The driver sits in the left front portion of the hull, with the engine to his right. Command and gunnery stations are in the turret. The hull and turret are built of welded aluminum. The armor, also aluminum, is reinforced with Kevlar anti-spalling liners designed to stop enemy small arms fire and shell splinters. The M109A2/3 turret has a full-width bustle that carries 22 rounds of 155mm ammunition.

The M109A2/3 has a 405 horsepower diesel engine capable of maintaining a road speed of 33 miles per hour. The M109A2/3 uses a torsion bar suspension system and has seven road wheels, with front-wheel-drive and a rear idler. There are no return rollers. This vehicle can ford streams as deep as six feet, or it can be fitted with nine air bags for amphibious use. Tracks can propel the M109A2/3 in the water at a rate of just under four miles per hour.

The main armament is the 16.66-foot M185 cannon, which fires a conventional high-explosive round to a range of 19,794 yards; the original M109 short-barreled cannon (M126) could achieve a range of just 15,996 yards. When firing a rocket-assisted projectile, the M109A2/3 can achieve ranges up to 26,246 yards. The gun can fire one round per minute or, for short periods, three rounds per minute. The gun tube can be elevated to 75 degrees, depressed five degrees below centerline, and traversed 360 degrees. All gun controls are hydraulic and have manual backup. The M109A2/3 can fire a complete range of U.S. 155mm ammunition, including high-explosive, smoke, illumination, tactical nuclear, chemical, and rocket-assisted high-explosive rounds. Secondary armament is a .50 caliber M2 heavy-barrel machine gun mounted on the turret near the commander's station.

The M109, M109A1, M109A2, and M109A3 are in service with the U.S. Army, Marine Corps, and National Guard. In accordance with the U.S. Division Plan 86, each U.S. armored and mechanized infantry division has three battalions of M109 series self-propelled howitzers. Each battalion comprises one fire-direction center and three batteries with eight guns each, divided into two platoons of four guns.

continued on page 204

Above: *The M109 Self-propelled Howitzer carries a 155mm main gun and one .50 caliber machine gun.*

The M109A2, shown here during Operation Bright Star exercises in Egypt, is supported by the M992 Field Artillery Ammunition Support Vehicle (right), which carries additional ammunition.

continued from page 201

M109 155mm SELF-PROPELLED HOWITZER

Caliber:	155mm
Length:	
Barrel:	16 ft., 8 in.
Overall:	29 ft., 11 in.
Width:	10 ft., 4 in.
Weight:	55,000 lbs.
Speed:	33 mph
Recoil system:	Hydropneumatic
Rate of fire:	
Maximum:	Three rounds per minute
Sustained:	One round per minute
Range (conventional ammunition):	19,794 yds.
Date of service:	1963

Above: *The M109 Self-propelled Howitzer has a road speed of 33 miles per hour and a range of 242 miles.* Opposite: *The armor on the M109 Self-propelled Howitzer is 0.75-inch-thick aluminum designed to protect the crew of six from small arms fire only.*

The M109 was due to be upgraded, but events in Eastern Europe and the Soviet Union may make that unnecessary.

G6 2C
G62C

M110A2 Self-propelled 203mm (8-Inch) Howitzer

The first M110 self-propelled howitzers were built in 1962, and the first M110 battalion was organized at Ft. Sill, Oklahoma, the following year. By the end of the 1960s, 750 M110s had been built.

In 1969, the U.S. Army began development of a longer-range version of the M110 to fire a new series of improved ammunition. Designated the M110A1, this gun entered service in January 1977. The new gun shared the old gun's chassis but carried a longer M201 barrel and a direct-fire M139 telescope. In 1978, the M110A2 was standardized and was nearly the same as the M110A1. A significant difference is that the cannon tube of the M110A2 was fitted with a muzzle brake so that it could fire heavier charges.

The M110 series has a crew of 13. The commander, driver, and three gunners ride on an open M110 chassis. The rest of the crew rides in the tracked M548 cargo-carrier, which hauls the ammunition. The hull of the M110 is all-welded aluminum and high-strength steel. The driver sits at the front left side of the hull. The engine is on the driver's right, and the main armament is at the rear. Only the driver is surrounded by armor.

The chassis has five road wheels, with the drive-wheel up front. The fifth road wheel serves as the idler. The M110 uses a torsion-bar suspension system. A General Motors Allison Division diesel engine generates 405 horsepower, giving the M110A2 series a road speed of 34 miles per hour and a cross-country speed of nine miles per hour; range is 450 miles. Because the M110's hull and turret are not enclosed, the M110 does not have night vision equipment or nuclear-biological-chemical warfare protection for the crew.

The M110A2's main gun can be elevated to 65 degrees, depressed to two degrees below centerline, and traversed 30 degrees left or right. Ammunition is loaded as three separate pieces—fuse, warhead, and propelling charge—by a hydraulic rammer and loader that lifts the ammunition and rams it into the chamber. The M110A2 can fire a rocket-assisted projectile to a distance of 32,800 yards. At the rear of the chassis is a large spade that is hydraulically lowered into the earth before the gun opens fire. Hydraulic power is backed up by a manual system.

The M110 series fires the complete range of 203mm ammunition in U.S. inventory. This includes chemical, nuclear, high-explosive, high-explosive rocket-assisted (HERA), and improved

Above: *The M110 Self-propelled 203mm (8-inch) Howitzer is the largest artillery piece still in U.S. military service.*

M110A2 203mm (8-INCH) SELF-PROPELLED HOWITZER	
Caliber:	203mm (8 in.)
Length:	
Barrel:	30 ft., 5 in.
Overall:	35 ft., 2.4 in.
Width:	10 ft., 4 in.
Weight:	58,496 lbs.
Speed:	34 mph
Recoil system:	Hydropneumatic
Rate of fire:	
Maximum:	Four rounds for three minutes
Sustained:	One round per two minutes
Range: (conventional ammunition):	23,293 yds.
Date of service:	1963

conventional munitions, which contain M42 grenades. The M650 HERA round is also fired as a spotting round for the rocket-assisted XM753 nuclear round. The fuse of the M106 high-explosive round can be set for air or ground burst. Due to the projectiles' weight and the difficulty of handling them, the M110A2 fires at a sustained rate of one round every two minutes. The maximum rate of fire is four rounds in the first three minutes.

The U.S. Army currently has 1,029 M110A2s in inventory. Under the U.S. Division Plan 86, M110A2 Self-propelled 203mm Howitzers are being integrated with Multiple Launch Rocket System (MLRS) batteries. All armored and mechanized infantry divisions have one battalion of 12 M110A2s divided into two batteries of six each; each battalion has one battery of nine MLRSs.

Top: *The M110 Self-propelled Howitzer entered service with the U.S. Army in 1963.* Bottom: *The M110A2 has a longer barrel than the original M110s and a double-baffle muzzle break to handle heavier powder charges.*

105mm Artillery Ammunition

U.S. 105mm ammunition is semi-fixed, i.e., the projectile and powder charges are in separate units. The projectile is loaded first into the gun's breech, then the powder charge is inserted.

Muzzle velocity and projectile range are dependent on a number of factors; two of the most important are the length of the cannon tube and the weight of the projectile. Most 105mm artillery rounds in current U.S service weigh an average of 42 pounds. When fired from the M102 Towed Howitzer with its 11-foot barrel, average muzzle velocity is 1,797 feet per second and its range is 16,513 yards.

Three 105mm artillery pieces remain in active service with the U.S. Army and Marine Corps: the M101, the M102, and the new M119, based on the British 105mm Light Gun. All three guns can fire any 105mm ammunition that is currently in U.S. inventory.

105mm ARTILLERY AMMUNITION

TYPE	WEIGHT/DESCRIPTION
M1 High Explosive	Weight: 46.43 lbs.
M60 Carrier Projectile	Weight: 42.9 lbs. Used for a number of different payloads, including smoke and chemical agents
M67 Target Practice-Tracer (TP-T)	Weight: 37.03 lbs.
M84 Smoke Projectile	Weight: 41.95 lbs.
M84B1 Leaflet Dispenser Projectile	Weight: 39.68 lbs.
M314 Illuminating Projectile	Weight: 46.43 lbs.
M327 High Explosive Plastic (HEP)	Weight: 33.66 lbs.
M360 Carrier Projectile	Weight: 43.85 lbs.
M413 High Explosive	Weight: 42 lbs. Carries 18 M35 antipersonnel grenades
M444 High Explosive	Weight: 42 lbs. Carries 18 M39 grenades
M546 Antipersonnel (APERS)	Weight: 38.25 lbs.
M548 High Explosive Rocket Assisted projectile (HERA)	Weight: 38.5 lbs. Maximum range: 16,513 yds. Used for a number of different payloads, including smoke and chemical agents

155mm Artillery Ammunition

The range of any projectile depends on a number of factors, the two most important of which are charge weight and tube length. As a rule of thumb, the M114A1 155mm Howitzer Towed with a tube length of 12.39 feet can fire the M483 projectile containing high-explosive antipersonnel grenades weighing 102.5 pounds to about 15,966 yards. The M198 155mm Towed Howitzer with a barrel length of 20 feet can fire the same projectile to about 24,059 yards.

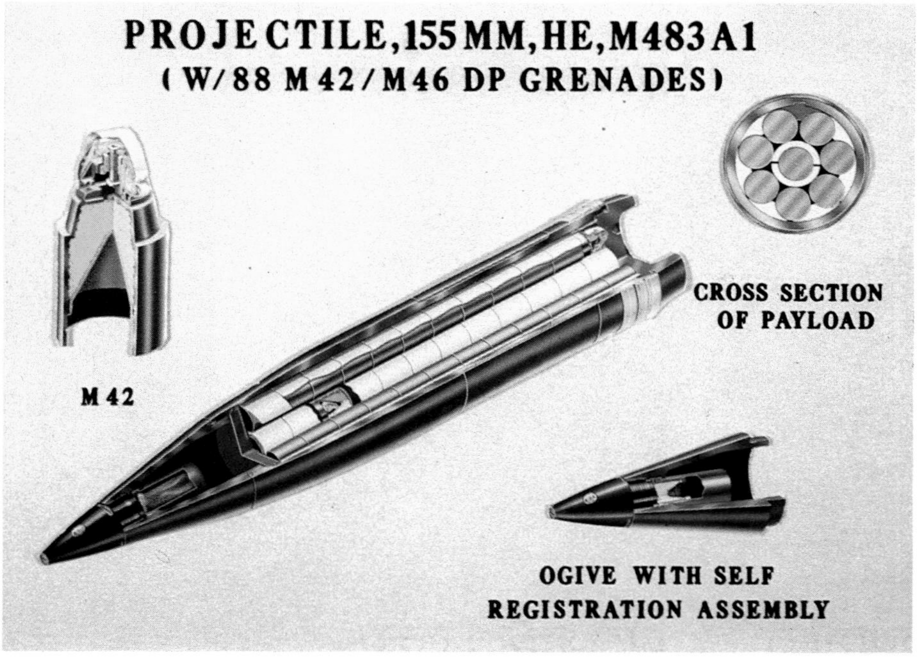

Few artillery rounds today contain only high explosive. Most carry submunitions—small, separate charges often referred to as grenades.

155mm ARTILLERY AMMUNITION

TYPE	WEIGHT/DESCRIPTION
M101 High Explosive Projectile	Weight: 95.7 lbs. Obsolete
M104 Smoke Projectile	Weight: 98.17 lbs. Obsolete
M107 High Explosive	Weight: 94.6 lbs. M114 and M198 Towed, M109A1 Self-propelled
M110 Carrier Projectile	Weight: 97.88 lbs. The M110 can carry a variety of warheads. M114 and M198 Towed, M109 Self-propelled
Chemical Warfare Projectile	Carries Mustard Gas (Agents H and HD)
White Phosphorus Smoke Projectile Series	
M112 Armor Piercing Projectile	Weight: 98.98 lbs. Carries white phosphorous smoke rounds. Obsolete
M116 Base Ejection Smoke Projectile	Weight: 93 lbs. M114 and M198 Towed, M109 Self-propelled
M118 Illuminating Projectile Series	Weight: 93.16 lbs. M114 and M198 Towed
M121A1 Chemical Warfare Projectile	Weight: 100.3 lbs. Carries VX or GB. M114 and M198 Towed, M109 Self-propelled
M449 Antipersonnel High Explosive Grenades	Weight: 95 lbs. An improved conventional munition projectile, the M449 contains 60 antipersonnel grenades. Short self-clearing time. M114 and M198 Towed, M109 Self-propelled
M454 Nuclear Projectile	Weight: 120 lbs. Carries the W48 nuclear warhead. M109 Self-propelled
M483 Antipersonnel High Explosive Grenades	Weight: 102.5 lbs. Contains 88 dual-purpose grenades (64 M42 and 24 M46) effective against personnel or lightly armored and unarmored vehicles. Long self-clearing time. M114 and M189 Towed, M109 Self-propelled
M549 High Explosive Rocket Assisted (HERA) Projectile	Weight: 102.5 lbs. Also known as a Rocket Assisted Projectile (RAP) because it has a small rocket motor in the base of the projectile that ignites after firing to increase velocity and

TYPE	WEIGHT/DESCRIPTION
M549 continued	therefore range. RAP 155mm shells increase muzzle velocity to 2,709.9 fps and extend range from 24,059 yds. to 32,808 yds.
M629 Area Denial Artillery Munition	Weight: 103 lbs. Contains 36 antipersonnel mines that are ejected in flight over the target area. Adjustable self-clearing time. Part of the ADAM system. M198 Towed, M109 Self-propelled
XM631 Tactical CS Gas Projectile	Weight: 100.3 lbs. M114 and M198 Towed, M198 Self-propelled
M650 High Explosive Rocket Assisted Projectile	M198 Towed
M687 Binary Nerve Gas Shell	Weight: 92.98 lbs. Carries VX or GB. Details classified. M198 Towed, M109A1 Self-propelled
M692 Antipersonnel High Explosive Grenades	Weight: 102.5 lbs. Contains 36 antipersonnel mines. Short self-clearing time. M198 Towed, M109 Self-propelled
M712 Cannon-Launched Guided Projectile (Copperhead)	Weight: 94.6 lbs. Also called HEAT CLGP. (High Explosive Antitank, Cannon Launched Guided Projectile). M198 Towed, M109 Self-propelled
M718 Antitank Mine	Weight: 93.9 lbs. Part of the RAAMS system. Short self-clearing time. This warhead can also be attached to a guided projectile. M198 Towed, M109 Self-propelled
M731 Antipersonnel High Explosive Grenades	Weight: 102.5 lbs. Contains 36 antipersonnel mines. Long self-clearing time. M198 Towed, M109 Self-propelled
M741 Antitank Mine	Weight: 93.9 lbs. Contains 9 antitank mines. Part of the RAAMS system. Long self-clearing time. This warhead can also be attached to a guided projectile. M198 Towed, M109 Self-propelled

155mm ARTILLERY AMMUNITION

TYPE	WEIGHT/DESCRIPTION
XM753 Nuclear Projectile	Details are classified. M198 Towed
XM785 Rocket Assisted Projectile with W82 Nuclear Warhead	Weight and details are classified. M198 Towed, M109A1 Self-propelled
XM795 High Explosive	This projectile will be used as a registration round for the M483 projectile. Registration rounds are fired to correct aim before committing the desired round. M198 Towed
M904 Practice Round	M109A1 Self-propelled
M823	Copperhead practice round. It is not fired.
M825 Base Ejection Smoke Projectile	Details classified. M198 Towed, M109 Self-propelled
M864 Dual Purpose Improved Conventional Munition	M198 Towed, MS109A1
Copperhead (Cannon Launched Guided Projectile)	Weight: 137.5 lbs. Range: 2 to 10 miles. M198 Towed, M109 Self-propelled

Above: *The Copperhead artillery projectile is an example of the new, technologically sophisticated smart weapons.* Left: *The Copperhead is a 155mm cannon-launched projectile. It contains a laser seeker and folding wings and tail surfaces that guide the missile to its target during the terminal phases of flight.*

203mm (8-Inch) Howitzer Ammunition

All 203 millimeter (8-inch) ammunition in U.S. Army service is separately loaded as propelling charge and projectile. Ammunition fired from the 203mm M115 Towed Howitzer, still in use with Reserve and National Guard units, has a range of about 18,372.7 yards.

Right: *Ammunition for the M110 Howitzer can weigh 200 pounds or more. The different types include conventional, chemical, and nuclear warheads.*

203mm (8-INCH) HOWITZER AMMUNITION

TYPE	WEIGHT/DESCRIPTION
M106 High Explosive Projectile	Weight: 204 lbs. M115 Towed, M110 Self-propelled
M404 High Explosive Projectile	Weight: 200 lbs. Carries 104 M43A1 grenades. M115 Towed, M110 Self-propelled
M422 Nuclear Projectile	Details are classified. Carries the W33 nuclear warhead, yields 5 to 10 kilotons. M115 Towed, M110 Self-propelled
M426 Chemical Warfare Projectile	Weight: 204 lbs. Carries GB or VX nerve gases. M115 Towed, M110 Self-propelled
M509 Improved Conventional Munition (ICM)	Weight: 205.6 lbs. High explosive projectile. Carries 195 M42 dual-purpose grenades. M115 Towed, M110 Self-propelled
M650 High Explosive Rocket Assisted Projectile	RAP version of the M106 projectile. Will also be used as a spotting round for the XM753 Nuclear Projectile. M110 Self-propelled
XM711 High Explosive Rocket Assisted Projectile	Weight: 200 lbs. To replace the M106. M115 Towed, M110 Self-propelled
XM736 Binary Nerve Gas Shell	Replacing the M426. M110 Self-propelled
M753 Nuclear Projectile	Details are classified. Replacing the M422 with the M33 nuclear warhead. Carries the W79 Enhanced Radiation nuclear warhead.

Lance Battlefield Support Missile (MGM-52C)

Above: The MGM-52C Lance missile is transported on the M752 tracked vehicle and is resupplied from the M688 Loader Transporter shown here.

The Lance Battlefield Support Missile, which is issued at corps level, is a general support weapon for use against rear enemy positions such as airfields, missile-launching concentrations, transportation, communications and logistics centers, and large concentrations of second-echelon troops. Mobile and easily moved, the missile and launcher can be quickly moved to a new position to avoid counterbattery fire.

The Lance missile replaced the "Honest John" and "Sergeant" in the 1970s. Its guidance system is self-contained; before launching, the location of the missile is entered into the guidance system, along with meteorological data at the launch and impact points. The missile is then guided in-flight by a directional-control and automatic meteorological compensation system known as DC-AUTOMET. The guidance system is virtually immune to electronic countermeasures.

The Lance uses a hypergolic fuel that ignites spontaneously in the presence of an oxidizer. While in flight, the Lance is stabilized via spinning, which is accomplished by venting propulsion gases through control vents just forward of the missile's midline.

The Lance is moved about the battlefield on the M752 vehicle, a specially adapted version of the M113 Armored Personnel Carrier that has been fitted as a launching vehicle. Another vehicle, the M688, carries two complete Lance missiles for reloading.

With a 1,000-pound conventional high-explosive submunition warhead (M251), Lance has a range of up to 43 miles. The M251 warhead is filled with 836 BLU-63 antipersonnel/anti-matériel bomblets. When equipped with the W70 Mod 1 or Mod 2 nuclear warhead weighing 465 pounds and yielding ten kilotons, or the W70 Mod 4 neutron warhead, the Lance's range is 75 miles.

The U.S. Army fields eight Lance battalions, with six stationed in Europe and two in the United States at Ft. Sill, Oklahoma. One independent battery is in South Korea. Each Lance battalion is equipped with six launchers.

Lance production ran from 1971 to 1980. In all, 2,133 missiles were produced. Two upgrade systems are now being developed. One is the Distance Measuring Equipment command-guidance system, which will give the Lance pinpoint accuracy, thus improving its effect with conventional munitions. On average, the Lance will fall within a 500-yard diameter of its target. Another system under development is the new Corps Support Weapon System, an improved Lance that carries a larger, more effective submunition program to a range of 124 miles.

LANCE BATTLEFIELD SUPPORT MISSILE (MGM-52C)	
Length:	20 ft., 3 in.
Diameter:	1 ft., 10 in.
Weight:	3,920 lbs. at launch
Speed:	Supersonic
Range with warhead:	
Conventional:	43 miles
Nuclear:	75 miles
Date of service:	1971

Left, top: *The Lance missile has a range of between 43 and 75 miles.* Left, bottom: *This Lance missile is being taken from its shipping container and loaded aboard the M688 Loader Transporter.* Right, top: *The Lance missile and its support system were designed to be as transportable as possible under combat conditions.* Right, bottom: *The Lance is launched directly from the M752 tracked vehicle.*

Multiple Launch Rocket System (MLRS)

The Multiple Launch Rocket System (MLRS), developed by LTV for the U.S. Army and Marine Corps, is intended to strike far into the rear of enemy armored forces. MLRS consists of a launcher, free rockets, a computerized aim and control complex, and a tracked vehicle. The system is capable of launching within one minute from one to 12 rockets to a range of 18 miles.

The system's tracked Armored Vehicle Mounted Rocket Launcher (AVMRL) is built on the same chassis as the M2 Bradley Infantry Fighting Vehicle. The AVMRL has a range of 300 miles, a top speed of 40 miles per hour, and considerable off-road capability. The Launcher Loader Module is bolted to the vehicle bed and can be raised to 60 degrees and traversed in a complete circle. Two boom-mounted electrical cable hoists can be used by crew members to reload the two rocket pod/containers.

The MLRS rocket is a tube-launched, free-flight vehicle weighing approximately 667 pounds. It is 12.9 feet long and 8.9 inches in diameter. Packed and sealed in its transport/launcher container at the factory, the MLRS has a ten-year shelf life, with no maintenance or special storage conditions required. The warhead, which comprises half the weight and length of the rocket, is a thin aluminum shell. Inside the shell are polyurethane foam containers holding 644 individual M77 antipersonnel/anti-matériel submunitions effective against personnel and light armor.

When the MLRS rocket reaches the target area, a black-powder charge in the center of the warhead is detonated by a timer and the submunitions are expelled in a circular or oval pattern, depending on the range. Each submunition is stabilized by a ribbon parachute as it falls, and explodes on contact. If all 12 rockets per MLRS launcher are fired in one mission and within one minute at the same target area, a total of 7,728 submunitions will fall into an area roughly equal in size to six football fields.

Electronics and other equipment are engineered for simplicity and ease of operation. The Fire Data Control System receives and stores information data by digital radio, then cues the gunner in plain language. Data can also be entered manually by the crew. Since the computer knows the exact location of the MLRS vehicle, the MLRS system needs only the target location and the latest meteorological report added to its data banks before conducting a fire mission. The MLRS system can plot its own location and then calculate a ballistic trajectory to the target, taking into account the weather en route. The system then tells the crew the exact moment to launch.

A range of new MLRS systems is under development. These include a Terminally Guided Warhead and a scatterable antitank mine warhead that uses the West German AT-2 antitank mine.

Above: *The Multiple Launch Rocket System (MLRS) can fire 12 ballistic missiles nearly 20 miles.*

Above: *The Multiple Launch Rocket System is used to smash rocket and artillery batteries, airfields, troop assembly areas, and other similar targets.* Right: *The MLRS is completely self-contained. An internal inertial navigation system provides pinpoint accuracy for the missiles anywhere on the planet.*

MULTIPLE LAUNCH ROCKET SYSTEM (MLRS)

Length:	12 ft., 11 in. per rocket
Diameter:	8.9 in. per rocket
Weight:	667 lbs. per rocket
Vehicle speed:	40 mph
Rate of fire:	12 rockets in 1 minute
Range:	
Rocket:	18 miles
Vehicle:	300 miles
Date of service:	1983

Above: *MLRS missiles are packaged six to a container. The container serves as a transport and storage crate as well as a launcher.* Left: *The MLRS rockets can be fired one at a time or in ripples.*

Tactical Missile System (TACMS)

The Multiple Launch Rocket System (MLRS) is designed to deal with highly mobile, fast-moving enemy formations within the forward battle area. But there remains the problem of striking at heavily air-defended C3I (Command, Communications, Control, Intelligence) facilities, rear-area airfields, reserve troop concentrations, and the like up to 60 miles away. Cruise missiles are no longer a viable alternative since all intermediate-range missiles have been banned by treaty.

In 1984, the U.S. Army began the development of a missile that would use the launch and guidance support equipment developed for the MLRS. The new weapon—which would have a longer range than the MLRS—was designated the Tactical Missile System (TACMS). Unlike the ballistic-trajectory, free-flight MLRS rocket, the Army's TACMS rocket is guided to its target by a Honeywell H700-3A integrated guidance unit that uses a ring-laser gyro guidance system.

The TACMS missile is the same length as the MLRS rocket but its diameter is 24 inches, nearly three times that of the MLRS rocket. As a consequence, the TACMS launcher will carry one missile per pod (a total of two) instead of the six missiles per pod (a total of 12) carried by the MLRS. The TACMS missile uses the Arcadene 360 solid rocket motor built by Atlantic Research Corporation. Four movable tail fins provide maneuvering ability and stabilization in flight.

The initial warhead—comprising M74 antipersonnel/anti-matériel grenades—will be the same as that used in the current Lance and MLRS missiles. Payload capability, number of M74 grenades, and the area of dispersion are classified. Under development is a "smart" submissile system similar to the system being developed for MLRS. This system will seek out, identify, and destroy various kinds of armored targets with either shaped-charge explosives or self-forging fragments. For this role, Martin-Marietta is developing a Phase II warhead with terminal guidance capability.

As with the MLRS system, TACMS will use the M270 tracked launcher, which is built on the M2 Bradley Infantry Fighting Vehicle chassis. TACMS carries a crew of three: driver, gunner, and section chief. The launcher weighs 25 tons, is 23 feet long, 8.2 feet high, and 9.5 feet wide. TACMS can reach a maximum speed of 40 miles per hour and has excellent cross-country ability.

The guidance system, carried on the M270, consists of a computerized fire control system, on-board stabilization reference package, a position-determining system, and a built-in reloading system. The position-determining system receives signals from the Department of Defense's navigation satellites to pinpoint its location anywhere in the world. The reloading mechanism enables the crew to draw reloads from a supply vehicle without leaving the armored launcher and exposing themselves to enemy small arms fire and shrapnel.

Below: *The Tactical Missile System fires a ballistic missile (foreground) that is more powerful and has a greater range than the MLRS missiles (background).*

TACTICAL MISSILE SYSTEM (TACMS)	
Length:	12 ft., 11 in. per rocket
Diameter:	2 ft. per rocket
Weight:	Classified
Vehicle speed:	40 mph
Rate of fire:	Classified
Range:	
Rocket:	60 miles
Vehicle:	300 miles
Date of service:	1990 (expected)

MAIN BATTLE TANKS

The main battle tank is the most awesome fighting machine yet developed for land warfare. Tanks are squat, ugly, menacing, and graceless. They have been so since Lieutenant Colonel E.D. Swinton climbed into the first Mark I tank and kicked its engine to life on September 15, 1915.

The tank changed the face of war. At a time when quick-firing artillery and the machine gun had driven soldiers into trenches during World War I, the tank reintroduced mobile warfare. Although tank development between the world wars was desultory at best, it had proceeded far enough in Nazi Germany and Imperial Japan that during the first two years of World War II, German and Japanese tanks contributed significantly to the smashing of eight armies.

Between 1939 and 1945, the tank developed from an armored carrier of machine guns and light guns into a mobile platform for heavy caliber artillery pieces. The United States neglected the tank between the world wars and was forced to play catch-up starting in 1939. By the time World War II ended, the U.S. was fielding the most advanced, most heavily armored, and most powerfully armed tank in the world—the M-26 Pershing. During World War II, the Soviet Union developed a fine medium tank in the T-34, which was rearmed in 1944 with an 84 millimeter gun that could punch through the armor of any tank then being fielded.

When the Cold War turned hot in Korea, the U.S. ordered the development of a medium-weight tank. Both the M-47 and M-48 Patton saw extensive service in Korea, and later in the Negev desert under the command of Israeli tankers. By the early 1960s, the pace of Soviet tank development had made the M-48 Patton obsolete, and a new tank—the M-60—was introduced. The M-60 sported a new turret on an M-48 chassis and a sophisticated, computerized fire control system for its new 105mm main gun.

In the early 1970s, after the failure of a joint venture among the U.S., West Germany, and Italy to develop a single main battle tank that could be used by all three nations, the U.S. developed its own main battle tank, the M-1 Abrams. The M-1 Abrams is thought to be the most powerful and sophisticated main battle tank in use in the world today.

The main battle tank of today is a far cry from the first armored boxes of World War I or even those of World War II. The basic definition of a tank is an armored box moving on an endless track and armed with a large caliber gun, but this is only a start.

That armored box has become a sophisticated blend of steel and ceramic capable of withstanding the strike of a 40- to 50-pound high-tensile-strength steel warhead traveling at speeds of 2,500 feet per second or faster. That armor is often supplemented by such "add-on" armor as additional plates of metal and/or ceramic, or Kevlar curtains and padding for the interior. Today's tank is powered by lightweight, reliable gas turbine engines that provide nearly instantaneous full power in emergencies. The tank is equipped with sophisticated laser range finding systems that can measure the distance to the enemy target, calculate a trajectory for a specific type of round,

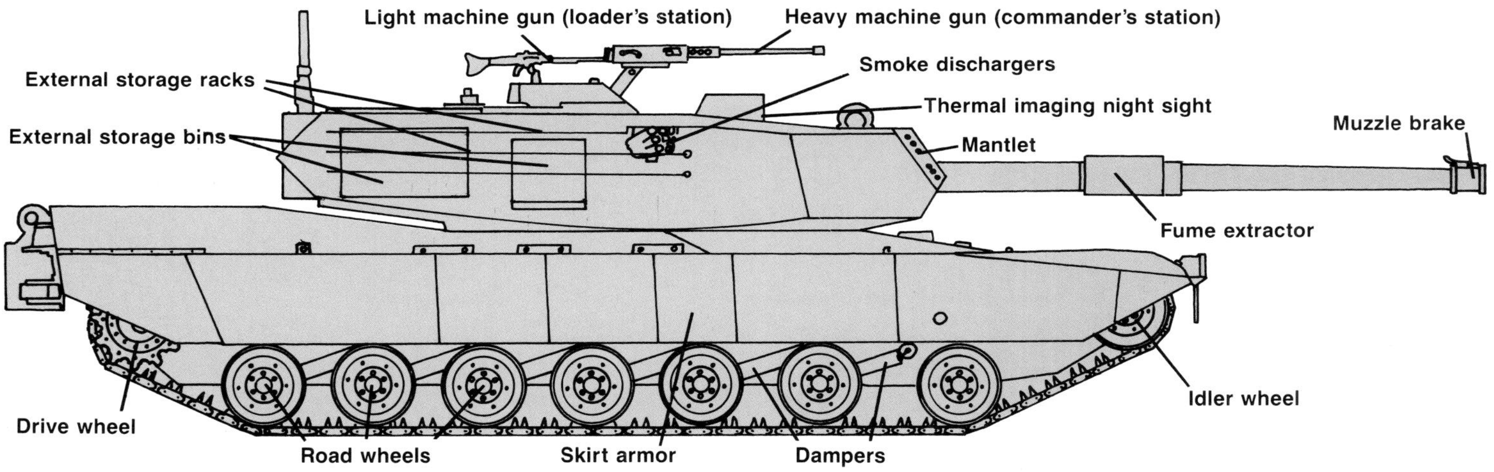

aim the gun, and fire. The tank's gun itself is a smoothbore that fires rounds with pop-up fins for in-flight stabilization.

Many of today's military critics decry the main battle tank as a dinosaur. They see the tank as a land battleship doomed to extinction in this age of one-man rocket launchers, recoilless rifles firing shaped-charge warheads, and powerfully armed, low-flying attack aircraft and helicopters. But the main battle tank is still the king of the battlefield, as events in Lebanon in 1982 and on the Iraq-Iran border in the 1980s demonstrated.

The tank works in conjunction with infantry soldiers, who provide protection from the enemy's antitank elements and who can move in behind the tank to hold the ground the tank helped take. The tank provides infantry with close fire support that would be impossible to obtain any other way. The tank will remain a major weapon into the foreseeable future.

Opposite, top: *The M-1 Abrams Main Battle Tank carries a 105mm main gun.* Opposite, bottom: *The M-60 Main Battle Tank is an upgraded version of the M-48 Patton.* Top: *The M-1A1 Abrams is armed with a 120mm main gun.* Bottom: *This illustration shows a modern main battle tank with features common to most of today's tanks.*

M-48 General George S. Patton Medium Tank

Above: *The M-48A1 Patton tank served with distinction in the Korean War and the Vietnam War.*

The Cold War began in earnest at the end of the 1940s. The Berlin Blockade, the fall of Nationalist China, the disappearance of Eastern Europe behind the Iron Curtain, Communist insurgencies in Malaya and the Philippines, and the invasion of South Korea by North Korea had many military planners convinced that war between the United States and the Soviet Union was only a matter of months away.

When the Korean War began in June 1950, the United States had only the obsolete M-4 Sherman Medium Tank in inventory; there was no newer medium tank in production. An interim medium tank, the M-47, was rushed into production, but the M-47's performance was not considered satisfactory against the new Soviet medium tank, the T-54, then entering service.

In 1950, the Detroit Tank Arsenal and the Chrysler Corporation were each awarded contracts to develop a new medium tank armed with a 90 millimeter gun. The new tank—to be developed as quickly as possible—was given the developmental designation T-48 and was to be based on the earlier T-42. Design work began in December 1950 and was completed one year later. Even before the first prototypes were finished in March 1952, production contracts were awarded to the Fisher Body Division of General Motors and to the Ford Motor Company. The first M-48 tank came off the assembly line in July 1952.

In the haste to get the M-48 into production, problems were overlooked or ignored. These problems came back to haunt the tank and its crews, earning the M-48 a reputation as a badly designed tank. Virtually all the early models had to be rebuilt to later configurations. Once rebuilding was accomplished, complaints and problems diminished. In the end, then, the Army had accomplished its purpose. The M-48 was a medium tank fully capable of standing up to the T-54 series of Soviet tanks.

The M-48 had a cast and welded hull with an escape hatch built into the floor. The turret was cast in one piece, the front wall of which was 4.3 inches thick. The M-48 Patton was the most heavily armored tank in American service to that date. Armor protection ranged from 4.72 inches on the hull's front to 4.3 inches on the turret front down to slightly less than one inch on the turret top.

The usual hull-mounted machine gun was eliminated in favor of more ammunition storage for the main gun. This design alteration allowed the driver to be seated in the center front of the hull. The gunner was located on the right side of the turret, the loader on the left, and the commander behind and higher. The loader had a hatch that opened to the rear. The commander's cupola could be traversed manually and had a sight for the .50 caliber Browning M2 HB machine gun.

The original General Motors Corporation 810 horsepower gasoline engine and a fire extinguishing system were mounted in the rear compartment. The engine drove the rear drive sprocket (the rear wheel that moves the tread) through a planetary gear transmission. The M-48 used torsion bar suspension with six relatively small road wheels per

M-48A5 GENERAL GEORGE S. PATTON MEDIUM TANK

Length:	20 ft., 1 in.
Width:	11 ft., 11 in.
Height:	10 ft., 1 in.
Combat weight:	50 tons
Engine:	Continental AVDS-1790-2D 750 hp diesel
Speed:	30 mph
Range:	310 miles
Obstacle/grade performance:	2.95 ft.
Armament:	One 105mm M68 main gun Three 7.62mm NATO M73 machine guns One .50 caliber Browning M2 HB machine gun
Crew:	4
Date of service:	1952

side. Five return rollers were used in the M-48 and M-48A1 configuration, but only three in the M-48A2 and later variations.

The M-48 was equipped with infrared driving lights, and an infrared/white light searchlight was mounted above the main gun. It was the first American tank to be fitted with a nuclear-biological-chemical warfare protection system and warm air heaters for crew comfort. A bulldozer blade kit was developed, and all M-48s had provisions for mounting it.

The 90mm M41 main gun used in the M-48 and M-48A1 was equipped with an evacuator, a muzzle brake, and a vertical sliding breech mechanism. The main gun range finder fed information to the commander's station and the gunner's station. The gunner's ballistic computer was electrically operated but worked on mechanical principles. Solutions to problems were simultaneously fed to gunner and commander.

The M-48 Patton has gone through seven model designations. In 1975 all M-48s of whatever configuration were modernized to the M-48A5 standard. This final modernization included improved armor, an improved fire control system, the 105mm M68 main gun, and a range of other modifications to increase service life. The diesel engine built by Continental was replaced with an improved model that gave an even greater range. The coaxial machine gun was changed from the 7.62mm Browning 1919A4E1 to the 7.62mm NATO M73 machine gun. A second 7.62mm NATO M73 machine gun was added at the loader's hatch position for antiaircraft use. The commander's hatch also had an antiaircraft machine gun.

No active Army units have been equipped with the M-48 Patton since 1984, when the last M-48s were withdrawn from South Korea. The last M-48s in Reserve and National Guard service are being replaced by the M-60.

Top: *The M-48A5 Patton, with a 105mm main gun, is still in service with the U.S. Army Reserve.* Bottom, left: *The M-48A5's turret and main gun were used to develop the M-60 Main Battle Tank.* Bottom, right: *This M-48A5 carries hitchhiking infantry troops.*

An M-48A5 Patton tank guards a convoy during Operation Team Spirit exercises in South Korea.

M-60 Main Battle Tank

In 1956, intelligence reports regarding tank development in the Soviet Union suggested that a tank more capable than the T-54/T-55 Main Battle Tank (MBT) was being developed. Even as the M-48 Medium Tank entered service in 1952, it was considered too heavy, too short-ranged, and too lightly armored to deal with the expected capabilities of the new Soviet tank. Upgrade programs were immediately undertaken, but the ultimate goal of up-gunning to the British L7A1 105 millimeter gun required a new turret. Authorization was obtained for a new tank design, and the first American MBT entered service in 1960 as the M-60.

Above: *An M-60 tank moves into firing position at the National Training Center in California's Mojave Desert.*

The M-60 hull is basically the same as that of the M-48's; it is divided into three compartments: driving, fighting, and engine/transmission. The new turret is better armored (information concerning the M-60's armor remains classified) and considerably larger, as it must be to mount the 105mm main gun.

The L7A1 105mm M68 main gun, of British design but built in the United States, is rifled and can fire between six and eight rounds per minute. The tank carries 63 rounds of main gun ammunition. The M-60 also carries two machine guns. The commander's cupola is equipped with a .50 caliber M85 antiaircraft machine gun. Mounted coaxially in the hull is the 7.62mm NATO M85 machine gun, due to be replaced with the M240 machine gun.

All M-60s were up-rated to the A3 configuration beginning in 1977. The first M-60A3s were sent to Europe and issued to the U.S. 1st Battalion of the 32nd Armor Division in 1979. Specific improvements included a new AN/VVG-2 laser range finder connected to an improved fire control system that uses an M21 solid state, rather than mechanical, computer. The new system allows either the gunner or the tank commander to fire the main gun. Bore sighting is made incomparably easier with the laser system.

A nuclear-biological-chemical warfare protection system was added in the M-60A3 configuration. It combines overpressure in the crew compartment with a high-capacity central air filtration system. Fresh air is brought directly to each crewmember through a tube. Complete night vision equipment has been fitted to the tank and includes an improved infrared/white light xenon searchlight.

A new track system with replaceable pads has been installed on the M-60A3, as well as a newer and more reliable diesel engine. An automatic Halon fire extinguisher system, a smoke-screen system using diesel fuel sprayed into the engine manifold, and the M219 smoke grenade launcher are included. A deep-water fording kit allows an M-60A3 fitted with a snorkel to traverse water up to 13 feet deep.

The last M-60A3 tank was built for the Army in 1983. The last of the older M-60A1s was completed for the Marine Corps in 1980. Conversion of all M-60A1s to the M-60A3TTS (tank, thermal sight) model is due to be completed by the early 1990s. The final version of the M-60, the M-60A3TTS, weighs close to 58 tons, eight tons more than the M-48, which in 1956 was already considered too heavy. More than 15,000 M-60s of various configurations were built before production ended.

Above: *The M-60 Main Battle Tank mounts a 105mm main gun.* Right: *The M-60A3 is an up-rated version of earlier M-60s. The upgrading included a laser range finder, thermal night vision, and a computerized fire control system.*

M-60A3 MAIN BATTLE TANK

Length:	22 ft., 7 in.
Width:	11 ft., 9.6 in.
Height:	10 ft., 8 in.
Combat weight:	58 tons
Engine:	Continental AVDS-1790-2D 750 hp diesel
Speed:	30 mph
Range:	298 miles
Obstacle/grade performance:	2.9 ft.
Armament:	One 105mm L7A1 main gun One 7.62mm NATO M73 machine gun One .50 caliber M85 machine gun
Crew:	4
Date of service:	1960

The M-60, like all American main battle tanks, was built to meet the Soviet military threat in Central Europe.

The M-60 saw extensive service with the Israeli Army, but it did not prove as survivable as hoped.

M-1 and M-1A1 Abrams Main Battle Tank

In the late 1960s and early 1970s there was a great deal of apprehension within the North Atlantic Treaty Organization (NATO) concerning the swift development of Soviet main battle tanks (MBTs). Soviet MBTs were heavily armored, fast, agile, and armed with the most powerful tank guns then mounted on vehicles of their class. The T-62 carried the 115 millimeter smoothbore gun, and the T-64 mounted the 125mm smoothbore gun. Both tanks were equipped with automatic loaders, and the T-64's gun could penetrate up to 18.7 inches of armor. The Soviet MBTs were superior in armament and speed as well as numbers. According to some estimates, Soviet MBTs outnumbered NATO MBTs by at least three to one.

After the collapse of a multinational project to design and build a new main battle tank to meet the Soviet threat, the United States contracted for the XM-1 tank, as the prototype M-1 was known, in June 1973. On May 7, 1979, the secretary of defense approved the production of the new M-1 MBT. The first two production tanks were delivered to the U.S. Army on February 28, 1980, and formally named for the late General Creighton W. Abrams, Army Chief of Staff and commander of the 37th Armored Battalion.

The M-1A1 Abrams evolved from the basic M-1 Abrams. The major difference between the M-1 and the M-1A1 was the mounting of the M256 120mm smoothbore Rheinmetall main gun developed in West Germany. M-1A1 upgrades also involved more armor protection, a new nuclear-biological-chemical warfare protection system that included air-conditioning for the crew, an improved suspension, and a better transmission. The M-1A1 was standardized in August 1984, and the first production models were delivered from the Detroit Arsenal in August 1985. In early 1989, other improvements were added, including a new commander's station with better weapons handling and a new independent thermal viewer, a carbon dioxide laser range finder, an improved tank-to-tank communication system, new ceramic and reaction-type armor, and a better thermal viewer for the driver.

The Marine Corps has requested the development of a deep-water fording kit and marinization so that the tank will not be affected by saltwater spray or a high-humidity environment. The Marine Corps hopes to replace its fleet of aging M-60 tanks with the M-1A1 Abrams in the 1990s. M-1 Abrams tanks already fielded in Europe are being replaced with the M-1A1. The returned M-1s are being distributed to the Army Reserve and National Guard.

The M-1 Abrams hull and turret are built of a material similar to the ceramic and steel plate Chobham armor developed in Great Britain. The same type of armor is also used on the British Challenger and the West German Leopard 2. The driver is seated in the middle of the hull in front in a reclining position because of the hull's steep slope. The commander and gunner are in the turret on the right, and the loader is on the left. The fire control system includes a laser range finder, a digital solid state computer, and a stabilized day/night thermal

Below: *The M-1 Abrams was designed to be able to meet Soviet T-72 and T-80 tanks on equal terms.*

sight. Armor plate separates the crew compartment from the fuel tanks and ammunition storage. A Halon fire extinguisher system reacts within 250 milliseconds to smother any fire. Ready ammunition is stored in the turret bustle, which projects from the turret rear. If an internal explosion occurs, three top panels (two in the M-1A1) would blow off, venting the force of the explosion upward and away from the crew.

The Abrams is powered by a Lycoming Textron gas turbine engine that burns diesel or aviation fuel; it can also operate on gasoline. The engine and transmission can be removed and replaced in less than one hour. The suspension system uses torsion bars. The Abrams can be identified by its very large, angular turret with an overhang and by its seven road wheels per side. The engine drives the treads through the rear drive sprocket. There are two return rollers, but these are hidden by the hinged, armored skirt.

The M68E1 105mm main gun fires the same ammunition as the M-60's gun. The ammunition has a combustible case (the case holding the ammunition burns up after firing) except for the percussion cap end, which is ejected. Stowage capacity is 40 rounds: 36 in the turret bustle and four in a rear hull compartment. A 7.62mm NATO M240 machine gun is mounted coaxially with the main gun. A 7.62mm NATO M240 machine gun at the loader's station and a .50 caliber Browning M2 HB machine gun at the commander's station are mounted on the turret roof for use against attacking aircraft, lightly armored vehicles, and personnel. Two M250 smoke dischargers with six barrels each are mounted one on either side of the turret front.

In March 1988, a program to develop and mount depleted uranium armor plate on the M-1A1 Abrams was instigated; depleted uranium is nonradioactive and is two and a half times as dense as steel. This new armor will raise the total weight of Abrams tanks so equipped to 65 tons.

continued on page 238

Above: *The original M-1 Abrams was fitted with the same 105mm main gun carried by the M-60 and M-48A5 tanks.*

The hooded projection on the Abram's turret (right) is the thermal night vision system.

The M-1 Abrams may well be the most powerful main battle tank in existence.

continued from page 233

M-1 AND M-1A1 ABRAMS MAIN BATTLE TANK

Length:	26 ft.
Width:	11 ft., 11 in.
Height:	7 ft., 9.6 in.
Combat weight:	63 tons
Engine:	Lycoming Textron AGT 1500 1,500 hp gas turbine
Speed:	45 mph
Range:	289 miles
Obstacle/grade performance:	3.5 ft.
Armament:	
All:	Two 7.62mm NATO M240 machine guns One .50 caliber Browning M2 HB machine gun
M-1:	One 105mm M68E1 rifled main gun
M-1A1:	One 120mm M256 smoothbore main gun
Crew:	4
Date of service:	1981

Above: *The M-1A1 Abrams carries three machine guns. In the foreground is the 7.62mm antipersonnel gun operated by the loader. Behind the loader is the tank commander, who operates the .50 caliber machine gun used against aircraft and light vehicles. Another .50 caliber machine gun is mounted coaxially with the main gun.*

120mm Tank Ammunition

Ammunition for U.S. tanks is of the semicombustible type. The propelling charge is contained in a plastic case that is consumed except for the metal base, which holds the primer and anvil. Honeywell Defense Systems and General Defense Corporation are the sole manufacturers of 120mm ammunition used in the M256 M1A1 120mm smoothbore gun mounted on the M-1A1 Abrams Main Battle Tank. Ammunition fired from tank guns can range up to 4.5 miles.

Armor-piercing (AP) projectiles are made from case-hardened metal, dense steel alloys, or other metals such as tungsten or depleted uranium (DU). Depleted uranium is one of the densest metals known. A by-product of Uranium 238 fuel, DU emits negligible amounts of radiation. Armor-piercing projectiles are often sub-caliber; that is, they are smaller in diameter than the bore of the gun. They are surrounded by sabots of light metal or plastic that are discarded as the projectile leaves the muzzle (DS). The smaller-diameter projectile thus has imparted to it the same force as a larger-diameter, heavier projectile; as a consequence, it strikes the target with greater force.

Tracer rounds (-T) emit a smoke trail that allows the gunner to see how closely the projectile strikes to the target. The gunner can then correct and adjust for the next shot. Antipersonnel rounds contain fragments of steel (FRAG) or high-explosive (HE) grenades. Some HE rounds are designed to be used against tanks (AT). Rounds containing grenades that are effective against both personnel and lightly armored vehicles are referred to as dual-purpose (DP). Similar rounds are also called improved conventional munitions (ICM). Base bleed (BB) shells emit gas through small holes in their base while in flight to lend additional stability. Rounds that can be used effectively against more than one type of target are referred to as multipurpose (MP).

The M1A1 120mm gun is smoothbored, which means that it has no rifling to cause the projectile to spin and stabilize itself while in flight. Smoothbore guns fire projectiles that are stabilized by fins that pop-up after firing (FS).

Squash head (SH) projectiles "squash" against, or spread out over, a large area of armor before detonating. The effect is to blow scabs of metal off the inside of the armor and cause the scabs to ricochet around the interior. Spotting rounds (-S) are used to mark targets and to check the gun's accuracy. Self-destruct (SD) projectiles have a built-in timer that causes them to explode or stop functioning after a set period of time so they will not be a danger to friendly troops or civilians. Target practice (TP) rounds contain a reduced load of explosive, usually only enough to cause smoke or a flare. Smoke-screen rounds contain white phosphorous (WP).

Tank ammunition is abbreviated as follows:

XM827 APFSDS-T	One-piece DU penetrator
M829 APFSDS-T **M830 HEAT-MP-T**	Two-piece DU penetrator
M831 HEAT-MP-T **XM859 HEAT-MP-T**	Training round for the M830
M865 TPFSDS-T **M866 TPFSDS-T**	Used for gunnery practice

105mm Tank Ammunition

All 105mm tank ammunition, like that for the 120mm gun, is semicombustible. It is used by the M-1 Abrams tank equipped with the M68E1 gun and the M-60 tank equipped with the M68; both the M68E1 and the M68 are rifled guns. The M-48A5 Patton is also armed with the M68 gun and can fire the entire range of 105mm ammunition, designations of which follow:

M392A2 APDS-T	**M724 TPDS-T**
M416 WP-T	**M728 APDS-T**
M456 HEAT-T	**M735/735A1 APFSDS-T**
M467 TP-T	**M737 TPS**
M490 TP-T	**M744 APFSDS-T**
M494 APERS-T	**M833 APFSDS-T**

ANTITANK WEAPONS

As the tank has assumed greater importance on the battlefield, the necessity to counter the tank's power and domination has grown. The tank first appeared on the battlefield in 1915; the antitank gun soon followed. At first, light artillery pieces fired from point-blank range were used to destroy enemy tanks. But these guns had limited mobility and often fell victim to the tank. During World War I, Peter Paul Mauser developed a 13 millimeter .512 caliber version of his famous bolt-action rifle as the first special-purpose antitank gun. From these early beginnings, antitank weaponry has grown into a major discipline.

At the beginning of World War II, the menace of Nazi Germany and the effectiveness of its Panzer divisions spurred the British to develop their highly effective six-pound 57mm antitank gun that replaced their two-pound 40mm unit. The British followed the six-pound antitank gun with a new 17-pound 76.2mm gun in 1942.

The United States, which had concentrated on developing the 37mm antitank gun that soon proved to be no match for tank armor, quickly adopted the British six-pounder as the 57mm Gun M1. The first American one-person antitank weapon was the bazooka, a metal tube containing an ignition mechanism that launched a rocket-propelled, shaped-charge warhead that could penetrate the armor of most tanks of the 1940s. The bazooka is no longer in U.S. service, having been replaced.

Concurrent with the development of more effective antitank guns came development in warheads. By the mid-1950s, it was possible to pack a more devastating punch into a smaller bore diameter. The British developed the composite projectile, a round with a tungsten penetrator surrounded by a light alloy discarding sabot. The sabot—designed to transmit thrust and to properly position the projectile in the barrel—was larger in diameter than the penetrator. This design allowed the round to be fired at a higher velocity.

Other types of ammunition were also developed. The squash head charge carries a plastic explosive that spreads over a large surface area before exploding. The blast blows scabs of metal off the inside of the armor plate to act like shrapnel. Armor-piercing rounds, which use thin-diameter rods of high strength steel, titanium, or depleted uranium, can literally punch holes in any tank armor in use today. The shaped charge focuses the force of the exploding charge against a small area of armor. The shaped charge was, until recently, the most devastating weapon that could be used against enemy armor. But reactive armor developed in Israel, and now used around the world, has decreased the effectiveness of the shaped charge.

The basic antitank weapon used today by both the Army and the Marine Corps is the TOW heavy antitank missile. The TOW missile can also be used against enemy bunkers, crew-served weapons, and under certain conditions, helicopters. The TOW missile is supported by smaller and more compact weapons like the M47 Dragon and the AT-4 recoilless rifle.

Opposite: *The BGM-71 TOW missile replaced the 105mm recoilless rifle.* Above: *The TOW is usually operated by a crew of two.* Left: *The M47 Dragon is a one-soldier, shoulder-launched antitank missile.*

The TOW missile launcher has been mounted on a variety of vehicles, including the HMMWV.

Tube-Launched, Optically Tracked, Wire-Guided (TOW) Missile (BGM-71)

In 1962, the U.S. Army's Missile Command issued a request for proposal for an antitank weapon to replace the SS11 and ENMTAC wire-guided missiles, and the 106 millimeter recoilless rifle. Hughes Aircraft submitted a winning design. In 1963, Hughes was awarded a contract for a heavy antitank assault weapon, a wire-guided, rocket-propelled weapon containing a high-explosive warhead.

TOW is a tube-launched guided missile that uses a semiautomatic, command to line of sight guidance system. The ground system consists of the missile in a container, sight unit, and launcher, for a total weight of 225 pounds. The BGM-71A rockets, the first production units, were 45.75 inches long, six inches in diameter, and weighed 46.1 pounds.

To use, the operator centers the target in the cross hairs of the 13-power optical sight. The operator presses the firing button to ignite a "blip" rocket, which pops the missile from its launch container. The blip motor burns for 1/20 of a second. To protect the TOW crew from injury, all fuel is consumed before the missile leaves the launch tube. At a distance of 120 feet to 180 feet, the smokeless sustainer motor ignites and the warhead arms. Before the sustainer motor accelerates the missile to 900 feet per second, four large wings unfold to provide lift. Combustion then stops and the missile glides to its target, two thin wires trailing behind.

The missile is steered by the operator, who watches through the launcher sight and uses a joystick to correct the missile's flight path. A sensor on the launcher watches the flare at the missile's base, computes the angular distance between the flare in the sight and the sight center, and automatically transmits correction signals along the trailing wires. Impact speed at the maximum range of 4,000 yards is greater than 225 miles per hour.

Recently, the Army began an improvement program to deal with the new armor being used in main battle tanks. The first program was a quick fix called I-TOW, shorthand for Improved TOW BGM-71C, which used a new warhead carrying a more powerful explosive and fitted with a standoff probe. The probe extends after the missile is launched; the probe causes the warhead to explode 15 inches from the armor plate to enhance penetration, unofficially said to be 34 inches.

The second TOW improvement program resulted in a larger missile that carries a three-segment standoff probe, a new sustainer motor delivering 30 percent more thrust, and a thermal infrared beacon mounted beside the xenon beacon to aid the operator when using a thermal-imaging night sight. The new missile, dubbed TOW 2 (BGM-71D), also received a new dual-digital microprocessor for more precise tracking and better accuracy at maximum ranges.

TOW became operational in 1970 with the United States and West German armies. Well over 500,000 Tube-Launched, Optically Tracked, Wire-Guided (TOW) missiles have been manufactured and sold. TOW will continue to be the U.S. Army's major tank buster into the 21st century.

Above: *The TOW missile, designed by Hughes, entered service in 1970.*

TUBE-LAUNCHED, OPTICALLY TRACKED, WIRE-GUIDED (TOW) MISSILE (BGM-71)

Diameter:	6 in.
Length:	55.1 in.
Weight:	47.4 lbs.
Range:	4,000 yds.
Speed:	625 mph
Date of service:	1970

Top: *The TOW missile uses a shaped-charge warhead. In this photo sequence, the fuse is seen being extended after firing.* Bottom, left: *The TOW missile is guided by commands sent from the tracking sight along two trailing wires.* Bottom, right: *The TOW missile launcher is shown here mounted on a Jeep.*

M47 Dragon II Medium Antitank Weapon

First fielded in 1972, the McDonnell Douglas Astronautics Dragon is being improved with a new warhead-retrofit program called the Dragon II, or Deluxe Dragon. Officially designated a medium antitank weapon system, the Dragon is lighter and has a shorter range than the TOW missile. The Dragon was designed to give a soldier the capability to destroy light, medium, and heavy armored vehicles; take out fortified bunkers; knock out concrete gun emplacements; and defeat other hardened targets.

Because the Dragon system is lightweight at 32.6 pounds, it has been an excellent weapon of choice for airborne and air mobile operations. Sufficiently portable to be used by a single soldier, the Dragon is packaged as a disposable round, with the missile sealed inside a launch tube container made of glass fiber composites. After the missile is fired, the tube is detached from the reusable tracker and discarded. Depending on circumstances, the Dragon missile unit can be outfitted with either a day or night tracker system.

The threat posed by new types of main battle tank armor has diminished the effectiveness of the original Dragon I warhead. In response, the U.S. Marine Corps has retrofitted all of its missiles with a new five-inch warhead that fits onto the basic Dragon missile. The resulting Dragon II has increased the armor-penetration capabilities of the weapon system by 85 percent.

The Dragon I and Dragon II have a range of between 65 and 1,000 yards. The system can track targets moving at speeds up to 30 miles per hour. Once launched, the Dragon takes approximately 11 seconds to fly to its extreme range of 1,000 yards. Once the projectile leaves the launch tube, the Dragon is guided to its target by the gunner via a wire filament that trails from the missile as it travels down range. From a concealed position, the gunner tracks the missile in relation to the gunner's line of sight through the telescopic sighting device. Corrections are transmitted through the wire to the missile. Thirty pairs of small rocket motors mounted around the missile's perimeter make the needed course corrections as well as assisting with acceleration and stabilization.

As the battlefield threat of today and tomorrow changes, antitank weaponry must change to ensure the survivability of a new generation of armored personnel carriers and tanks. In that vein, the "fire" of the Dragon II answers the challenge. The U.S. Army is believed to have upwards of 20,000 Dragon I missiles in inventory at present; these units will be converted to the improved Dragon II configuration. The Dragon II will serve as an interim measure until the Advanced Antitank Weapons System-Medium (AAWS-M) is ready to be fielded.

Above: *The Dragon antitank missile and launcher are light enough to be carried by one soldier.*

M47 DRAGON II MEDIUM ANTITANK WEAPON	
Diameter:	4.72 in.
Length:	
Weapon:	46.2 in.
Missile:	33.8 in.
Weight:	
Weapon:	32.6 lbs.
Missile:	15.4 lbs.
Speed:	330 fps
Range:	1,000 yds.
Date of service:	1972

Top: *The Dragon has a range of 3,000 feet and carries a shaped-charge warhead effective against heavy plate armor.* Bottom, left: *After firing the Dragon missile, the operator discards the fiberglass tube.* Bottom, right: *The sight unit contains a telescopic sight, an infrared detector, and the required electronics to fire the missile and guide it to its target.*

Above: *The slow speed of the Dragon missile requires the operator to hold still during the missile's flight so that the sight unit is not disturbed.*

AT-4 Light Antitank Weapon

In the U.S. military's ongoing search for lighter and more effective antitank weaponry, U.S. ground forces have selected the Swedish-designed AT-4. This lightweight and simple disposable weapon is among the most effective in its class. Tipping the scales at 13.2 pounds, the AT-4 is easily transported: An individual soldier can carry the weapon unassisted. Unlike most antitank and anti-armored vehicle weapons systems, the AT-4 does not require a crew for operation, nor a tripod or bipod. It is launched from the operator's shoulder while standing, kneeling, or lying down.

The AT-4 measures just over three feet in length and fires a very potent 3.31-inch diameter projectile to an effective range of 500 yards. This weapon is designed to replace the less effective M72 Light Armor Weapon (LAW). Deliveries of the new system are currently underway. Honeywell will eventually produce the AT-4 in the United States under license from the Swedish defense firm FFV.

The AT-4 has a plastic tube body reinforced with glass fiber. Inside the basic unit is a firing mechanism, sights, and a self-contained round. After firing, the launcher is disposed of. This high-tech weapon comes with a variety of charges, including High Explosive Anti-Tank (HEAT), High Explosive Dual Purpose (HEDP), White Phosphorous (WP) smoke, and an Illumination Bomb (IB) round for lighting up the battlefield at night.

The AT-4's primary mission is to stop armored vehicles and light tanks. The HEAT round fired by the AT-4 reaches speeds of more than 985 feet per second and can penetrate up to 11.8 inches of armor at ranges of 300 yards or more. The warhead features the "behind armor secondary effects" charge: After the projectile cuts through the vehicle's armored protection, a high-pressure incendiary effect occurs. This action, which is accompanied by a blinding flash, is designed to effectively knock out the crew of the enemy vehicle even if the penetration hole is relatively small.

With the addition of the AT-4 to the U.S. military inventory, the individual soldier can act not only as a rifleman against advancing troops but also as an effective armored vehicle/light tank stopper. The modern battlefield dictates that both sides will rely more heavily on a host of armored personnel carriers, armored fighting vehicles, and light tanks. The task of equipping frontline soldiers with an effective means of stopping advancing armor may well be one of the vital keys to combat success today and in the future.

Below: *The AT-4 is a recoilless rifle that is light and easy to transport.*

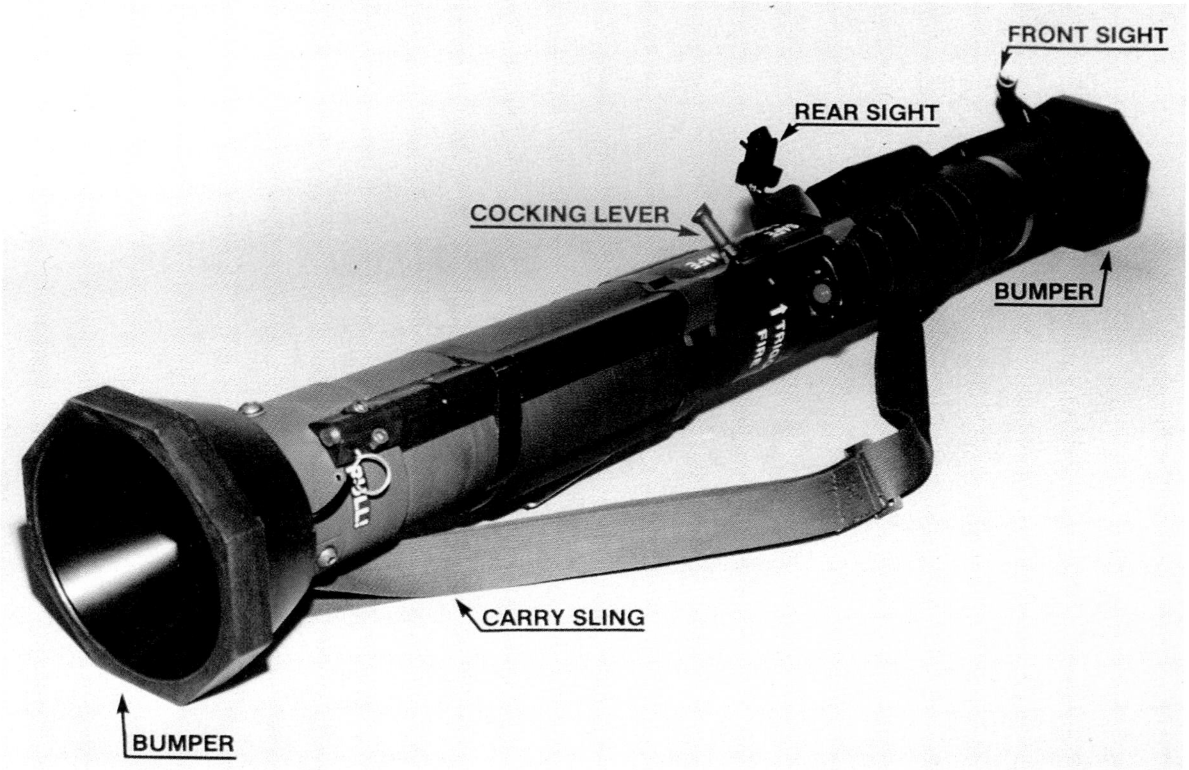

AT-4 LIGHT ANTITANK WEAPON	
Caliber:	84mm
Weapon length:	39 in.
Weight:	
Projectile:	6.6 lbs.
Weapon:	13.2 lbs.
Muzzle velocity:	985 fps
Range:	500 yds.
Date of service:	1989

ARMORED FIGHTING VEHICLES

Mobility is the key to success in warfare; this often-stated dictum has become vital on the modern battlefield. The evolution of the armored fighting vehicle began during World War I. The armored fighting vehicle—primarily the tank—provided the foot soldier with a traveling machine gun and artillery post that could support him in the front lines.

During World War II, the Allies were ill-prepared to fight Germany's tank-led war of mobility and fast maneuverability. As late as May 1945, no nation had managed to field a professional military force or employ tactics equal to those of the German Army. The Allies achieved victory only because they relied on a strategy of attrition based on their superior manpower and productivity.

The lessons of the 1940s remain relevant today. The Soviet Union and its Warsaw Pact allies have adopted the German concepts of mobility and maneuverability and coupled those concepts with overwhelmingly superior forces, all backed with sufficient inventory, production capacity, and manpower to win by attrition. The United States and its North Atlantic Treaty Organization (NATO) allies plan to strike back with superior weapons, but in inferior numbers. To even the odds, NATO depends on European-based U.S. reinforcements and, as a final option, nuclear weapons.

A major area of concern remains armored fighting vehicles. The Soviets have long recognized the value of armored vehicles to carry troops to support armor and armor/infantry operations. The Soviets can now deploy 75,000 armored personnel carriers (APC) and armored fighting vehicles (AFV) in Europe alone, compared with a total NATO force of 35,700.

Today, there are four classes of armored vehicles: armored personnel carriers (APC), armored fighting vehicles (AFV), infantry fighting vehicles (IFV), and cavalry fighting vehicles (CFV). Tracked and wheeled variations are nearly the equal in speed, mobility, agility, and gun power to the medium tanks of World War II. Armored vehicles are armored against small arms fire and carry powerful main guns for protection against enemy tanks and gunners, or for offensive purposes. The armored vehicle is needed to enable American infantry to keep pace with the main battle tank (MBT), both to protect and support the MBT and to occupy territory against enemy counterattack once the MBT has moved on.

The United States Marines Corps uses the Light Assault Vehicle (LAV) 25, an eight-wheeled combat vehicle armed with the Hughes M242 Bushmaster 25 millimeter chain gun. The U.S. Army uses the tracked Bradley M2 and M3 Fighting Vehicles.

Opposite: *The M113 Armored Personnel Carrier is the most ubiquitous vehicle in the U.S. Army.* Above: *The M2 Bradley Infantry Fighting Vehicle can carry a fully equipped infantry squad.* Left: *The M998 High Mobility, Multipurpose Wheeled Vehicle is replacing the M151 Jeep, the M274 Mule, the M561 Gamma Goat, and the M880 truck.*

M113 Armored Personnel Carrier

The FMC Corporation's M113 Armored Personnel Carrier (APC) and its variations are perhaps the most widely used armored fighting vehicles in the world today. To date, more than 75,000 have been built in more than 20 different models. The amphibious M113, which has been in production since 1964, carries a crew of two plus an infantry squad of 11. It can maintain a road speed of 42 miles per hour, averages 2.78 miles per gallon of fuel, and has a range of 300 miles.

FMC's M113 has been heavily criticized because its light armor barely stops a non-armor-piercing rifle bullet. The M113 is particularly vulnerable to heavier-caliber weapons, and crew and passengers suffered casualties during the Vietnam War due to spalling, an effect produced by shaped charges used in antitank guns or missile warheads. When the shaped-charge warhead strikes, molten metal is sprayed into the interior of the vehicle, striking passengers and equipment.

Survivability of armored fighting vehicles can be increased by adding armor, but only so much extra armor can be added before the powertrain can no longer move the vehicle. To improve survivability and counter spalling, FMC and other manufacturers of armored fighting vehicles, as well as independent companies such as Israeli URDAN Industries, Ltd., have developed bolt-on aluminum armor panels for the exterior and Kevlar liners for the interiors of crew/passenger and cargo compartments. A current version, the M113A3, has external fuel tanks and spall-suppressant, bolt-on interior armor to increase crew survivability. An up-rated powertrain that, even with the added armor, gives the vehicle a cross-country speed of 22 miles per hour is available.

The M113A3 is armed with a .50 caliber M2 machine gun with 2,000 rounds. Basic hull armor is 5083 aluminum. Bottom surfaces have anti-mine appliqués. The M113A3 is not fast enough to keep pace with the M-1 Abrams Main Battle Tank, so is retained only in mechanized units having the M-60 Main Battle Tank.

The M113 chassis has been used as the basis for a number of other vehicle weapon systems. Among them are the M106A2 Carrier for the 4.2-inch mortar, the M125A2 for the 81 millimeter mortar, the M577A2 Command Post Vehicle, the M548 Unarmored Cargo Carrier, the M752 Lance Missile Carrier, the M730 Chaparral Missile Carrier, the M981 Artillery Fire Integration Support Team Vehicle, the M1059 Smoke Generator Vehicle, and the M1015 Electronic Warfare Shelter Carrier.

Above: *The M113 Armored Personnel Carrier is being upgraded with add-on armor to make it more resistant to small arms fire.*

Left: *The M113 is perhaps the most widely used armored fighting vehicle in the world.* Below: *The M113 Armored Personnel Carrier is used by both the Army and the Marine Corps.*

M113 ARMORED PERSONNEL CARRIER	
Length:	16 ft.
Width:	8 ft., 9.5 in.
Height:	8 ft., 1 in.
Weight:	24,595 lbs.
Engine:	Detroit Diesel 6V-53, turbocharged, 215 hp
Speed:	
Road:	42 mph
Swimming:	3 mph
Range:	300 miles
Date of service:	1964

The M113 Armored Personnel Carrier can reach a cross-country speed of 22 miles per hour.

M2/M3 Bradley Infantry and Cavalry Fighting Vehicles

Above: *The M2 Bradley is a fighting vehicle designed to carry infantry troops and keep up with main battle tanks.*

The Bradley Infantry and Cavalry Fighting Vehicles were selected by the U.S. Army in 1976 to carry troops to protect tanks, to conduct mounted warfare, and to consolidate gains made by armor. The Bradley was designed to fire on the move; to defeat tanks and other fighting vehicles; to conduct troop-suppression and day/night, high-speed, cross-country missions; and to swim. Troops can fight from inside the Bradley, and then quickly exit to fight outside the vehicle. Of the infantry combat vehicles commonly in use today, only the Soviet BMP-2 comes close to the Bradley's capabilities, but it lacks the Bradley's day/night, high-speed, and cross-country capabilities.

The Bradley weighs nearly 50,000 pounds and is capable of speeds of 41 miles per hour on a hard surface. Using its tracks for propulsion, the Bradley can swim at the rate of 4.2 miles per hour. The vehicle's cruising range is 300 miles. The vehicle is powered by a Cummins VTA-903 diesel engine and is equipped with thermal imaging sights for the gunner, an optical relay for the commander, and an AN/VVS-2 night-vision sight for the driver.

The M2 infantry version, or Infantry Fighting Vehicle (IFV), carries a squad of nine, including a driver, gunner, and commander, with the latter two in the turret. The turret contains a McDonnell Douglas M242 25 millimeter chain gun. Three hundred rounds of ready ammunition are carried in the turret, with an additional 600 rounds stowed aft in the hull. Because of the Bradley's stabilized turret drive, the M242 chain gun can be fired with extreme accuracy when the vehicle is moving at speed over virtually any terrain.

An M240C machine gun is mounted coaxially to the right of the 25mm main gun. Other armament includes a TOW missile launcher mounted in a hinged, rectangular box on the left side of the turret. The TOW can defeat Soviet main battle tanks at an extreme range of 4,000 yards. The M2 Bradley carries seven TOW missiles—two in the launcher and five in a storage space in the vehicle's hull. The vehicle is also equipped with six ball-mounted M231 Colt 5.56mm, port-firing automatic weapons, an M60 7.62mm squad machine gun, and ten M16 automatic rifles.

The M3 cavalry version, or Cavalry Fighting Vehicle (CFV), is externally identical to the M2 Infantry but carries a cavalry squad of five. The M3 stores twice as many rounds as the IFV (1,200 for the 25mm main gun) and ten additional TOW antitank missiles to complement the pair loaded in the side-mounted launcher. The CFV can also carry five Dragon shoulder-launched antitank missiles in place of the stowed TOW missiles. The CFV is not equipped with firing ports and carries just five M16 automatic rifles.

Above: *The M2 Bradley Infantry Fighting Vehicle is the most combat capable light armored tracked vehicle in existence today.* Right: *The M2 Bradley Infantry and the M3 Bradley Cavalry Fighting Vehicles are both equipped with a 25mm chain gun and a TOW missile launcher.*

M2/M3 BRADLEY INFANTRY AND CAVALRY FIGHTING VEHICLES

Length:	21 ft., 2 in.
Width:	10 ft., 6 in.
Height:	9 ft., 9 in.
Weight:	49,802 lbs.
Engine:	Cummins diesel VTA-903, turbocharged, 500 hp
Speed:	
Road:	41 mph
Swimming:	4.2 mph
Range:	300 miles
Date of service:	1981

Marine Corps Light Assault Vehicle 25

The U.S. Marine Corps' Light Assault Vehicle (LAV) 25 is an eight-wheeled, armed, armored fighting vehicle and personnel carrier. Originally designed by MOWAG of Kreuzlingen, Switzerland, as a 6 x 6 wheeled vehicle and known as the PIRANHA, this armored fighting vehicle (AFV) was adopted by the Canadian Army in 1977 as Armored Vehicle, General Purpose (AVGP). Before selecting the Swiss-Canadian 8 x 8 version, the Marine Corps evaluated three other light armored vehicles: the tracked British Scorpion, Cadillac Gage's V-150, and Cadillac Gage's six-wheeled V-300. Both the Canadian AVGP and the U.S. Marine Corps LAV are built by the Diesel Division of General Motors, London, Ontario, Canada. The LAV is street legal in the U.S. and can be driven along any highway without a Department of Transportation waiver.

The LAV-25 is armed with a stabilized Hughes M242 Bushmaster 25 millimeter chain gun and a coaxial M240C 7.62mm machine gun mounted in a power-driven, two-personnel turret. This AFV can also mount a Mark 19 40mm grenade launcher, a M2 .50 caliber machine gun, or a M60 7.62mm machine gun on a pintle mount. The 25mm Bushmaster fires ammunition that can defeat all Soviet or Warsaw Pact light-armored vehicles and armored personnel carriers out to a range of 8,202 feet.

Six versions of the LAV-25 are currently in service: LAV-25 with a 25mm chain-gun, LAV logistics carrier, LAV mortar vehicle armed with the 81mm mortar, LAV antitank vehicle carrying a twin TOW missile launcher, LAV command and control vehicle, and LAV maintenance/recovery vehicle. The LAV-25 carries a crew of three (commander, driver, and gunner) and has room for six combat-ready marines in the cargo compartment. The marines sit three to a side, facing outward, and fire their weapons through ports. Above each port is a periscope.

Above: *The Marine Corps' answer to the M2/3 Bradley is the Light Assault Vehicle 25, which has eight wheels rather than tracks.*

The LAV-25 is air transportable, carried inside the C-130 Hercules, C-141 Starlifter, or the C-5 Galaxy. It can also be carried in a sling beneath the CH-53E Super Stallion helicopter; the helicopter can ferry the LAV-25 from amphibious assault ships directly to the beach.

When the LAVB program is completed, 758 LAVs will be deployed in four Light Armored Vehicle Battalions (LAVB), one for each Marine division, and in six additional companies located with prepositioned naval flotillas around the world. The four battalions are 1st LAVB at Camp Pendleton, California; 2nd LAVB at Camp Lejeune, North Carolina; 3rd LAVB at 29 Palms, California; and 4th LAVB, which is still to be assigned a location. Each LAV battalion will include 1,038 personnel and 145 LAV-25s.

The Marine Corps is investigating a variation of the LAV, the LAV-90. This vehicle is armed with the Belgian MECAR Kenerga 90mm, high-velocity, low-recoil tank gun mounted in a two-person turret. The turret contains a modular sight and laser range finder, a navigation system capable of interrogating positioning satellites, the M240 coaxial machine gun, and 66mm smoke-grenade launchers. The MECAR turret can be mounted in place of the 25mm gun turret in less than two hours.

Above: *The LAV-25 is based on a Canadian Armed Forces version of a Swiss armored personnel carrier.* Right: *The LAV-25 is fast enough to operate with the M-60 Main Battle Tank (background).*

MARINE CORPS LIGHT ASSAULT VEHICLE 25

Length:	21 ft.
Width:	7 ft., 2.5 in.
Height:	8 ft., 2.5 in.
Weight:	27,559 lbs.
Engine:	Detroit Diesel 6V-53T, turbocharged, 175 hp
Speed:	
Road:	63 mph
Swimming:	6 mph
Range:	485 miles
Date of service:	1984

M998 High Mobility, Multipurpose Wheeled Vehicle (HMMWV)

Although far less "glamorous" than tracked fighting vehicles and heavy tanks, wheeled military vehicles are integral to the world of modern U.S. combat forces throughout the world. Because the official name of the U.S. military's newest multipurpose, wheeled vehicle is a bigger mouthful than the name of the venerable vehicle it replaced—the Jeep—the M998 High Mobility, Multipurpose Wheeled Vehicle (HMMWV) is popularly known as the "HummVee" or "Hummer."

Officially, the 2.5-ton Hummer is a multifaceted utility vehicle designed to fill a variety of military roles for modern ground forces. The Hummer is produced by the AM General Division of LTV, and it was originally adopted by the U.S. Army to replace the aging series of Jeep vehicles. The Hummer's host of capabilities have enabled it to replace the M274 MULE, the M880 pickup truck, and the M792 ambulance.

The Hummer's low silhouette and extreme maneuverability allow far greater battlefield movement than the older Jeeps and trucks it replaces. The Hummer is basically a four-wheel drive, go-anywhere vehicle that can be used for everything from field car to roving, tank-busting TOW missile carrier.

With versatility a key element of the Hummer's design, it's no surprise that 60,000 of the vehicles are being delivered to the U.S. Army, Air Force, and Marine Corps. The Hummer family of vehicles consists of up to 18 different vehicles. In addition to its antitank "shoot and scoot" role, the Hummer provides battlefield assistance as a staff car, supply vehicle, troop carrier, communications center, command post, medical evacuation vehicle, and armament carrier.

Depending upon need, the vehicle can be equipped with a host of weaponry, including the 7.62 millimeter and .50 caliber machine guns, TOW I and TOW II missile launchers, the Mark 19 grenade launcher system, and the Stinger antiaircraft missile system. The Hummer can travel up to 351 miles on a single tank of diesel fuel, and it can even run—and fight—on flat tires. All Hummer variations use the same chassis, engine, and transmission, so locating replacement parts is a relatively easy task both on and off the battlefield.

Adopted by the U.S. military in 1982 and in service since 1984, the Hummer has proved itself a tough combat vehicle that gets troops in and out of harm's way quickly.

Above: *The HMMWV is a do-everything unarmored vehicle.*

M998 HIGH MOBILITY, MULTIPURPOSE WHEELED VEHICLE (HMMWV)	
Length:	15 ft.
Width:	7 ft., 1 in.
Height:	5 ft., 7.5 in.
Weight:	4,969 lbs.
Wheelbase:	10 ft., 8 in.
Engine:	General Motors V8 6.2 liter diesel
Speed:	65 mph
Range:	351 miles
Date of service:	1984

Top: *The HMMWV is sturdy enough to mount the TOW 2 antitank missile launcher.* Center: *The HMMWV is powered by a diesel engine and has an automatic transmission.* Bottom: *As part of the Forward Air Defense System, the HMMWV has been equipped with the Stinger antiaircraft missile.*

The HMMWV can mount a gun/missile combination called the Line-of-Sight Forward Heavy. The gun is a .50 caliber heavy machine gun and the missile is the Stinger.

MINES

There are few weapons more feared by combat soldiers than land mines. Mines cause higher casualties than any other weapon except artillery fire.

Little more than 70 years ago, a land mine was nothing more complex than a tunnel dug by sappers beneath an enemy's defensive position. The tunnel was packed full of explosives and usually exploded in the middle of the night to cause the most panic and confusion. (In one British action in 1917, a one-million-ton charge of ammonal was detonated beneath German positions at 3 A.M.)

Within months of the appearance of the tank on the Western Front in World War I, Germany developed the first antitank mine—an artillery shell buried in the earth with only the fuse exposed. With this innovation, the race between armor and land mines was on. During World War II, minefield laying was developed to a high art. Land mines by the millions were laid from Cairo to Casablanca, from Normandy to Kursk. The Soviets have estimated that they alone laid over 200 million mines. Twenty percent of all Allied tank losses during World War II were due to land mines. During the Korean War (1950–53), this figure rose to 60 percent of all United Nations tank losses. Land mines caused an incredible 70 percent of all U.S. and ARVN (South Vietnamese) tank losses in South Vietnam from 1964 to 1975.

Today's mines can be placed by hand, tossed from a vehicle, dropped from an aircraft, or strewn from a rocket or artillery warhead. They can discriminate between friendly and enemy tanks by recognizing infrared and magnetic signatures. They can activate themselves on cue, and can use infrared, acoustical, or magnetic sensors to detect the presence of an enemy. Mines can bound in the air to a predetermined height before exploding. They can drive a shaped charge against the soft underbelly of a tank or blow off a tank tread. They can even deactivate themselves at a preset time to allow the passage of friendly forces.

The Land Mine and Minelaying Systems

Land mines fall into two basic categories, antipersonnel (AP) and antitank (AT). Antipersonnel mines are laid to deny the enemy access to an area or to defend a fixed position. One type of AP mine in current U.S. service is the M16A2. When the M16A2 is disturbed, a preliminary charge explodes, blowing the mine from its container, which is buried from three to six feet deep. The main charge then explodes and hurls shrapnel 24 feet or more. Other antipersonnel mines, such as the U.S. M14 "Cupcake" or "Toe Popper," cause injuries by blast effect. A third type of mine—the fragmentation mine—is attached to a stake and detonated by trip wire.

Above: *The Claymore mine can be detonated electrically or by percussion fuse.*

The Claymore mine is the fourth category of antipersonnel mine. The U.S. M18A1 has a slightly curved surface in which 700 steel balls are embedded in a plastic matrix. The mine can be detonated electrically or by a percussion fuse attached to a tripwire or a remote-control device. An explosive charge of 1.5 pounds of Composition 4 (C4) explosive causes the plastic matrix to fragment, driving the steel balls outward in a 60-degree arc.

Antitank mines are designed to immobilize or destroy vehicles. These mines can be detonated by pressure, the movement of a vertical tilt rod, or a magnetic sensor. The pressure-fused AT mine is the most common. A spring-loaded striker is held back from an explosive cap. When a weight in excess of a set amount releases the striker, the cap explodes and detonates the main charge. To prevent detection by mine detectors searching for magnetic abnormalities, the preferred mine casing today is aluminum or plastic.

Antitank mines often contain a magnetic sensor that measures the amount of iron and steel in an approaching vehicle. When a preset level is exceeded, the detonator first explodes an uncovering charge that blows off the layers of camouflage, allowing the shaped charge an unobstructed path. The shaped charge is a jet of extremely hot gas that forms in milliseconds and melts its way through the softer armor of the tank's underbelly into the tank's interior.

Mines are laid in patterns called minefields. Whether intended for people or vehicles, minefields fall into certain basic types. *Protective* minefields provide close protection for friendly positions or warn of an enemy's approach. They are always laid within range of the defender's small arms but beyond the range of hand grenades. *Tactical* minefields are intended to disrupt, delay, and reduce the enemy's mobility; to channel the enemy in a desired direction; or to stop him. U.S. Army practice is to lay a minimum of three mine belts. The outer belt is covered by antitank weapons such as the TOW missile; the second belt is protected by a combination of antitank and tank weapons. The innermost belt is protected by all weapons. *Point* minefields are laid to disorganize an enemy and to deny access to specified areas. These minefields are usually irregularly shaped and include both AP and AT mines, complete with anti-handling (booby trap) devices. *Interdiction* minefields are established in enemy-held areas by special operations forces or by rocket- and aircraft-delivered AP and AT mines, usually in mixed configurations. They can be used to deny or discourage the use of airfields, ports, and staging or population areas. *Phony* minefields are used to extend the effectiveness of real minefields. They are also used to misdirect enemy forces into real minefields or into areas that can be brought under fire.

The U.S. Army and Marine Corps have opted for a mix of mechanical and scatterable mine systems. The mechanical minelaying system is known as the M128 Ground Emplaced Mine Scattering System (GEMSS) and is mounted on a towed trailer. Two dispensers hold up to 400 mines each. The mines are ejected out to 98 feet on either side of the trailer, forming a 196-foot-wide belt. The GEMSS system can dispense its full load of M75 antitank mines and M74 antipersonnel mines in 15 minutes. The mines arm themselves after impact.

Scatterable mines are usually small and quite powerful. Since they are not buried, they are designed to blend in with the background. They usually arm themselves after impact or during flight, and they contain neutralizing or self-destruct mechanisms to render the area safe for friendly forces or civilians after a specified period. The scatterable mines in use by American combat forces are referred to as FASCAM—Family of Scatterable Mines—and currently include four operational systems: ADAM, RAAMS, M56, and VOLCANO.

Scatterable mines can be strewn by aircraft, long-range rockets, or artillery cargo shells. These mines are particularly useful against airfields. Surface-penetrating variations are used to punch craters in the runway surface to prevent aircraft usage and damage vehicles attempting repairs. Antipersonnel variants make it dangerous or impossible for maintenance and flight crews to operate.

A complete listing of all land mines and minelaying systems currently in use by U.S. land power forces is shown in the accompanying table.

U.S. LAND MINES

DESIGNATION	TYPE	DISPENSING METHOD	SYSTEM	COMMENT
M2	AP	M		Bounding, obsolete
M6A2	AT	M		Obsolete
M7A2	AP/AT	M		Obsolete
M14	AP	M		Cupcake
M15	AT	M		Tilt-rod capability added
M16A1	AP	M		Bounding
M18 Series	AP	M		Claymore
M19	AT	M		Plastic version of M15
M21	AT	M		Plate charge, tilt-rod
M24	AT	M		Rocket charge/off-route
M74	S-AP	Gv/Ac/Helo	M128 GEMSS	80 AP mines in normal load
M75	S-AT	Gv/Ac/Helo	M128 GEMSS	320 AT mines in normal load
M74	S-AP	Ac	GATOR	60 or 94 mines
M75	S-AT	Ac	GATOR	Three self-destruct mines available
M77	AP	M	MOPMS XM133	Candidate mine-system
M78	AT	M	MOPMS XM133	Candidate mine-system
M692	S-AP	Ar	ADAM	Long self-destruct life
M718	S-AT	Ar	RAAMS	Short self-destruct life
M731	S-AP	Ar	ADAM	Short self-destruct life
M741	S-AT	Ar	RAAMS	Long self-destruct life
XM84	AT	M	WASPM	Project on hold/SFF warhead
XM87	S-AT/AP	Ac	VOLCANO	Mine canister—holds 40 M74/75-type mines

Key: AP = Antipersonnel
AT = Antitank
S- = Scatterable
M = Manually laid
Gv = Ground vehicle
Ac = Aircraft
Helo = Helicopter
Ar = Artillery

PROJECTILE, 155MM, AT, M718/741

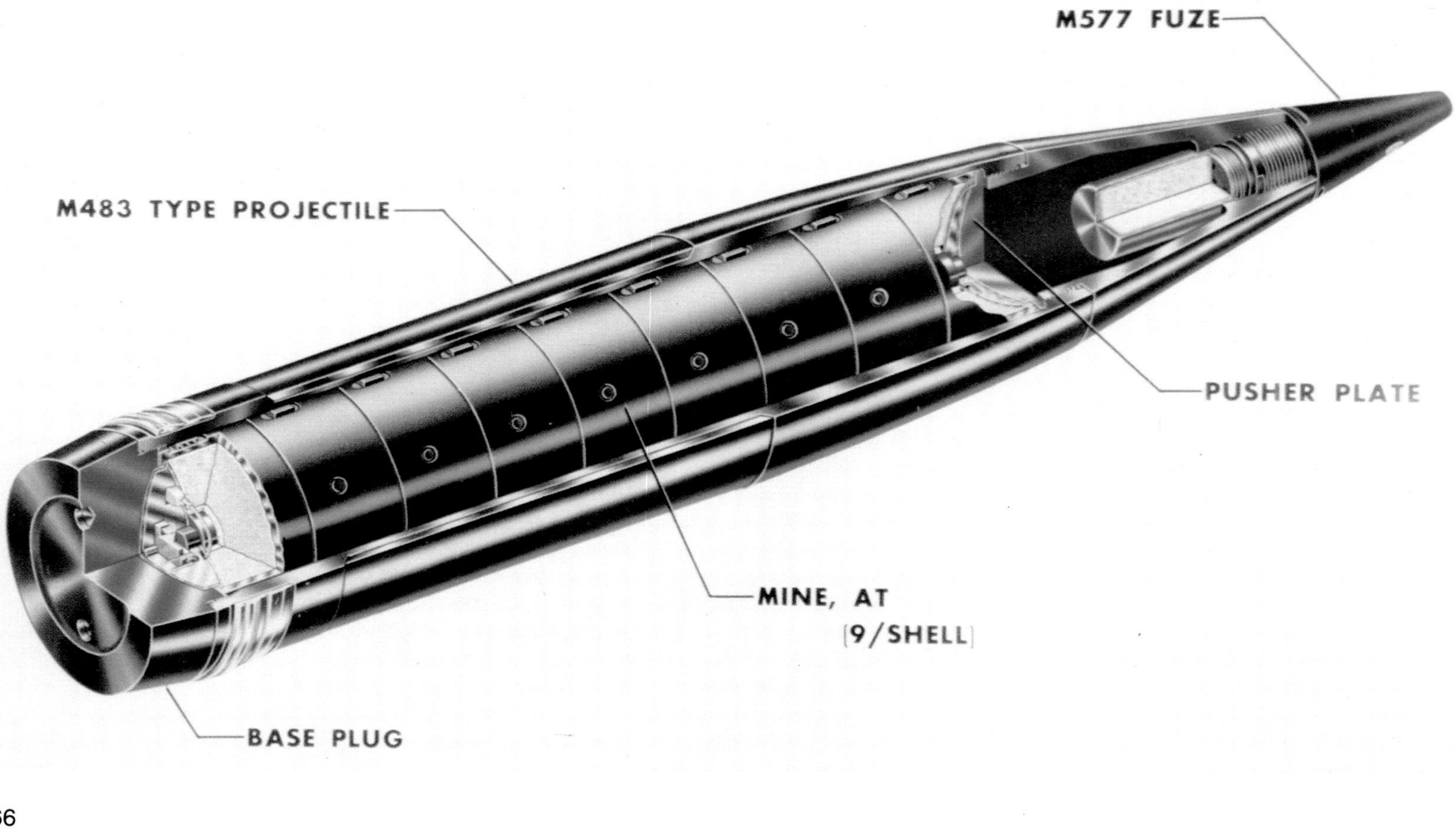

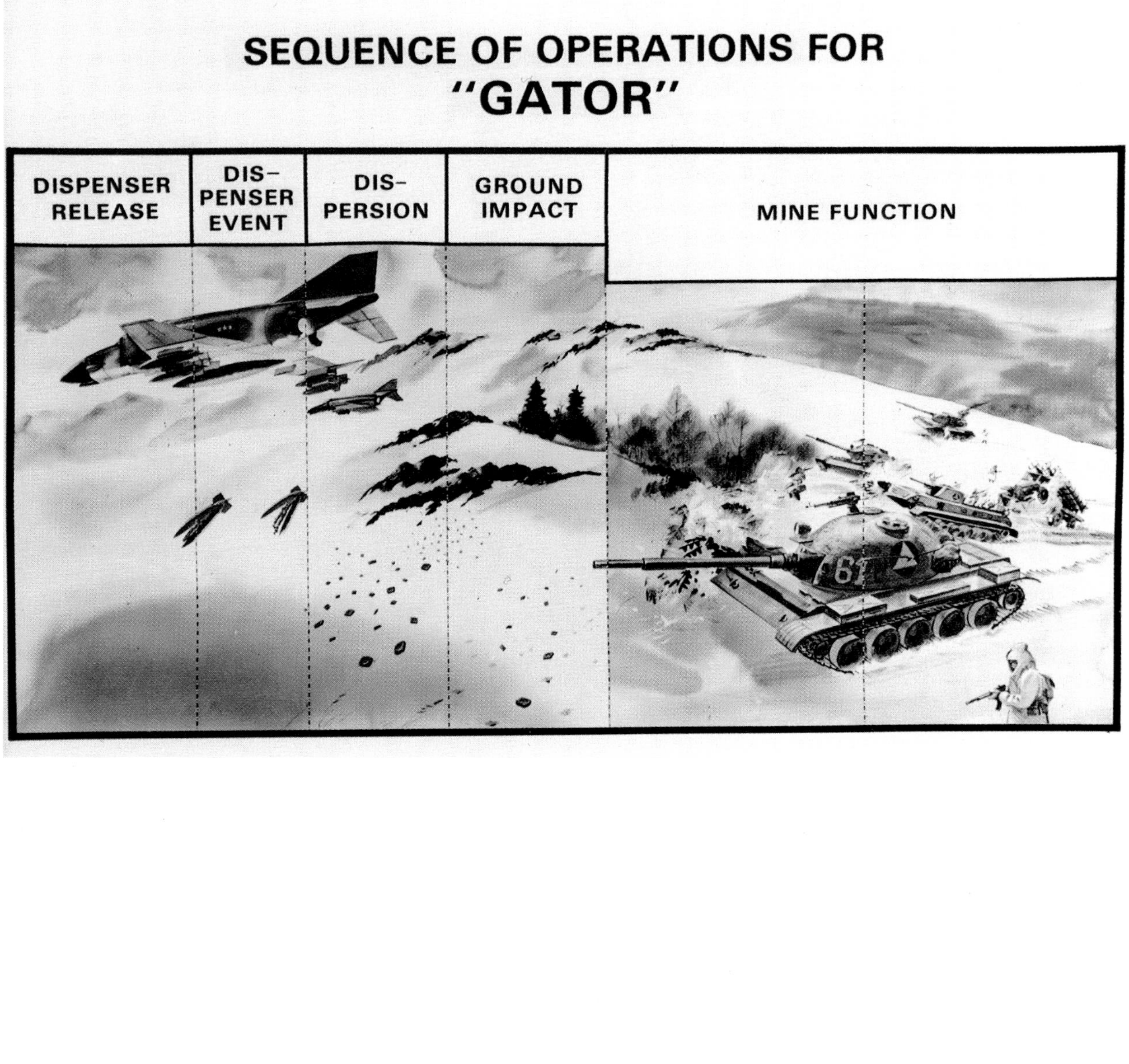

Opposite, top: *The 155mm ADAM system is, in effect, a minefield that can be laid by artillery fire.* Opposite, bottom: *The 155mm M718/741 projectile is typical of today's artillery rounds. The projectile carries nine mines that are effective against most tanks in service today.* Above: *The ADAM round dispenses a series of small pop-up mines that are effective against personnel and unarmored vehicles.* Left: *GATOR is an airborne antitank mine system dispensed from low-flying aircraft against approaching armored columns.*

BATTLEFIELD ELECTRONICS

As late as the end of World War II, battlefield electronics primarily meant communication systems. Today's battlefield electronics offer much more than secure and reliable communications. Specialized radar and computer systems track enemy artillery and missile fire and trace it back to its source with remarkable speed and accuracy. Battlefield electronics detect and track the movement of enemy forces, and they enable the individual soldier to call in artillery or attack aircraft with unparalleled accuracy.

Counterbattery fire—determining the trajectory of incoming artillery and missile fire and tracing it back to its source—has been elevated to a science. Specialized radar and computer systems spot the enemy round as soon as it clears the horizon. The system then watches the incoming round, calculates its trajectory and impact area, and displays the geographical coordinates of the point from which the round was fired. Today's systems can even transmit this data to friendly guns or missiles so fast that return fire is on its way before the enemy round strikes.

A team of two soldiers can use a hand-held system to guide a smart bomb to an area where enemy tanks are encamped. One soldier speaks into a radio to an attack aircraft circling a few miles away while the other points an instrument that looks like a small searchlight at the tanks below. When the soldier presses the trigger, nothing visibly happens. But the smart bomb released by the attack aircraft and now swooping in on the camp sees a tank glowing with laser light. The sensor in the bomb's nose acquires the target. The bomb's sensor focuses on the laser-lit tank and directs the steering mechanism. The bomb is so accurate that it can strike the top of the tank's turret, where the armor is thinnest.

Today's soldier is far more technologically aware and capable than at any time in the past. These sophisticated new weapons, while expensive, compensate for what the U.S. military and its North Atlantic Treaty Organization allies lack in numbers against the far more numerous Soviet and Warsaw Pact military forces.

Above: *The AN/TPQ-37 Artillery Fire Finder Radar system can identify and track a fired artillery or rocket round back to its source.* Left: *The Fire Finder system provides tracking data on enemy fire to U.S. artillery or missile batteries.*

AN/PPS-5B Battlefield Surveillance Radar

The U.S. military's standard battlefield surveillance system dates back to the early 1960s, when it was designed as a soldier-portable system. Having been used extensively throughout the Vietnam War, the AN/PPS-5B remains in service today; more than 1,350 units are in use by the U.S. Army and overseas customers.

Capable of detecting both moving and stationary targets, battlefield radar can automatically scan a given area for a long period of time to protect soldiers from attack. The radar can be rotated by hand or by motor to scan the surrounding area for unseen enemy threats. The system uses doppler radar to search for, and distinguish between, a host of fixed and moving targets. When set to locate moving targets, the system can pick up and identify even those targets creeping along at speeds under one mile per hour.

The entire transmitter/ receiver radar is portable in three pack units, and the unit can be assembled and operational in less than ten minutes. The AN/PPS-5B radar system can also be used in a vehicle-mounted configuration, usually in a Jeep or High Mobility, Multipurpose Wheeled Vehicle (HMMWV). The radar unit is usually affixed to the same pintle-mount system used for the .50 caliber machine gun. Thus the unit can be dispatched to wherever the threat appears greatest, replacing a host of stationary surveillance systems that would require additional operating crews.

The battlefield surveillance system has been used to monitor troop movements, detect enemy patrols, and provide perimeter defense and target coordination for artillery batteries. The PPS-5B remains in production today on an "on order" basis. Spare parts continue to be produced. Although the AN/PPS-5B Battlefield Surveillance Radar may not reflect the state-of-the-art electronics that many think are needed in the modern combat zone, the system has continued to prove its battlefield efficiency in virtually every region and climate of the world.

Upgrades to the existing system include a longer-range scanning capability that enhances detection performance to nearly ten miles and a new remote control system for the receiver/ transmitter's elevation aiming. Additionally, the radar system has a new mast mounting system to raise its elevation for enemy surveillance to a greater distance.

Top: *The Marine Corps' AN/PPS-5B uses lasers to mark targets for smart weapons.* Bottom, left: *The AN/PPS-5B can be serviced and operated by one soldier.* Bottom, right: *The relatively simple keyboard of the AN/PPS-5B is rugged enough for field use under combat conditions.*

AN/PPS-5B BATTLEFIELD SURVEILLANCE RADAR

Weight:	272.80 lbs.
Sections:	Three pack units
Power source:	6v battery or 24v dc generator
Frequency:	16 to 16.5 GHz tunable
Range:	
Soldier-portable:	Three miles
Vehicle-mounted:	Six miles. New optional detection package makes unit capable of detection to ten miles.
Date of service:	1963

AN/TPQ-36/37 Mortar/Artillery Fire Finder Radar

Above: *The AN/TPQ-36 Mortar Fire Finder Radar is a smaller version of the AN/TPQ-37.*

Counterbattery fire is artillery or missile fire aimed at the artillery or missile battery of an attacking enemy. In the era of muzzle-loading cannons, a battery simply aimed its cannons at the enemy artillery within sight across the battlefield.

By World War I, short-range, rapid-firing guns shelled opposing forces in their trenches while long-range guns farther back from the battle line tried to destroy the short-range guns. Coordinates and corrections—either from observation balloons or from specially trained soldiers sent to the forward trenches—were fed to gunners over telephone lines or by semaphore signal. During World War II, light observation aircraft replaced observation balloons.

Today, tactical ballistic missiles have ranges up to 60 miles, and tube artillery firing rocket-assisted projectiles can strike up to 18 miles away. Forward artillery observers are not a viable alternative at these distances, and the air space over the battle area is too hostile to operate spotter aircraft.

The AN/TPQ-36/37 Mortar/Artillery Fire Finder Radar can spot incoming artillery shells, mortar rounds, or tactical missiles. The Fire Finder measures the trajectory of the rounds and predicts where they will fall. It also traces the enemy rounds back to their point of origination. The origination coordinates are then automatically fed to friendly tube or missile artillery units, which can accurately return fire before the enemy has a chance to move to a new position.

The Fire Finder system employs a range-gated doppler radar system. Range-gating establishes artificial parameters, or gates; when a gate is passed, a unique signal is transmitted. When a second gate, or parameter, is violated, another unique signal is transmitted. The parameters mark the progress of an object, and the doppler radar measures its speed.

When activated, the Fire Finder radar divides the world into four equal sectors and examines each sector in turn every few milliseconds. The Fire Finder sends out an array of pencil-thin radar beams at set intervals, forming an "electronic fence." The radar signals sample the area, looking for any object that violates the preset gates, or parameters. The system is capable of tracking a large number of incoming shells and rockets, including volley fire, at the same time. If the enemy attempts to jam the system, Fire Finder can trace the jamming signal to its source and direct fire at the signal.

The entire Fire Finder system is mounted in an eight foot by eight foot square box on the frame of a truck. Antenna, electronics, and powerplant are mounted on a trailer. A crew of three is needed to operate the system, which can be set up within 15 minutes.

Fire Finder was developed by Hughes Aircraft Company. The AN/TPQ-37, which covers a broad area, went into service in 1980. The AN/TPQ-36, which watches a relatively small area and is used to support mortar batteries, entered service in 1983. The Fire Finder system was used by the Marines in Lebanon to direct counterbattery fire from the battleship *New Jersey.* Normal disposition along a division front is two AN/TPQ-37 systems 6.2 to 7.5 miles to the rear and three AN/TPQ-36 systems within two to four miles of the front lines.

Above: *The Mortar Fire Finder Radar is deployed well forward in combat areas.* Right: *The AN/TPQ-36 can track mortar, short-range artillery, rockets, and other incoming rounds back to their source.*

AN/TPQ-36/37 MORTAR/ARTILLERY FIRE FINDER RADAR

Weight:	
Antenna, transceiver, generator:	3,206 lbs.
Operations shelter:	2,575 lbs.
Antenna height:	12 ft., 1.7 in.
Computer:	Digital HMP 3637
Memory:	65,536 words
Word length:	16 bit
Memory cycle time:	600 nanoseconds
Power source:	Ten kw generator
Frequency:	400 Hz, 3 Phase
Voltage:	115/200 v
Date of service:	1980

Laser Designators

Above: *The Army uses the AN/TVQ-2 laser designator to mark targets for smart weapons.*

The "dumb" projectile weapon does not have a guidance system and so cannot make course corrections to seek out a specific target. The "smart" weapon contains a guidance system that can steer it to its target. But smart weapons need something on which to fasten their sensors and serve as a guide. One method to accomplish this is to use a laser to illuminate the target so that the smart weapon's sensors can "see" it. Several versions of laser target designators and locators are in use with U.S. forces. Two of the most common are the AN/PAQ-3 MULE, or Modular Universal Laser Equipment, and the AN/TVQ-2 Ground/Vehicular Laser Locator Designator, G/VLLD, more commonly, GLLD

For the Marines, the MULE is a real workhorse, with a portable tripod unit using a laser range finder, and target designator system that will work with all laser-guided weapons in use by U.S. forces. This includes the Maverick and Hellfire missiles, the Copperhead, and all laser-guided bombs. The system identifies the target, reads out the range, enables the operator to send this information back to a command center, and then literally "paints" or "bathes" the target in laser light so that the smart weapon can find its way.

With batteries and a stabilized tracking module (complete with traversing feature), the MULE's range finder/designator unit tips the scales at 38 pounds. With its optional thermal imaging sight, the MULE can locate enemy targets at night or in heavy battlefield smoke.

The Army's GLLD is used by forward soldiers and observers whose job it is to spot enemy positions, armor, and high-priority targets, then relay information back to a command center as quickly as possible. The GLLD system consists of a laser designator, range finder, tripod, batteries, and a tracking unit. The weight of the GLLD—52 pounds—requires two soldiers to move it about the battlefield. Once set up and in place, the sighting operator locates a target and relays this information via conventional radio to the command center, artillery/mortar battery, or incoming strike aircraft that are using any of the new generation of smart weaponry.

The sighting operator then focuses ("paints") a laser beam on the target. The projectile can "see" the laser-designated spot and will fly to it. The exact frequency and pulse of the GLLD laser beam allows smart weapons to discriminate between other designator systems operating in the area. This cuts down on the error factor and prevents all weapons from converging on a single target.

The manufacturer, Hughes, is developing a smaller, hand-held laser target designator for the individual soldier. Resembling a stumpy rifle, the designator can be used to guide all laser homing weapons. The new designator can also indicate to friendly aircraft the positions of various units and mark supply drop zones, medevac emergencies, troop extractions, and other vital information. This new unit is known as the AN/PAQ-1 Hughes Laser Target Designator.

Above: *The GLLD is usually operated by a two-soldier team, although it can be carried and used by one soldier.* Right: *Once the target is marked with laser light, smart weapons guided by laser seekers will home in to destroy the target.*

LASER DESIGNATORS

Models:	AN/PAQ-3 Modular Universal Laser Equipment (MULE) AN/TVQ-2 Ground/Vehicular Laser Locator Designator (G/VLLD)
Users:	
MULE:	United States Marine Corps
GLLD:	United States Army
Width:	
MULE:	1 ft., 7 in.
GLLD:	1 ft., 6 in.
Height:	
MULE:	2 ft.
GLLD:	2 ft., 1 in.
Weight:	
MULE:	38 lbs.
GLLD:	52 lbs.
Date of service:	
MULE:	1986
GLLD:	1982

AIR-DEFENSE SYSTEMS

A major threat today to the ground forces of any nation is the attack aircraft. Attack aircraft can carry heavy bomb loads as well as ammunition and rockets that can penetrate any armor thickness in use today on any main battle tank or armored vehicle. The attack aircraft can appear with little warning over a rise or from behind a screen of trees before ground forces have time to take cover.

World War I saw the introduction of the ground-attack aircraft. Airplanes were heavily armored against small arms ground fire and equipped with powerful engines to enable them to carry extensive bomb and weapons loads. During World War II, the German Stuka and the Soviet Stormovik brought the concept of ground-attack aircraft to the attention of the world's military planners in a most forceful way. These planes successfully led wave after wave of tanks against enemy opposition. Today, the American A-10 Thunderbolt, the Soviet Su-25 Frogfoot, and the Argentinean Pucara are the preeminent ground-attack warplanes. And there are also ground-attack helicopters, such as the Soviet Union's Mi-8 Hip and the Mi-24 Hind.

To counter the attack aircraft, sophisticated air-defense weapons have been developed. Today's battle area is more heavily defended against low-flying attack aircraft than at any other time in history. The U.S. Army and Marine Corps deploy mobile, radar-directed antiaircraft missile weapons and one-person, shoulder-launched missiles, including the Chaparral, Stinger, and Redeye missiles. All modern air defense is rocket propelled and either internally guided or terminally guided from the ground. Systems have been developed to provide protection at high altitudes and long ranges, at medium altitudes and distances, and at low altitudes and short ranges. Air-defense weapons can be carried on self-propelled vehicles or on an infantry soldier's back.

A new generation of air-defense weaponry is under development and will be fielded in the early 1990s. This new weaponry will extend the capability of the U.S. fighting soldier to defend against air attack. And certain of these new weapons will also be effective against tanks and other armored vehicles.

Opposite, top: *The Vulcan is a towed trailer mounting a 20mm Gatling Gun used to provide defense against low-flying aircraft.* Opposite, bottom: *The Redeye is a shoulder-launched antiaircraft missile that can be carried by individual soldiers.* Top: *The Roland 2 is a U.S. version of a French-German antiaircraft missile system.* Bottom, left: *The Chaparral is an antiaircraft missile system based on the Sidewinder series of missiles.* Bottom, right: *The Stinger is a technologically advanced shoulder-launched antiaircraft missile system.*

The Hawk antiaircraft missile system has been in service since 1960.

MIM-23B Hawk Air-Defense Missile System

The Hawk air-defense missile is one of the oldest antiaircraft missile systems remaining in active service with U.S. forces. This system is widely deployed throughout the U.S. Army and Marine Corps and serves with the air-defense units of 21 other nations. Although the Hawk is somewhat large, heavy, and cumbersome, the U.S. Department of Defense decided in 1982 to keep the system in service until after the turn of the century.

Hawk (Homing-All-the-Way-Killer) was developed by the Raytheon Company in the mid-1950s and was first deployed by the U.S. Army in 1960. The Hawk is a surface-to-air guided missile designed to provide protection against attacking aircraft flying at altitudes between 15,000 and 60,000 feet. It is powered by the Aerojet General M112 booster/sustainer solid-fuel rocket motor. The Hawk's warhead carries a proximity fuse and a 120-pound warhead filled with high explosive. Upon detonation, the explosion fragments the surrounding casing and destroys the target with shrapnel.

The Hawk missile launcher is mounted on the self-propelled M727 launcher unit, which is based on the chassis of the M113 Armored Personnel Carrier. The entire system, though heavy, is air-transportable. The Hawk missile originally depended on a ground-launch facility to direct it to the target. Of course, this made the Hawk subject to enemy electronic countermeasures.

A typical Hawk battery consists of six three-round launchers; a tracked loading vehicle carrying three rounds; a pulse-acquisition radar unit to acquire medium-altitude enemy aircraft; the continuous wave acquisition radar, which searches for low-altitude enemy intruders; two target-illuminating radars; a range-only radar that measures the distance to the target on a real-time basis and then supplies that distance to the continuous wave radar; and the battery control center. By modern standards, the Hawk battery is "noisy" in the electronic sense, making it a target for enemy aircraft equipped to detect and destroy radar installations.

The Hawk has undergone two major improvement programs since 1972. The first, Improved Hawk, substituted solid-state electronics to improve reliability. Also added were a larger warhead, improved propellant, and a system that automatically coordinates data supplied by the various systems and then selects and assigns priorities to targets in order of threat. The second improvement program began in the mid-1980s, in keeping with the Army's 1982 decision to use the Hawk into the 21st century. Tracking and fire control systems are being redesigned to allow the upgrading of electronic countermeasures capability and information processing. This improvement will result in enhanced capability and a deadlier air-defense missile. Despite its bulk and complexity, the Mach 2.5 Hawk missile remains one of the best air-defense systems in the world for medium-altitude interdiction.

Above: *Despite its age, the Hawk is still an extremely effective antiaircraft missile system.*

Top: *The Hawk can be launched singly or in threes.* Center, left: *The Hawk missile is mounted on the self-propelled M727 launcher unit.* Center, right: *The Hawk has a range of 25 miles and a speed of Mach 2.5.* Bottom: *The Hawk may be cumbersome by today's standards, but it will probably remain in service well into the next century.*

MIM-23B HAWK AIR-DEFENSE MISSILE SYSTEM

Length:	16 ft., 6 in.
Diameter:	1 ft., 2 in.
Weight:	1,382 lbs.
Speed:	Mach 2.5
Range:	25 miles
Altitude:	15,000 to 60,000 ft.
Date of service:	1960

The MIM-23B Hawk is powered by an Aerojet General M112 rocket motor.

FIM-43A Redeye Antiaircraft Guided-Missile System

Above: *The FIM-43A Redeye missile carries an infrared seeker that locks onto the hottest target within its range of view.*

The Redeye is an antiaircraft guided missile that can be carried and launched by one infantry trooper. The missile employs a heat-seeking, infrared (IR) sensor in its nose to detect and home in on the heat emissions from an enemy aircraft. The Redeye has three major components: launcher, missile, and battery and coolant unit. The missile itself travels at supersonic speeds and has a flight time of 15 seconds. If the Redeye has not found its target after 15 seconds, the warhead detonates and destroys itself to prevent danger to friendly aircraft or ground troops beneath its flight path.

To fire the Redeye, the operator inserts the battery and coolant unit and attaches an umbilical cord to electrically connect the missile to the launcher. When a target is detected, the operator peers through the sight and finds the aircraft. With the thumb of the right hand, the operator depresses the safety/actuator switch, which allows the operator 45 seconds to complete the firing sequence. When the safety/actuator switch is depressed, freon gas flows to the missile's IR sensor and cools it, making it very sensitive to any heat source. Since there is no Identification, Friend or Foe (IFF) system, the operator must be certain that he is aiming at a hostile aircraft.

When the IR seeker senses a preset heat level, it produces a high-pitched tone, indicating that the missile's guidance system is now tracking the aircraft. A gyroscope, which stabilizes the missile, begins to spin, and the operator depresses the uncaging switch, allowing the gyroscope to take command of the missile's stability. The operator now only has to pull the trigger.

An ejector motor fires the Redeye missile from its launcher, and a sustainer motor fires after a preset distance to protect the operator. When the missile accelerates to 28 Gs (one G equals the force of gravity on an object at rest), a fuse timer-switch closes and 1.6 seconds later, the warhead arms.

In flight, the guidance command system measures the difference between the direction the gyroscope indicates the missile is pointing and the position of the target as observed by the IR seeker. A small computer makes adjusting calculations and feeds these calculations to the guidance system. The guidance system uses fins, which pop open from the missile's fuselage after firing, to change the direction of flight. As the missile approaches the target, the guidance system continues to make ever smaller course corrections. The Redeye is detonated either by striking a solid object or by decelerating suddenly when it strikes a part of the aircraft too thin to activate the primary detonator.

Since the Redeye can only track an enemy aircraft moving away from its launching position, its value is limited to post-attack situations. The Redeye was the first self-seeking, one-soldier, portable antiaircraft missile placed in U.S. service. It is now being replaced by the Stinger.

Left: *The Redeye is effective only when fired at an aircraft moving away from the launcher.* Below: *The Redeye missile system is lightweight and has a range of about two miles.*

FIM-43A REDEYE ANTIAIRCRAFT GUIDED-MISSILE SYSTEM	
Length:	4 ft.
Diameter:	2.8 in.
Weight:	18 lbs.
Speed:	Mach 1.8
Range:	2.1 miles
Altitude:	8,200 ft.
Date of service:	1964

Vulcan Air-Defense System

The Vulcan Air-Defense System (VADS) provides low-altitude air defense for fixed positions and for armored, infantry, and supply columns and convoys. VADS is based on the Vulcan 20 millimeter aircraft cannon developed by General Electric. The system is mounted on a modified M113A1 Armored Personnel Carrier or, more commonly, on a two-wheeled trailer that is towed by the M715 or M37 truck or by the High Mobility, Multipurpose Wheeled Vehicle (HMMWV). The Vulcan was originally intended as an interim light antiaircraft system until the Sergeant York system became available. But the Sergeant York was canceled, and VADS has been in service since 1968.

VADS uses the Vulcan M61 six-barrel cannon. The fire control system employs the gyroscopically controlled M62 sight developed by Lockheed Electronics. To operate, the gunner acquires the target visually. As the operator tracks it, the radar unit attached to the sight calculates the range of the target. That information is fed to a computer that converts it to lead angle and elevation.

The lack of electronic sensors limits the Vulcan's use to daytime, clear weather operations only, a tremendous handicap in the European area. The Vulcan can be fired at 1,000 or 3,000 rounds per minute in bursts of ten, 30, 60, or 100 rounds. When borne by an armored personnel carrier, the system carries 500 rounds of ammunition ready to use; when trailer-mounted, the system carries 1,100 rounds. When on an armored personnel carrier, the Vulcan's turret can be traversed and the guns elevated by power switches.

A Product-Improved Vulcan Air-Defense System (PIVADS) is currently being fielded. A new fire control system is being retrofitted to the existing M163 and M167 gun systems. This new fire control system can deal with the new, faster aircraft deployed by the Soviet bloc. A new sight replaces the previous M62. A new solid state computer replaces the present analog computer to conduct ballistic computations and conduct tests of the entire system. A new drive system is being installed that will improve the gun's tracking ability.

The Vulcan Air-Defense System is usually deployed with the Chaparral antiaircraft missile system at battalion level in two batteries of 12 Chaparral launchers and 12 VADS each. In the absence of any other rapid-fire, mobile antiaircraft system, the Vulcan will remain in service through the 1990s.

VULCAN AIR-DEFENSE SYSTEM
(M167 Towed Version)

Length:	16 ft.
Width:	6 ft., 5 in.
Height:	6 ft., 7 in.
Weight:	3,500 lbs.
Range:	1,750 yards
Date of service:	1968

Opposite, top: *The Vulcan antiaircraft gun system's radar measures range only.* Opposite, bottom: *The Vulcan gunner must aim the cannon with optical sights once the enemy aircraft is within range.* Above: *The Vulcan's 20mm Gatling Gun is a modification of the one used in helicopters and other aircraft.* Left: *The Vulcan fires at a rate of either 1,000 or 3,000 rounds per minute, depending on the gunner's selection.* Below: *The towed Vulcan carries 500 rounds of ammunition.*

The M167 Vulcan antiaircraft gun carries 1,100 rounds of ammunition.

M48A1 Chaparral Low-Altitude Self-propelled Surface-to-Air Missile System

The Chaparral is a low-altitude air-defense system developed to protect troops on the front line of battle from enemy aircraft. The missile itself is a refinement of the Sidewinder air-to-air missile.

The Chaparral system was first delivered to the U.S. Army in 1969. The M48A1 system is presently deployed with the Army in composite battalions with the Vulcan self-propelled antiaircraft gun. Each battalion has 24 Chaparral systems and 24 Vulcans, divided into two batteries of 12 missile systems and guns each. More than 700 Chaparral systems have been built for the U.S. Army.

Chaparral is a mobile, heat-seeking missile effective against high-performance aircraft flying at low altitudes to attack troops. The system is normally mounted on a vehicle, with four missiles carried on a railed launcher. Eight more missiles are contained in special storage compartments in the vehicle. The Chaparral is usually mounted on the M730 tracked carrier, an offshoot of the M113 Armored Personnel Carrier. The launch control station consists of a collapsible crew cab and missile-launching turret. In 1989, the Army completed an upgrade program for this vehicle, giving it a stronger and more reliable powertrain.

The missile itself is a slender tube, five inches in diameter and 9.5 feet long, with four fixed wings and movable control surfaces aft. To reduce the battlefield infrared signature of the entire system, the missile is equipped with smokeless rocket motors. The Chaparral missile is a fire-and-forget system. Once launched, the missile is on its own, continuing to track and guide itself toward the enemy aircraft using its on-board infrared heat-seeking sensors. This "smart" feature allows the gunner to begin looking for other hostile aircraft as soon as the missile is away.

The missile's M250 warhead contains a proximity fuse. At a specified (and classified) distance, the warhead explodes. A high explosive turns the missile warhead and the explosives case into shrapnel. The MIM-74E and MIM-74F missiles are effective at altitudes from 164 feet to 19,685 feet and ranges up to 3.78 miles.

The Chaparral system has been upgraded by its designer and manufacturer, Ford Aerospace, with a new Rosette Scan Seeker (RSS) that replaces all previously used infrared systems. The RSS can be reprogrammed to cope with infrared countermeasures and differing infrared heat signatures that might be encountered on the battlefield. This also extends the missile's effective range.

Above: *The Chaparral antiaircraft guided missile was designed for low-altitude air interdiction.*

Above: *The Chaparral launcher is carried on the M730 tracked vehicle.* Left: *The launch unit of the Chaparral holds four missiles on a manually tracked launcher.* Below: *The Chaparral's warhead uses an infrared sensor in its nose to guide the rocket to its target.*

M48A1 CHAPARRAL LOW-ALTITUDE SELF-PROPELLED SURFACE-TO-AIR MISSILE SYSTEM

Vehicle:	M730A2
Length:	19 ft., 11 in.
Width:	8 ft., 9.5 in.
Weight:	28,712.5 lbs.
Engine:	Detroit Diesel 6V-53, 202 hp
Speed:	38 mph
Range:	313 miles
Armament:	Twelve Chaparral AA missiles
Length:	9 ft., 6 in.
Diameter:	5 in.
Weight:	185 lbs.
Altitude:	19,685 ft.
Speed:	Mach 2.5
Range:	3.78 miles
Date of service:	1969

FIM-92A Stinger

Air defense in the battle zone against high- and low-performance aircraft has become a high military priority. Attack aircraft are now equipped with "smart" bombs, cluster munitions, fuel-air munitions, high-capacity machine guns, and guided and free-flight rockets. All this weaponry is intended to destroy or disrupt troop and vehicle movements, airfields, junctions, communications centers, and troop concentrations. Even entrenched infantry platoons can come under attack by specially equipped attack aircraft.

The FIM-92A Stinger provides infantry soldiers with a weapon to protect vital installations as well as their own formations. The Stinger system weighs less than 35 pounds and can be carried anywhere a soldier can take a rifle. The Stinger missile is five and a half feet long. It is launched from a lightweight, reusable, pistol-gripped launcher that contains the Identification, Friend or Foe (IFF) system antenna and the necessary electronics to control launching. The Stinger tracks an enemy aircraft via an infrared sensor in the missile's nose. The aircraft can be in any position relative to the soldier—approaching, departing, or parallel. The missile's sensor can detect the heat of the aircraft's exhaust plume and track it to the source.

Above: *The FIM-92A Stinger portable antiaircraft missile was designed in the mid-1960s as a replacement for the Redeye.*

The operator inserts the missile—carried in its individual transportation/launcher tube—into the launch unit, arms it, and clips the IFF unit to a belt. The IFF's electrical cord is attached to the launcher unit. When an enemy aircraft appears, the operator lifts the launcher unit and sights the target through an open, or iron, sight system, which resembles a three-sided box. The soldier activates the missile's infrared sensor while pointing the launcher at the target. When the sensor has detected and locked onto the enemy aircraft's engine exhaust, a steady high-pitched tone is emitted. The IFF system is then used to interrogate the enemy aircraft. If the response is incorrect, the soldier pulls the trigger.

The missile blasts from the launch tube and its solid-fuel rocket motor quickly pushes it to Mach 2. Eight control surfaces, four at the nose and four at the tail, "pop up" from the missile's fuselage. The infrared seeker in the missile's nose continues to home in on the target's exhaust plume, providing flight path steering corrections to the missile's guidance command system. The Stinger missile is fitted with a hit-to-kill warhead that detonates 6.6 pounds of high explosive to destroy the enemy aircraft.

The Stinger has proved so successful that several variants are currently under development. One is the Stinger Passive Optical Seeker Technique (POST), which increases infrared countermeasures capability. Soviet and Afghan government pilots discovered that ejecting flares would often decoy Stinger missiles. The Stinger is also being developed to arm helicopters and land vehicles, such as the M2/3 Bradley and the High Mobility, Multipurpose Wheeled Vehicle (HMMWV).

Left, top: *The Stinger's operator acquires the enemy aircraft in the sight and waits for the infrared sensor in the missile's nose to lock on.* Left, center: *The infrared sensor sends guidance commands to the missile's steering surfaces, steering the missile to the target.* Left, bottom: *The Stinger carries a fragmenting-case warhead that destroys with high explosive and shrapnel.* Above: *The wire running from the sight unit to the back of the launcher tube connects the power pack to the rocket's igniter and infrared sensor.*

FIM-92A STINGER

Length:	5 ft., 6 in.
Diameter:	2.76 in.
Weight:	34.76 lbs.
Speed:	Mach 2
Range:	3.12 miles
Altitude:	15,750 ft.
Date of service:	1981

The Stinger has a range of more than three miles and travels at Mach 2.

MIM-104 Patriot Tactical Air-Defense Missile System

The MIM-104 Patriot grew out of a 1964 U.S. Army requirement for a new missile system that could defend against medium- to high-altitude high-performance aircraft and ballistic missiles. This new missile system was intended to replace the Nike Hercules and the Hawk missile systems. The Patriot's single command and control system was envisioned as a replacement for the nine separate command and control systems used in the Nike Hercules and Hawk systems. And it was intended to function in the high-intensity battlefield expected in the 1980s.

The Patriot missile system is a 17.4-foot-long rocket powered by a Thiokol TX-486 solid-fuel motor that propels the missile at Mach 3. Equipped with a high-explosive warhead detonated by a proximity fuse, the Patriot destroys its target with shrapnel. The Patriot can also be fitted with a nuclear device if so desired.

The missile is carried in a storage/transportation container that also serves as the launcher. Four Patriot missiles in their containers are mounted on a wheeled launcher unit that is towed by the M818 six-wheel tractor. The engagement control station is mounted on the M818 and contains all the necessary command and control equipment. Another trailer, parked a short distance away, houses subsidiary ground control radar.

The Track Via Missile (TVM) guidance system, which caused extensive development delays and cost overruns, is the heart of the Patriot system and accounts for its great accuracy. The missile control operator acquires a target and verifies it as hostile on a multifunction phased-array radar that can track more than 100 targets at the same time.

Above: *The MIM-104 Patriot was originally designed to be a successor to Hawk, but its long development period and high cost reduced the number of units acquired.*

After launch, the missile and the target are tracked on a "time-sharing" basis, which means that the radar switches back and forth between the two in milliseconds and sends steering commands to the missile's guidance system. During the last ten seconds of flight, the main radar holds steady on the target, illuminating it with a radar beam. The reflected radar beam is detected by an antenna in the nose of the approaching missile. The missile then relays the beam to the ground; the beam is analyzed by the engagement control computer that then sends revised steering commands to the missile. As the missile approaches its target, the course corrections it receives via this process become very refined, steering the missile with unerring accuracy.

The Patriot missile system is so versatile that it can track and steer eight missiles to different targets at the same time, with any three in the TVM stage of flight. Since signal processing does not take place in the missile itself, the system is difficult to jam effectively. A single computer performs all functions—search, acquisition, tracking, and guidance—and switches between these functions ten times a second.

The Patriot was approved for development in 1965 but did not enter service until 1984. Eight battalions of Patriot systems are now fully deployed, and the Army plans to purchase some 6,200 missiles.

MIM-104 PATRIOT TACTICAL AIR-DEFENSE MISSILE SYSTEM

Length:	17 ft., 5 in.
Diameter:	1 ft., 4 in.
Weight:	2,200 lbs.
Range:	42.5 miles
Altitude:	79,000 ft.
Speed:	Mach 3
Date of service:	1984

Top: *The Patriot is launched directly from its storage/shipping container. Each container holds four missiles.* Bottom, left: *The Patriot's phased-array radar system searches the area, acquires the target, tracks it, and guides the missile to it.* Bottom, right: *The combination of phased-array radar and a powerful Thiokol TX-486 single-thrust motor gives the Patriot a range of 42 miles at a speed of Mach 3.*

Roland Air-Defense Missile System

The Roland air-defense system, designed and manufactured by France's Aerospatiale and West Germany's Messerschmitt-Bolkow-Blohm defense companies, is a low-altitude guided-missile air-defense system that can knock out high-performance enemy aircraft. It can protect moving columns of troops and armored units as well as stationary targets such as airfields and depots. The U.S. Army purchased the all-weather Roland 2 system in 1975.

The U.S. Roland air-defense system is mounted on the bed of a five-ton, cross-country, 6 x 6 truck. It can also be mounted in a permanent ground emplacement as a static airfield defense system. Roland carries two missiles on its turreted, railed, two-arm launcher, with eight more held in reserve. Reserve missiles are loaded automatically from two rotating-drum magazines in less than ten seconds. The crew of four comprises the commander, gunner, assistant gunner, and driver, but all systems can be operated by only two crew members if necessary.

The Roland 2 incorporates a pulse-doppler search radar with a range of ten miles, an optical sight, and an infrared sensor. The commander watches the search radar for a target, then designates the target. The launcher automatically positions itself to the proper heading, and then tracking radar measures elevation and locks onto the target. The missile launches automatically; within the first 1,300 feet, the infrared sensor in the missile's nose and the radar in the launcher begin to guide the missile toward the target.

The Roland missile uses two solid-propellant motors. The first, or booster, stage produces 3,250 pounds of thrust for 1.7 seconds. The second, or sustainer, stage burns for 13.2 seconds and produces 400 pounds of thrust, propelling the missile at a velocity of 1,640 feet per second (Mach 1.5). The missile spins during flight and is steered by a deflector in the exhaust, which is controlled by signals transmitted from the launcher.

Reaction time from target detection to missile launch is approximately six to eight seconds. A second round can be fired at the same target within two seconds. The Roland is not a fire-and-forget system but rather concentrates on one enemy aircraft threat at a time. Roland uses a proximity fuse that detonates a warhead to destroy the target with shrapnel. The probability of a single shot striking the target is 60 percent or higher.

Originally, the U.S. version of the Roland was intended to be the major low-altitude air-defense system for the U.S. military. Successive cutbacks, however, reduced total purchases to only 27 systems. The Roland 2 was deployed in 1985 with the New Mexico Army National Guard, which is part of the Rapid Deployment Force assigned to the Army's Central Command.

Above: *The Roland antiaircraft guided missile is a French-German development.*

Above: *The Roland missile has a range of 3.9 miles and is effective at altitudes between 16,400 and 66,000 feet.* Right: *The Roland system is mounted on the same chassis that is used for the M113 Armored Personnel Carrier.*

ROLAND AIR-DEFENSE MISSILE SYSTEM	
Vehicle:	M939 5-ton 6 × 6 truck
Launch unit:	
Length:	22 ft., 8 in.
Width:	10 ft., 6 in.
Height:	9 ft., 7 in.
Missile:	
Length:	7 ft., 10 in.
Diameter:	6.3 in.
Weight:	139 lbs.
Speed:	Mach 1.5
Range:	3.9 miles
Altitude:	66,000 ft.
Date of service:	1985

LAND-BASED INTERCONTINENTAL BALLISTIC MISSILES

Before and during World War II, the development of large rocket engines was almost completely ignored by the military services of the United States and Great Britain. But in Germany, development of rockets large enough to carry explosive warheads several hundred miles began in 1934 under the direction of Colonel Walter Dornberger. While still a university student, Wernher von Braun, who would later contribute so much to the American defense and space programs, was hired to work on the development of rocket engines at the artillery testing grounds near Berlin and later on Peenemude Island in the Baltic.

The V-2 rocket (V for vengeance) and the V-1 pulse-jet powered cruise missile were used by Germany to bombard London and other military and civilian targets in England shortly after the Normandy Invasion in 1944. During their short operational life, both missiles subjected the British people, especially in London and the surrounding areas, to a bombardment that was, in some ways, more intense than the Blitz. Only a concentrated effort to destroy the production facilities for, and launching sites of, both missiles mitigated the threat by January 1945.

The success of the V-1 and V-2 missiles convinced American, British, and Soviet military planners that national security lay in nuclear-tipped missiles with intercontinental range that threatened the enemy with complete destruction should the enemy attack. In the West, the concept is referred to as Mutual Assured Destruction (MAD). Work on missiles began immediately after World War II, using captured German stocks of missiles and many of their rocket scientists.

The first American missile with intercontinental range was the SM-62A Snark cruise missile, deployed for the first time in 1957. Snark was to be followed by the SM-64 Navajo and the MX-774, but both were canceled. Resources were devoted to rocket-propelled ballistic missiles, which were far less vulnerable to countermeasures.

The first intercontinental ballistic missile (ICBM) in American service was the liquid-fueled Atlas, a descendent of Wernher von Braun's V-2. The Atlas—spurred on by the Soviet development of the hydrogen bomb some years earlier and the Soviet's ambitious and continuing development program of ICBMs—was first deployed in 1959. The Atlas was a complicated and expensive missile but, with the related Titan I missile, provided the United States with an effective deterrent force against nuclear aggression.

Liquid-fueled missiles were difficult to launch because of their complexity. And liquid-fueled missiles were even more difficult to store for the long periods of time envisioned for a weapon that would be used only as a last resort. The solution to these problems was a solid-fuel missile in which the oxidizer and fuel were mixed together into a solid—actually a gel or rubbery type of compound. When ignited, the compound burns fiercely and quickly to provide the propulsive gases for the missile.

The Minuteman (always ready) was the first of the third-generation ICBMs to be deployed. Like the Titan missile, the Minuteman was secured in silos—specially constructed launch tubes buried in the ground and protected by immense steel and concrete blast doors. The missile silos were connected electronically to control centers that were also deeply buried.

The Minuteman III and the Peacekeeper are the two currently deployed land-based ICBMS. They form a key component of America's nuclear defense triad.

Opposite: *The Peacekeeper ICBM can carry up to ten warheads, here being attached to the reentry vehicle; each warhead can be individually targeted.* Right: *These Minuteman III ICBMs are being test-fired from Vandenberg Air Force Base in California to a test range in the central Pacific Ocean.*

Above, left: *A Minuteman III, a four-stage, solid-fuel rocket, being assembled.* Above, right: *Minuteman III ICBMs are launched from underground silos.* Left: *The Peacekeeper is housed in specially hardened underground silos.*

Minuteman III (LGM-30) Intercontinental Ballistic Missile

Above: *These two Minuteman III ICBMs will reach their targets, 5,000 miles away, in less than 15 minutes.*

The Minuteman intercontinental ballistic missile (ICBM) was the first solid-fueled, nuclear-tipped missile to enter U.S. service. Its purpose was to carry a nuclear warhead to targets in the Soviet Union, or any other nation, should the United States be attacked. In this respect, the Minuteman, like all American and Soviet ICBMs, is a deterrent to a surprise attack. The Minuteman III evolved from the original Minuteman I and its successor, the Minuteman II; it can carry three individual warheads a distance of 6,800 miles.

The Minuteman III is a four-stage rocket built by Boeing Aerospace Company. The first stage is powered by a Thiokol TU-120 rocket motor that produces 200,000 pounds of thrust. The second-stage rocket motor is an Aerojet SR19-AJ-1 rocket engine producing 60,000 pounds of thrust. Both these stages burn for 60 seconds. The third stage uses an Aerojet/Thiokol SR37-MJ-1 rocket motor that delivers 34,000 pounds of thrust for 59.6 seconds. The fourth stage, which distinguishes the Minuteman III from its predecessors, is built by Bell Aerospace and is referred to as the Post Boost Control System (PBCS).

The Minuteman III's current warhead is the W-78, which yields an equivalent of 331 kilotons of TNT. Three W-78s are carried in the General Electric Mark 12A reentry vehicle, which sits atop each Minuteman III along with various and classified penetration aids, electronic jamming devices, chaff to confuse radar, and decoy missile reentry vehicles. The decoy reentry vehicles so closely resemble the actual reentry vehicle that they can fool optical, radar, and infrared detection devices. Thus, an enemy antimissile defense system must deal with 12 or more reentry vehicles, all diverging to different targets, rather than just three.

The Minuteman was originally designed to be transported from place to place on specially built railroad flatcars that would also serve as launching platforms. The idea was to make enemy targeting of missile launch sites as complicated as possible to prevent their destruction in an all-out first strike. But Congress objected to the cost of such a system, and the Minuteman missiles were deployed in fixed silos.

The Minuteman silo is buried more than 80 feet deep. It is heavily constructed of concrete and steel and capped with massive retractable steel covers to withstand near misses or air bursts from enemy ICBMs. To further reduce the chance of all missiles being knocked out of

MINUTEMAN III (LGM-30) INTERCONTINENTAL BALLISTIC MISSILE	
Length:	59 ft., 8 in.
Diameter:	6 ft., 2 in.
Weight:	76,000 lbs.
Armament:	Mk 12A reentry vehicle with 3 W-78 331 kt nuclear warheads
Number of stages:	4
Range:	6,800 miles
Date of service:	
Minuteman I:	1963
Minuteman II:	1966
Minuteman III:	1971

action, the silos are spaced at least 4.5 miles apart, and the control facilities are located in a separate underground bunker 11.5 miles away. Minuteman III missiles are deployed in six wings. Each wing contains three or four squadrons, and each squadron has 50 missiles. Each squadron is divided into five flights; each flight controls ten silos. Missile silos are unmanned; the control facility for each flight is crewed 24 hours a day by two officers. The officers must individually and simultaneously verify the launch code and then turn separate keys in their individual launch consoles before a missile can be launched. And then only if the President has initiated the command sequence.

If the wing launch control facility is knocked out of action, the Minuteman missiles can also be launched, and even retargeted, by a control officer in an airborne command post known as the Emergency Airborne Command Post. The missiles can also be launched and retargeted via the National Emergency Airborne Command Post, which is contained in an E-4B aircraft.

Production of the Minuteman III ended in 1977. Currently, the Minuteman III is deployed as the first line ICBM in the U.S. arsenal.

Bottom, left: *The LGM-30 Minuteman III has a range of over 6,000 miles.* Right, top: *The entrance to a Minuteman III ICBM silo.* Right, bottom: *Originally, the Minuteman III was to be mounted on a train that would move from point to point at random to confuse enemy attempts to target the missile, but cost considerations dictated that the Minuteman III be housed in underground silos.*

Peacekeeper (LGM-118) Intercontinental Ballistic Missile

Above: *The rectangular tiles around the Peacekeeper's fuselage are sabots that form a smooth, tight fit with the silo walls. The tiles fall way after launch.*

The Peacekeeper intercontinental ballistic missile (ICBM) has had a long and checkered developmental history. Like the Minuteman, it was not intended to be based in silos. The Peacekeeper began life as a road-deployable system intended to complicate enemy targeting programs.

The basing system was to be a series of long, deep trenches along which the missiles would be moved at random. The missiles were to be encased in special containers that would also serve as launchers when jacks aboard the railroad cars lifted segments of the trench roof.

But as with the Minuteman, congressional sentiment turned against such a mobile system because of cost, and other alternatives were sought. A mobile Peacemaker was also perceived by many as a "first strike" system and therefore provocative to the Soviets. The missile, built by Martin-Marietta Denver Aerospace Company was finally deployed in former Minutemen silos in 1986. A total of 100 Peacekeeper missiles will be installed before the project is completed in the mid-1990s. Currently, nearly 60 of the authorized 100 have been built and installed in missile silos. Because of the delays—mostly political—the Peacekeeper has proved to be the most expensive ICBM built to date.

The Peacekeeper serves as the heavyweight counterpart to the Minuteman III. The Peacekeeper was designed and built to counter the threat of the Soviet Union's SS-18 and SS-19 heavy ICBMs, and to replace the aging and less capable Titan II liquid-fueled missiles. The Strategic Arms Reduction Talks (START) agreement places a limit of 4,900 nuclear warheads that may be used on deployed strategic delivery systems, covering both land-based and submarine-launched ICBMs. The Peacekeeper carries ten W-78 warheads; so for every Peacekeeper installed, ten Titan IIs or Minuteman IIs must be withdrawn.

The Peacekeeper is a three-stage missile. The first two stages are solid-fueled; the first motor is built by Thiokol and the second by Aerojet-General. The Thiokol motor can be angled through 15 degrees for precise control after launching. The third stage is built by Hercules and contains the same high-energy propellant used in the Navy's Trident submarine-launched missile. Both the second and third stages have extendable nozzles that reduce the length of the rocket before firing.

The Peacekeeper missile is contained in a launch canister installed in the silo. The missile is ejected from the canister by pressurized gas—a procedure known as a cold launch. The first-stage rocket motor ignites when the missile is between 50 and 100 feet in the air.

The Peacekeeper uses a unique guidance system based

PEACEKEEPER (LGM-118) INTERCONTINENTAL BALLISTIC MISSILE	
Length:	70 ft., 8 in.
Diameter:	7 ft., 6 in.
Weight:	195,015 lbs.
Armament:	Mk 21 reentry vehicle with 10 W-78 331 kt warheads
Range:	6,800 miles
Number of stages:	3
Date of service:	1986

on the Advanced Inertial Reference System (AIRS) designed by Draper Laboratories and built by Northrop. The in-flight computer can perform 200,000 operations per second. The computer monitors missile status, aligns the inertial platform, monitors the missile's progress toward the target, and sends adjustment signals to the guidance system. The guidance system is so accurate that the missile's warheads can be expected to fall within 175 feet of their targets.

The Peacekeeper carries ten warheads in the Mark 21 reentry vehicle. Each warhead yields the equivalent of 331 kilotons of TNT, and each warhead can be independently targeted. There is sufficient space in the reentry vehicle to carry as many as two additional warheads. The reentry vehicle also carries a range of penetration aids, electronic and other sensor jammers, and inflatable warhead decoys to confuse enemy antimissile defense systems.

Top: *Each Peacekeeper warhead holds a 331-kiloton-yield nuclear weapon.* Bottom, left and right: *A Peacekeeper ICBM is loaded into an above-ground silo during developmental testing. This same missile was successfully launched as part of the testing.*

CHEMICAL WARFARE

Chemical warfare made its debut in World War I, when both sides released terrible clouds of poisonous hydrogen cyanide and chlorine gas. Because of the primitive state of the art in protective gas masks and clothing, casualties were appalling.

By unspoken agreement, neither the Allied nor Axis powers used chemical weapons during World War II, although both sides stockpiled huge tonnages of bombs and artillery shells filled with deadly chemical gases.

Until recently, much of the chemical weaponry in U.S. inventory was World War II-vintage in design, if not in actual production. All branches of the United States military have developed extensive protective clothing and techniques to guard troops from the effects of all kinds of chemical weapons from nerve to tear gases. At the same time, as a deterrent to enemy use of chemical weaponry against the United States or its allies and friends, the United States has developed new chemical gases and delivery vehicles that are safer to store and transport, but more lethal to an enemy. But the United States and the Soviet Union stand on the threshold of an historic treaty that would ban not only the use but also the manufacture and stockpiling of chemical weapons.

Above: *An estimated 15 nations now stockpile chemical weapons. At least eight nations have used them within the past two decades.*

Chemical Warfare Capability

The United States Army's recent chemical warfare program has been directed toward upgrading its chemical warfare and chemical warfare protection capabilities to meet the massive buildup of Soviet chemical arsenals in the past 15 years. Three weapons are involved: the XM687E1 155mm binary chemical artillery shell, loaded with the nonpersistent agent GB2; the BIGEYE bomb, which contains the persistent agent VX2; and the XM-135 specialized warhead for the Multiple Launch Rocket System

Left: *In the U.S. military, protective chemical clothing is standard issue and chemical warfare defensive training is routine.*

(MLRS), which can carry either compound.

The 155mm chemical artillery shell would be the Army's first response to an enemy attack. The shell forces enemy frontline troops into protective gear and degrades their combat capability. The XM-135 warhead is carried by MLRS rockets, which have a range up to 18 miles. They are fired against enemy reinforcements moving into the battle area and against nearby logistical and communication/control targets. The BIGEYE aerial bomb is delivered by tactical aircraft against rear-area troops, airfields, and larger logistical and communication/control complexes.

All three types of chemical weapons employ a new binary technology. The toxic compound is not formed until two components, which are stored in separate containers, are mixed while the weapon is in flight. The two components of the compound GB (Sarin) are liquid isopropanol and methylphosphonyldifluoride, or difluor. The two compounds used to produce VX (Soman) are dimethylpolysulfide and ethyl 2-[diisopropylamino]ethyl-methylphosphonite. The formulas of these and other toxic compounds can be modified to produce persistent (long-lasting) and nonpersistent compounds. For example, GB2, which is methylphosphonyl-difluoride in an isopropanol solution, is nonpersistent because it evaporates within a matter of hours.

Chemical warfare involves more than just weaponry; *protection* against enemy chemical weapons is paramount. Protection from nerve and chemical agents ranging from CN to mustard gas requires airtight protective clothing. An efficient gas mask that filters air through canisters of chemicals that deactivate the chemical agent being used is also needed. The clothing and mask are hot, sweaty, and claustrophobic. The wearer finds it difficult to manipulate equipment and weapons—harder still to walk or run. Exertion produces considerable body heat and increased discomfort inside the protective clothing. Visibility is hampered by gas masks that steam up and hearing is reduced. It is estimated that chemical-protective clothing reduces combat efficiency by 30 to 50 percent.

A treaty between the United States and the Soviet Union to end the production and stockpiling of chemical weapons is imminent. If such a treaty is signed, not only will all American and Soviet stockpiles of toxic chemical agents be destroyed but both countries will exert overwhelming pressure on all other nations to follow suit.

Above: *In future wars, U.S. military personnel—such as these infantry troops preparing to board a C-130 transport—may still have to know how to cope with chemical warfare weaponry.*

U.S. CHEMICAL WARFARE AGENTS

(Compiled from open sources; may not be exhaustive)

AGENT	COMMON NAME/ ACTION	DELIVERY METHOD
Toxic Nerve Agents:		
Tabun	GA—Cholinesterase inhibitor	A/R/AB
Sarin	GB—Cholinesterase inhibitor	A/R/AB
Soman	GD—Cholinesterase inhibitor	A/R/AB
—	GP—Unknown composition; action thought to cause cholinesterase inhibition	A/R/AB
Thickened Soman	VX—Cholinesterase inhibitor	A/R/AB
BUZZ	BZ—Hallucinogenic LSD derivative	
Blue X	Unknown composition: incapacitating; variously estimated for 1 to 2 and 8 to 12 hours	
Tear Gases:		
Brombenzyl-cyanide	CA—Eye discomfort and tears; long acting	
Chloraceto-phenone	CN—Smarting and tearing of eyes; short acting	
Chloraceto-phenone in Chlorpicrin	CS—Eye discomfort, tears; choking	
	(The following agents have been developed and used in the past; many remain in inventory.)	
Blister Agents:		
Ethyldichlorarsine	ED—Blister agent	
Lewisite	L—Irritation of nasal passages, with skin and membrane burns; poisonous	
Mustard	H, HD, HN, HS—Inflammation of skin and membranes; blindness	
Phosgene Oxime	CX—Destruction of skin and membrane tissue	
Blood Agents:		
Arsine	SA—Gasping; choking, asphyxiation	
Cyangen Chloride	AC—Convulsions, asphyxiation	
Hydrogen Cyanide	CK—Convulsions, gasping, choking, asphyxiation	
Choking Agents:		
Chlorpicrin	PS—Severe coughing, lung edema, choking, asphyxiation	
Chlorine	CL—Severe coughing, choking, skin and membrane burns, asphyxiation	
Phosgene	CG—Severe coughing, choking, asphyxiation	
Nausea Gases:		
Adamsite	DM—Sneezing, nausea; depression	
Diphenyl-chlorasine	DA—Sneezing, nausea; depression	

Key: A = Artillery R = Rocket AB = Aerial bomb

Right: *This soldier—wearing a gas mask but no protective clothing or gloves—is prepared for non-lethal chemical warfare only.*

U.S. SEA POWER

U.S. sea power takes many forms, such as these amphibious assault ships and combat stores ships.

U.S. SEA POWER

Above: *The USS* Iowa *battleship fires its powerful 16-inch guns.*

THE IMPORTANCE OF SEA POWER

Sea power defines the strong nations of the world, regulates and permits trade, and defends national borders in a way that no army can. No landlocked nation has ever risen to be a major world power or sustained itself for long in a major war without control of the seas.

Even into the 20th century, sea power remained the ultimate determiner of the outcome of war. Kaiser Wilhelm paid lip service to the goal of German sea power, but his government was never willing to commit Germany's full resources to building a navy powerful enough to challenge Great Britain's Royal Navy successfully in World War I. Adolf Hitler also failed to realize, when he forged his Nazi military machine, that sea power was needed to protect it.

During World War II, sea and air power worked together in close cooperation. The role of the battleship and its guns was taken by the carrier-borne aircraft, which extended the naval task force's striking power from 20 miles to 300 miles and more. Although both the United States and Japan understood this concept in 1941, only the United States possessed the resources needed to sustain a powerful navy through the end of the war.

The end of World War II left the United States as the most powerful force in the Pacific region. With American trade and interest growing in the Pacific Rim nations, the only way to secure peace in the Pacific was to maintain a powerful naval presence. At the same time, the deepening Cold War had placed recovering Europe at risk. To contain Soviet expansionism, which had already swallowed up Eastern Europe, the North Atlantic Treaty Organization (NATO) alliance was established as a united front. The main cornerstone of NATO was the promise of the United States to sustain its West European partners in case of Soviet attack. A strong American military presence was established in Europe, and it was maintained and replenished by an equally strong naval presence in the Mediterranean Sea and the North Atlantic.

Just as before 1941, when many fleet sailors considered bombing aircraft more a nuisance than a danger, before the 1982 Falkland Islands War, the idea that surface ships might be vulnerable to modern guided missiles, aircraft, and submarines was not seriously considered. That brief and bloody engagement in the remote South Atlantic left that vulnerability no longer in doubt, and every major navy in the world is taking steps to reduce it. Air-defense systems have received the highest priority. Ships have been reconstructed to replace fragile and flammable aluminum structural members in vulnerable areas with steel. New self-defense weapons and tactics are assiduously being developed.

In the last decades of the 20th century, sea power has assumed far more responsibility for deterring not only strategic war but lower levels of conflict as well. Since 1945, the United States has been engaged in nine major military actions, and American naval power has played a pivotal role in all. Sea power offers the most efficient means for the United States to keep outlaw nations in check. The presence of the Sixth Fleet off the Libyan coast in the Mediterranean Sea has restricted Libyan adventurism through the 1980s. A multinational task force of surface warships—largely American—was deployed to the Persian Gulf in 1986 to protect private vessels sailing those waters from Iraqi and Iranian attack. That task force, in combination with United Nations diplomacy, was instrumental in bringing an end to the shooting between Iran and Iraq.

ORGANIZATION OF U.S. SEA POWER IN THE 1990s

The U.S. Navy is headed by a Naval Chief of Staff, who sits on the Joint Chiefs of Staff and serves as the naval adviser to the President of the United States. The Naval Chief of Staff has authority and responsibility only for planning and operational training of the Navy. Operational command is vested in the commanders-in-chief of the three major American naval fleets.

The United States possesses a three-ocean naval fleet, which operates within the three U.S. military Unified Commands. The naval component of the Atlantic Command is the Atlantic, or Second, fleet, which is headquartered at Norfolk, Virginia. The Second Fleet is responsible for supporting NATO and, in case of war, for carrying out NATO strike attacks against the Soviet Union and Warsaw Pact navies. It is also responsible for all naval operations in the Caribbean and the Central American Atlantic coastal areas, and for the maritime security of the United States in these areas.

The European Command's naval component is Naval Forces Europe, which is the Sixth Fleet. The Sixth Fleet is responsible for the American

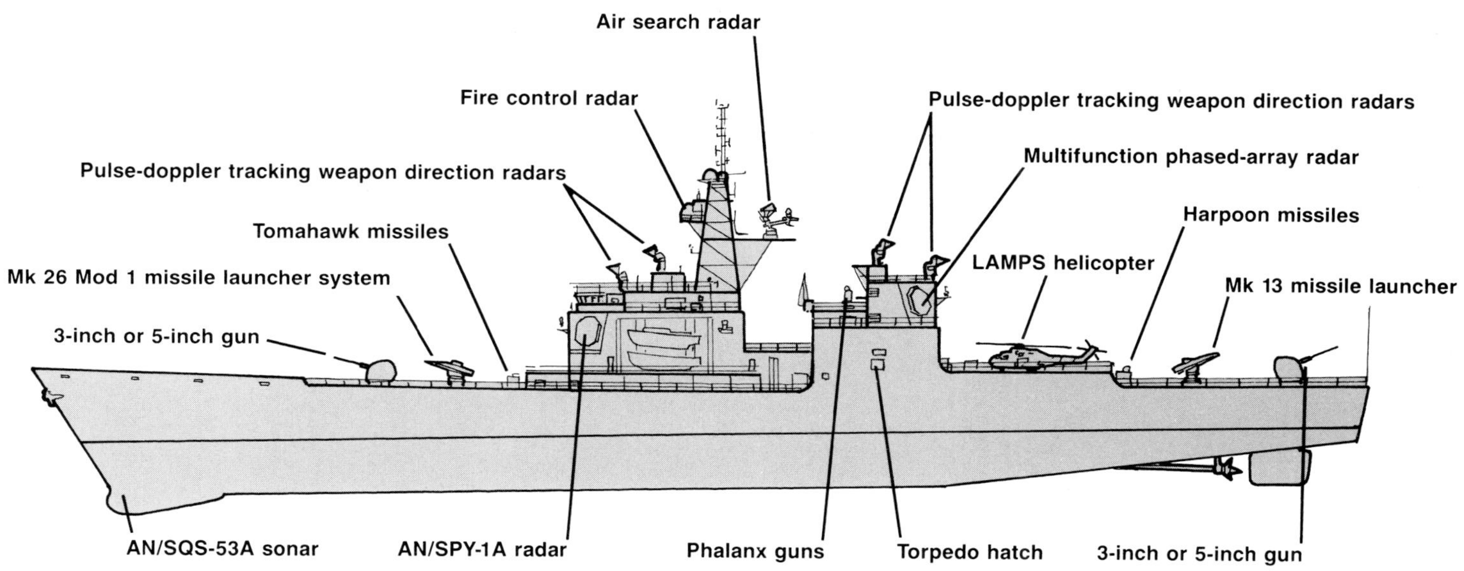

Above: *An illustration of a modern navel ship showing elements common to most of today's ships.* Left: *An artist's rendering of an* Ohio-*class submarine; nuclear-powered submarines form an integral part of U.S. sea power.*

phases of the security of southern Europe and the Mediterranean Sea area as part of the NATO Striking and Support Force. Vessels and personnel rotate routinely between the Sixth and Second fleets.

The naval component of the Pacific Command is the Pacific fleet, which includes the Third and Seventh fleets. The Third Fleet operates in the eastern Pacific. Recently it has placed a heavier emphasis on north Pacific maneuvers since Soviet naval activity has increased in that region. The Third Fleet also provides the ships that deploy to the Seventh Fleet in the western Pacific. The Seventh Fleet's area of responsibility includes the northwestern Pacific from the Kamchatka Peninsula at the Bering Sea to the South China Sea around into the Indian Ocean and up into the Persian Gulf. Since 1979, at least one aircraft carrier and task force has been kept on station in the Indian Ocean. To do so, carriers have sometimes had to be moved into the Indian Ocean from the Atlantic fleet.

It should be noted that the specification chart at the end of the discussion of each ship class is representative only. Actual ships within the class may vary from this representative norm.

THE NAVAL CHALLENGE IN THE 1990s

The four major naval fleets in the world today in terms of numbers, capability, and firepower are those of the United States, France, Great Britain, and the Soviet Union. All four are equipped with nuclear weapons, all four possess aircraft carriers, and all four deploy nuclear submarines carrying ballistic missiles.

Left: *America protects its interests worldwide through the deployment of powerful aircraft carrier task forces.* Right: *The* Oliver Hazard Perry-*class frigate USS* Doyle *steams through the waves.*

At the end of World War II, the Soviet Navy was primarily a coastal defense force operating with a few heavily gunned cruisers, short-range coastal submarines, and various surface warships. None of them was capable of extended ocean voyages or of being organized into major ocean-going task forces. The Soviet Navy had restricted itself to a coastal force for historical and geographic reasons. Despite its extensive coastlines, the Soviet Union is considered to be a landlocked nation because of its lack of accessible warm-weather ports.

The Soviet leadership understood that to successfully project its influence and military power outside the European and Asian landmasses, they must possess a strong, oceangoing navy. The first of four Soviet aircraft carriers was launched in the 1980s. New classes of cruisers, destroyers, and frigates—all with deep-ocean capability—have been deployed farther and farther afield in stronger and stronger task forces. Soviet nuclear submarines have become nearly the equal of American nuclear submarines in fire and stealth. And they have surpassed American submarines in numbers.

Since the mid-1970s, 12 major new classes of surface and submarine warships have been constructed in the Soviet Union, all suitable for extended seagoing operations. In all, the Soviet Union has some 70 ship classes in service, all developed since the 1950s.

A spirit of accommodation is emanating from the Soviet Union. The new generation of pragmatic technocrats that has assumed leadership recognizes that the Soviet Union can no longer compete with the West in defense expenditures and at the same time improve living conditions for its citizens. In 1985, the political leadership of the Soviet Union began to take steps to reduce their military establishment. However, the Soviet government has not reduced its naval establishment. Further, there has been no indication that it will do so. Soviet naval construction programs continue to roll along at the accelerated pace established in the early 1980s.

The question facing the national leadership of the United States is whether or not they will diminish their own naval construction and, by extension, their sea power. The United States is remote from the world's major conflict areas—the European continent and the southeast and southwest Asian landmasses. Nevertheless, as a nation, it maintains strong military, political, and commercial alliances and interests in these areas. Although the United States imports little oil directly from southwest Asia, its major allies in Europe and Asia do. More U.S. international trade crosses the Pacific than the Atlantic, and the disposition of the United States' major military bases—sea, air, and land—reflects this distribution. Air power holds enemies in check through the threat of nuclear retaliation. But sea power is the only means the United States has, short of nuclear war, to protect its overseas interests and those of its allies and friends.

Strong, modern U.S. sea power is still vitally necessary for securing the sea lanes to permit free, uninterrupted trade between nations. The United States has a global responsibility to secure those sea lanes, not only for its own interests and those of its friends and allies, but for all the nations of the world. That can only happen by continuing to maintain a modern, well-equipped U.S. Navy.

39

AIRCRAFT CARRIERS

The United States Navy deploys the largest and most powerful ship in the world, the nuclear-powered aircraft carrier. Aircraft carriers lead heavily armed squadrons of smaller fighting and support ships in task forces. The job of these task forces is to maintain the security of, and protect the interests of, the United States and its allies and friends, to keep the peace, and to permit free travel along the international waterways of the world.

The United States Navy currently possesses two classes of nuclear-powered carriers, *Enterprise* and *Nimitz,* and four classes of conventionally powered carriers, *Midway, Forrestal, Kitty Hawk,* and *Kennedy.* In addition, one aircraft carrier of World War II-vintage, the *Lexington,* is operated as an aviation training ship.

In the opening days of World War II, the British Royal Navy demonstrated the aircraft carrier's viability both as a means of protecting a fleet and as a way of extending the range of the fleet's weapons far beyond the horizon. In November 1940, Swordfish aircraft from the British aircraft carrier HMS *Illustrious* bombed the port of Taranto, sinking half the capital ships (the biggest and most important ships) in the Italian battlefleet in one swift action and foreshadowing the Japanese attack at Pearl Harbor.

The United States was fortunate that the aircraft carriers belonging to the Pacific fleet were conducting exercises at sea on December 7, 1941, and so were spared destruction. The existence of these carriers, as well as the production of dozens more, helped to defeat the Japanese Navy. Within the year following Pearl Harbor, American and Japanese carriers traded decisive blows at the Battle of the Coral Sea; American aircraft carriers at the Battle of Midway turned the tide of Japanese conquest.

After World War II, American naval forces were constructed around the idea of powerful aircraft carriers that carried two types of aircraft. Short-range fighters had the job of providing security for the task force against hostile aircraft and surface vessels. Medium-range bombers, armed with both nuclear and conventional weapons, posed a distinct threat to the coastal and inland areas of any hostile power.

But the development of sea power via large carrier task forces was not automatic. In the immediate postwar years, the Air Force saw the long-range manned bomber and the ballistic missile as the prime guarantor of

Opposite: *The aircraft carrier USS* Nimitz *is one of the most powerful naval vessels afloat.* Above: *The USS* Independence, *shown here being refueled, is a conventionally powered aircraft carrier.*

peace. That vision, however, was shaken by the Korean War. The aircraft carrier again played a pivotal role, as it had during World War II. Carriers sent bomb-laden aircraft winging inland to destroy North Korean and Chinese Communist communications, logistics, armor, and troop transport facilities.

The 1960s saw the large carrier assuming the central position in the nuclear-armed task force. Early in the Kennedy administration, some critics thought the aircraft carrier was too vulnerable to submarines and ballistic missiles. The carrier admirals fought a major skirmish to retain the large aircraft carrier. Their victory was a partial one, because the new *Kitty Hawk* class was built with conventional rather than nuclear propulsion. Later, carrier operations off the coast of Vietnam once again proved the usefulness of the aircraft carrier.

The Soviet invasion of Afghanistan, coupled with Soviet support of a host of liberation wars and Communist-dominated insurgency campaigns in the late 1970s and early 1980s, galvanized the Reagan administration. It reconsidered not only the Navy's readiness and capability but also that of the military service as a whole. The number of aircraft carriers in operation was increased, and three new ships of the *Nimitz* class were ordered—the *Theodore Roosevelt,* the *Abraham Lincoln,* and the *George Washington.*

Although the United States currently has 15 aircraft carriers in operation excluding the *Lexington*, only four carriers are deployed at any one time—two in the Mediterranean and two in the western Pacific. The remaining carriers are in transit to or from their stations; engaged in fleet exercises or other training; or in port for overhaul, repair, or modernization. Normally, a carrier can expect to spend six months on active duty and the next 12 in training or overhaul.

Midway-Class (CV) Aircraft Carriers

The *Midway* class of aircraft carriers was originally designed to replace the *Essex* class; the design was based on experience gained in the battles of the Coral Sea and Midway in 1942. Only three ships of this class were built: USS *Midway* (CV 41), USS *Franklin D. Roosevelt* (CV 42), and USS *Coral Sea* (CV 43). Two others intended for this class were canceled. The *Roosevelt* was decommissioned after being replaced by the USS *Nimitz* in late 1977.

Above: *The USS* Midway *and the USS* Coral Sea *are the last World War II-era regularly commissioned warships in U.S. Navy service.*

The *Midway*-class carriers were all built with heavy gun armament that varied through their service lives. Included at various times were five-inch, three-inch, 40 millimeter, and 20mm batteries. The carriers were twice as heavy as their predecessors; they had armored flight decks and were designed to take aboard 137 aircraft.

Although they are considered World War II-vintage carriers, none of this class saw action. *Midway,* the first, was not commissioned until September 1945 and the *Coral Sea* not until October 1947. Both carriers have been extensively remodeled. Angled decks were added to both in 1977, and their open bows were closed in when hurricane bows were added later in the yards. Their wide variety of guns have all been removed and replaced by the Phalanx Close-In Weapons System Mark 15 multibarrel guns and two eight-cell Sea Sparrow missile launchers.

Midway initially operated with the Sixth Fleet until it was sent to the Pacific in 1965. *Coral Sea* served with the Atlantic fleet until September 1960, when it was shifted to the Pacific fleet. Both carriers took part in operations off the coast of Vietnam.

Although huge by World War II standards, they are smaller than other aircraft carriers currently in service. Both *Midway* and *Coral Sea* are 900 feet long, at the waterline, and they have flight decks 1,006 feet long and 1,003 feet long, respectively. *Midway* displaces 1,800 more tons than *Coral Sea* when fully loaded. Both are powered by four Westinghouse steam turbines that develop a total of 212,000 horsepower. Both have Babcock & Wilcox boilers and both are capable of 32 knots (36.8 miles per hour).

Neither ship operates F-14A Tomcats, but they do carry 65 aircraft divided into three F/A-18 Hornet fighter squadrons, two attack squadrons of A-6E Intruders, one tactical electronic warfare squadron of EA-6B Prowlers, one early airborne warning squadron of E-2C Hawkeyes, and one squadron of helicopter antisubmarine warfare SH-3H Sea Kings.

Coral Sea is currently serving with the Atlantic fleet and is home-ported at Norfolk, Virginia. It will replace the World War II veteran USS *Lexington* in 1992 as the Navy's only pilot-training ship at Pensacola, Florida. *Midway* will continue to serve as a first-line carrier with the Pacific fleet until the late 1990s. It will then be replaced by USS *Ranger* (CV 61). *Midway* is the only American aircraft carrier to be based in a foreign port—Yokosuka, Japan.

Both *Midway* and *Coral Sea* are tributes to the people who designed and built them and the crews that man them. More than 40 years after they were built, they are still in service.

MIDWAY-CLASS (CV) AIRCRAFT CARRIERS

Operational (commissioned):	CV 41 USS *Midway* (September 1945) CV 43 USS *Coral Sea* (October 1947)
Displacement:	
CV 41:	67,000 tons
CV 43:	65,200 tons
Dimensions:	
Length overall:	
CV 41:	1,006 ft.
CV 43:	1,003 ft.
Beam:	121 ft.
Draft:	36 ft.
Propulsion:	Four Westinghouse steam turbines Twelve Babcock & Wilcox 600-psi boilers
Speed:	32 knots (36.8 mph)
Armament:	
CV 41:	Two 20mm Phalanx CIWS 3-barrel guns Two Sea Sparrow Mk 29 missile launchers
CV 43:	Three 20mm Phalanx CIWS 3-barrel guns
Fire control:	
CV 41:	Two Mk 115 fire control systems
CV 43:	None
Aircraft:	F/A-18 Hornets, A-6E Intruders, EA-6B Prowlers, E-2C Hawkeyes, SH-3H Sea Kings
Surveillance radar:	
All:	SPS-48C 3D search SPS-49 air search
CV 41:	SPS-65 navigation
CV 43:	SPS-67 navigation
Sonar:	None
Crew:	
Navy:	
CV 41:	2,826
CV 43:	2,502
Naval air wing:	
CV 41:	1,860
CV 43:	2,220
Marines:	72

Top: *The USS* Midway *originally had a straight-line flight deck, but it was rebuilt in the 1950s after British experiments showed the value of the angled flight deck.* Above: *The USS* Coral Sea *currently serves with the Mediterranean fleet.* Left: *F/A-18 Hornets from the* Coral Sea *flew air strikes against Libya in 1986.*

The Coral Sea *carries three squadrons of F/A-18s, two squadrons of A-6Es, one squadron of EA-6Bs, one squadron of E-2Cs, and one squadron of SH-3H helicopters.*

Forrestal-Class (CV) Aircraft Carriers

In 1949 the U.S. Air Force persuaded the Truman administration that the long-range bomber and missile would be the ultimate arbiter of any future wars, all of which were expected to be nuclear. As a result, the first American aircraft carrier to be designed since the end of World War II, the USS *United States,* was canceled. A subsequent "revolt" by the Navy, as well as the experience of the Korean War, convinced a reluctant Department of Defense and the new Eisenhower administration that aircraft carriers still had an important role to play. It was a lesson that would have to be learned again and yet again.

The *Forrestal*-class aircraft carriers were the first to be both designed and built after World War II, and they were the first "supercarriers." The British had experimented with the angled deck, and subsequently the Americans tested it by adding an angled deck to the *Essex*-class carrier, USS *Antietam*. The *Forrestal* was originally scheduled to have a straight deck, but these tests proved the usefulness of the new configuration. British design work played a significant role in equipping the *Forrestal*-class carriers and all subsequent American carriers. In addition to the angled deck, the *Forrestal* class also received four British-designed steam catapults able to launch aircraft up to 80,000 pounds—the F-14A Tomcat weighs 73,000 pounds—and the mirror landing system, with which the pilot keeps a ball of light centered in a large mirror to make a safe landing.

Since it was originally designed for the large 100-aircraft wing of the World War II era, the *Forrestal* class can store up to 750,000 gallons of aviation fuel. The air wing complement was reduced to its present 85 aircraft as aircraft capability and size increased.

The *Forrestal* was laid down (construction began) in July 1952, launched in December 1954, and commissioned in October 1955. The speed with which it and subsequent carriers in the class were built reflect the Cold War anxieties of the period. The last of the four ships in the class, the USS *Independence,* was commissioned less than four years later, in January 1959.

Forrestal, Saratoga, and *Independence* served in the Atlantic and Mediterranean until the mid-1960s. In late 1965, the *Independence* joined Task Force 77 in the Gulf of Tonkin and launched aircraft against targets in North and South Vietnam. The *Forrestal* sailed to join the task force in 1967, but its tour was cut short by a fire that caused 194 casualties and required seven months for repairs. *Saratoga* remained with the Atlantic fleet and took over antisubmarine warfare duties (CVS) in 1972, when the last of the *Essex*-class carriers were withdrawn from service. By 1975, all four *Forrestal*-class ships had been fitted with antisubmarine warfare equipment and aircraft, and they were redesignated as multipurpose carriers (CV). Aircraft from *Saratoga* were

Above: *The USS* Midway *and the USS* Coral Sea *are the last World War II-era regularly commissioned warships in U.S. Navy service.*

engaged by Libyan fighters in 1986.

The *Forrestal* and *Saratoga* have flight decks that are 20 feet shorter than *Ranger* and *Independence. Forrestal* has a top speed of 33 knots (37.95 miles per hour), but the other three are one knot faster because of improved engines. All are powered by four steam turbines built by Westinghouse that develop a total of 260,000 horsepower in *Forrestal* and 280,000 horsepower in *Saratoga, Ranger,* and *Independence.* All four are capable of steaming 12,000 nautical miles (13,800 miles) without refueling. All four ships carry an average complement of about 2,880 officers and men, plus an additional 3,400 members of the air wing when aboard and 72 officers and enlisted Marines.

Their air wings are similar to those in service with other CV or CVN class carriers: two fighter squadrons (VF) of F-14A Tomcat fighters, three attack squadrons (VA) of A-6E Intruders and two attack squadrons of A-7E Corsair IIs, one squadron of electronic warfare (VAQ) EA-6B Prowlers, one squadron of early warning (VAW) E-2C Hawkeyes, one squadron of antisubmarine warfare (VS) S-3A Vikings, and one squadron of helicopter antisubmarine (HS) warfare SH-3H Sea Kings. *Independence* currently has two squadrons (VFA) of F/A-18 Hornets, and *Ranger* has only two A-6E squadrons and no A-7E Corsair IIs. Carrier Air Wing-6 (CVW) currently serves aboard *Forrestal,* CVW-17 aboard *Saratoga,* CVW-2 aboard *Ranger,* and CVW-10 aboard *Independence.* All four carriers in this class have surface-search and air-detection radars.

Originally intended to be withdrawn from service at the end of their 30-year life spans, all but *Ranger* have undergone the Service Life Extension Program (SLEP), which has added a minimum of 15 years of additional service. *Forrestal* underwent SLEP between January 1983 and May 1985, *Saratoga* between October 1980 and February 1983, and *Independence* between April 1985 and August 1987. *Ranger* will replace the USS *Midway* at its home port in Yokosuka, Japan, in the early 1990s and will be modernized there.

Above: *The USS* Ranger *will replace the* Midway *at Yokosuka, Japan in 1992.* Left: *The* Saratoga *is a conventionally powered aircraft carrier.*

Top: *The* Independence *was one of the first four "supercarriers" in the U.S. Navy.* Center: *The* Saratoga *currently serves with the Atlantic fleet.* Bottom: *Construction of the* Forrestal *began in 1952; the ship was commissioned just three years later.*

FORRESTAL-CLASS (CV) AIRCRAFT CARRIERS

Operational (commissioned):	CV 59 USS *Forrestal* (October 1955) CV 60 USS *Saratoga* (April 1956) CV 61 USS *Ranger* (August 1957) CV 62 USS *Independence* (January 1959)
Displacement:	
CV 59:	59,650 tons
CV 60:	60,000 tons
CV 61:	78,200 tons
CV 62:	79,200 tons
Dimensions:	
Length overall:	
CV 59, CV 60, CV 61:	990 ft.
CV 62:	1046.5 ft.
Beam:	130 ft.
Draft:	37 ft.
Propulsion:	
All:	Four Westinghouse steam turbines
CV 59:	Eight Babcock & Wilcox 600-psi boilers
CV 60, 61, and 62:	Eight Babcock & WIlcox 1,200-psi boilers
Speed:	
CV 59:	33 knots (37.95 mph)
CV 60, CV 61, CV 62:	34 knots (39.1 mph)
Armament:	
All:	Three 20mm Phalanx CIWS 3-barrel guns
CV 61, 62:	Three Sea Sparrow Mk 29 launchers
CV 59, CV 60:	Two Sea Sparrow Mk 29 launchers
Fire control:	Two Mk 91 fire control systems
Aircraft:	F-14A Tomcats, F/A-18 Hornets, A-7E Corsair IIs, A-6E Intruders, EA-6B Prowlers, E-2C Hawkeyes, S-3A Vikings, SH-3H Sea Kings
Surveillance radar:	SPS-10 search SPS-48C 3D search SPS-49 air search
Sonar:	None
Crew:	
Navy:	
CV 59:	2,958
CV 60:	2,896
CV 61:	2,889
CV 62:	2,793
Naval air wing:	3,400
Marines:	72

Kitty Hawk-Class (CV) Aircraft Carriers

The *Kitty Hawk* class contains four conventionally powered aircraft carriers, the *Kitty Hawk, Constellation, America,* and *John F. Kennedy.* This last carrier is often considered to be in a class of its own.

The *Kitty Hawk* was laid down in December 1957 at the New York Shipbuilding yards in Camden, New Jersey. It was launched in May 1960 and commissioned in April 1961. Its entire service life was spent with the Pacific fleet. In 1987, it entered the Philadelphia Naval Shipyard to undergo a modernization process, officially known as the Service Life Extension Program (SLEP), that will add 15 years to its service life, from 30 years to 45 years. *Kitty Hawk* is expected to return to service in early 1990.

The USS *Constellation,* commissioned in October 1961, was the second carrier in this class to be completed, and it was similar to the *Kitty Hawk.* Both were intended to be improved versions of the *Forrestal* class of carriers, with a larger flight deck and better aircraft-handling arrangements. The port-side elevator was repositioned so that it can be used during flight operations, and both it and the center deck elevator were redesigned to handle longer aircraft.

The *America* was laid down in January 1961 and commissioned in January 1965. It can be distinguished by a narrower smokestack. It also has a bow sonar dome. The SQS-23 search sonar was installed, but it was removed in 1981 on the determination that escorts could perform the sonar search function more efficiently.

The *John F. Kennedy* was to be the first in a new series of nuclear-powered carriers, but it was not laid down until 1964 because the Secretary of Defense, Robert S. McNamara, was not convinced that the Navy needed another large carrier. Projections of carrier operations off the coast of Vietnam finally persuaded the secretary to approve the new ship, but only as a nonnuclear vessel. Congress had refused to fund another nuclear carrier. The *John F. Kennedy* can be distinguished by its funnel, which is angled at about 40 degrees outboard to keep smoke from interfering with flight operations.

The *Kitty Hawk*-class carriers were originally intended to be an attack carrier class (CVA). Between April 1973 and June 1975, all four carriers in this class were modified to multimission carriers (CV) and took aboard antisubmarine warfare aircraft. The *Kitty Hawk, Constellation,* and *America* were originally armed with the Terrier RIM-2 missile system, which was capable of carrying a nuclear warhead, and SPQ-55B missile-control radars. These were replaced by the Sea Sparrow RIM-7 missile system to counter Soviet antiship missiles. The Sea Sparrow takes up far less room on deck and does not interfere with flight operations. The Sea Sparrow is fired from the Basic Point Defense Missile System's eight-tube launcher. Sea Sparrows must be reloaded by hand.

Kitty Hawk-class carriers displace 80,800 tons when fully loaded, provisioned, and armed for sea, except for the *Kennedy,* which displaces an additional 140 tons. They are powered by four steam turbines built by Westinghouse that develop a total of 280,000 horsepower and are driven by eight boilers built by Foster Wheeler. They are 990 feet long at the waterline and 130 feet wide. The flight decks of all four are nearly 1,050 feet long and 252 feet wide, except for the *Kennedy,* which has a flight deck 12 feet wider. The

Above: *The USS* John F. Kennedy *was the last aircraft carrier in Navy service to be built with a conventional rather than a nuclear powerplant.*

top speed of these carriers is classified information, but they are known to have speeds over 30 knots (34.5 miles per hour).

This class of carrier has a normal crew complement of between 2,773 and 3,045 officers and men plus an additional 2,500 members of the air wings when aboard. They also carry 72 officers and enlisted Marines, who provide for the vessel's security.

Each *Kitty Hawk*-class carrier has aboard about 85 aircraft when on station. The usual complement is two fighter squadrons (VF) of F-14A Tomcat fighters and three attack squadrons (VA) of A-6E Intruders, A-7E Corsairs, or (VFA) of F/A-18 Hornets. They also carry one squadron of electronic warfare (VAQ) EA-6B Prowlers, one squadron of early-warning (VAW) E-2C Hawkeyes, one squadron of antisubmarine warfare (VS) S-3A Vikings, and one squadron of helicopter antisubmarine warfare (HS) SH-3H Sea Kings. *America* is manned by Carrier Wing-1 (CVW), *Kennedy* by CVW-3, and *Constellation* by CVW-14. The *Kitty Hawk's* air wing, CVW-8, was redeployed to the *Theodore Roosevelt* when it entered the yard for SLEP.

Kitty Hawk-class carrier decks have two launching areas for simultaneous operations, each with two steam catapults. Each carrier also has surface search, air detection, and threat detection radars. Three 20 millimeter Phalanx Close-In Weapons System three-barrel Gatling guns provide close-in protection, and all are equipped with three eight-tube Sea Sparrow missile launchers for longer-range protection out to 10 nautical miles (11.5 miles).

The *Kitty Hawk* is completing its modernization program. *Constellation* has just begun its SLEP program, and *America* and *Kennedy* will follow suit in 1994 and 1996, respectively.

Below: *The* John F. Kennedy *served as flagship on Independence Day 1986 during the rededication of the Statue of Liberty.*

KITTY HAWK-CLASS (CV) AIRCRAFT CARRIERS

Operational (commissioned):	CV 63 USS *Kitty Hawk* (April 1961) CV 64 USS *Constellation* (October 1961) CV 66 USS *America* (January 1965) CV 67 USS *John F. Kennedy* (September 1968)
Displacement:	
CV 63, CV 64, CV 66:	80,800 tons
CV 67:	80,940 tons
Dimensions:	
Length overall:	
CV 63, CV 64:	1,045 ft.
CV 66:	1,047 ft.
CV 67:	1,051 ft.
Beam:	
CV 63, CV 64, CV 66:	130 ft.
CV 67:	128.5 ft.
Draft:	37 ft.
Propulsion:	Four Westinghouse steam turbines Eight Foster Wheeler 1,200-psi boilers
Speed:	Classified
Armament:	Three 20mm Phalanx CIWS 3-barrel guns Three Sea Sparrow Mk 29 8-tube launchers Small arms
Fire control:	Three Mk 91 fire control systems
Aircraft:	F-14A Tomcats, F/A-18 Hornets, A7E Corsair IIs, A-6E Intruders, EA-6B Prowlers, E-2C Hawkeyes, S-3A Vikings, SH-3H Sea Kings
Surveillance radar:	SPS-10F/28B search SPS-48C 3D search SPS-49 air search
Sonar:	None
Crew:	
Navy:	
CV 63:	2,773
CV 64:	3,017
CV 66:	2,983
CV 67:	3,045
Naval air wing:	2,500
Marines:	72

Top: *The USS* America *serves with the Atlantic fleet.* Bottom: *The USS* Constellation *is named after one of the first 36-gun frigates to be built for the U.S. Navy in 1794.*

The America *was commissioned in 1965; it will undergo modernization in the early 1990s.*

Enterprise-Class (CVN) Aircraft Carrier

When it began flying air strikes against North Vietnam in 1965, the *Enterprise* was the first nuclear-powered ship to see combat. Laid down in February 1958, it was the first nuclear-powered aircraft carrier to be built by the United States and also the first in the world.

The *Enterprise* was intended to be a two-ship class, but the Eisenhower administration did not release the funds voted by Congress, and the second ship in this class was never built. In fact, the next nuclear-powered ship to be built was the USS *Nimitz.* A fierce debate raged within the government and the military over the future of the aircraft carrier. In the view of one side, aircraft carriers were rendered obsolete by advances in submarine and missile technology, and no value could come from spending the $451 million that the *Enterprise* cost. The other side saw the nuclear-powered carrier, surrounded by a powerful task force providing air and sea defense, as an influential deterrent to nuclear war and as a big stick in limited conflicts.

In spite of the debate, the *Enterprise* was built. Its hull was a modification of the USS *Forrestal*-class of conventionally powered aircraft carriers that had just been built. Since the *Enterprise* was nuclear-powered and therefore had no stacks to be positioned aft of the island, the bridge was built in the shape of a box with an inverted cone atop that housed the SPS-32/23 phased-array "billboard" radars. These were replaced during modernization in 1979–81 because of their low reliability and high frequency of maintenance.

The nuclear power plants—eight A2Ws—were designed by Westinghouse in 1950 but were not completed until 1954. In the meantime, the latest technology developed in the nuclear submarine program was applied to a redesign. The nuclear reactors heat pressurized water to turn four steam turbines that produce a total of 280,000 horsepower. When the *Enterprise* was commissioned, it was estimated that its nuclear fuel would enable it to sail 200,000 miles. In fact, its first fuel cores were not replaced for 207,000 miles.

The use of nuclear power plants meant that aviation fuel and other stores could be kept in space normally devoted to storing fuel needed to power oil-fired boilers. Weapons storage space is minimal, because the *Enterprise* carried no guns until the Phalanx Close-In Weapons System (CIWS) three-barreled chain guns were installed. A scheduled Terrier missile system was never installed, and it was not until the 1979 modernization that two Sea Sparrow missile launchers were installed. A third will be added in the mid-1990s.

When the *Enterprise* was commissioned in November 1961, it was the largest ship ever built. It rivals the *Nimitz*-class carriers in size and displaces 9,300 more tons when fully loaded. *Enterprise* is 1,040 feet long at the waterline and 133 feet wide. The flight deck is 1,101 feet long and 257

Above: *The USS* Enterprise *was the first nuclear-powered aircraft carrier built for any navy in the world.*

ENTERPRISE-CLASS (CVN) AIRCRAFT CARRIER

Operational (commissioned):	CVN 65 USS *Enterprise* (November 1961)
Displacement:	90,970 tons
Dimensions:	
Length overall:	1,101 ft.
Beam:	133 ft.
Draft:	39 ft.
Propulsion:	Four steam turbines Eight Westinghouse A2W pressurized-water nuclear reactors
Speed:	Classified
Armament:	Three 20mm Phalanx CIWS 3-barrel guns Two Sea Sparrow Mk 25 launchers
Fire control:	Two Mk 91 fire control systems
Aircraft:	F-14A Tomcats, A-7E Corsair IIs, A-6E Intruders, EA-6B Prowlers, E-2C Hawkeyes, S-3A Vikings, SH-3H Sea Kings
Surveillance radar:	SPS-10F/28B search SPS-48C 3D search SPS-49 air search SPS-85 threat warning
Sonar:	None
Crew:	
Navy:	3,319
Naval air wing:	2,625
Marines:	72

Top: *The cone-shaped appearance of the* Enterprise's *island structure was changed when the SPS-32/33 phased-array radars were removed.* Bottom: *The* Enterprise *traveled 238,000 miles without refueling.*

feet wide. Its top speed is classified, but it is known to be over 30 knots (34.5 miles per hour). *Enterprise* normally carries a crew of 3,319 officers and men, plus an additional 2,625 members of the air wing when aboard. It also has a complement of 72 officers and enlisted Marines, who provide for the vessel's security.

The air wing for the *Enterprise* is CVW-11 and contains the usual complement of two fighter squadrons (VF) of F-14A Tomcat fighters; three attack squadrons (VA), one of A-6E Intruders and two of A-7E Corsair IIs; one squadron of electronic warfare (VAQ) EA-6B Prowlers; one squadron of early warning (VAW) E-2C Hawkeyes; one squadron of antisubmarine warfare (VS) S-3A Vikings; and one squadron of helicopter antisubmarine (HS) warfare SH-3H Sea Kings.

Enterprise was originally a modified *Kitty Hawk*-class design. It has two deck launching areas for simultaneous operations, each with two steam catapults and four deck edge elevators. The carrier also has surface search, air detection, and threat detection radars. Originally called an attack carrier (CVAN), its mission and designation was changed to multimission carrier (CVN) in June 1975.

In 1964, three years after being commissioned, the *Enterprise* joined with the nuclear-powered missile cruiser USS *Long Beach* (CGN 9) and the nuclear-powered cruiser USS *Bainbridge* (CGN 25) to form the world's first nuclear-powered task force. They traveled 37,522 miles around the world, without refueling or replenishing, in 64 days, with time included for official visits to foreign ports.

The USS Enterprise *completed a major overhaul and modernization in 1982. It is scheduled to be overhauled again by the mid-1990s.*

Nimitz-Class (CVN) Aircraft Carriers

There are currently five *Nimitz*-class aircraft carriers in commission plus one more under construction; they are the largest warships ever built. The *Nimitz*-class carriers were originally proposed in the late 1950s as replacements for the *Midway* class. But the Kennedy administration was not convinced that large aircraft carriers were still viable, and in its early days neither was the Johnson administration. Aircraft carriers were considered too vulnerable to silent-running nuclear-powered submarines and air- and sea-launched ballistic missiles in time of war.

But the Vietnam War showed that the large aircraft carrier still had a major role to play in naval warfare that no other ship could accomplish. Attack and bombing aircraft operating from carrier decks could hurt an enemy far inland. And in an age of limited conflict, they could inflict cumulative and intolerable pressure on the enemy's economic and military capacity to wage war.

Once approved, the original three ships of the *Nimitz* class were further delayed by labor and scheduling problems. The USS *Nimitz* was finally commissioned in May 1975 and the USS *Dwight D. Eisenhower* in October 1977. In the late 1970s, the Carter administration sought to wind down large, expensive military programs and wanted to cancel the third carrier in the class. The Soviet invasion of Afghanistan persuaded Congress to demand that the third and fourth carriers be built. The USS *Carl Vinson* was commissioned in March 1982; the USS *Theodore Roosevelt* was begun in October 1981 and commissioned in October 1986.

The upsurge in defense spending that appeared at the beginning of the Reagan administration in 1981 had actually begun during the last fiscal year of the Carter administration. In his call for a 600-ship Navy, the Secretary of the Navy, John Lehman, approved the construction of two more *Nimitz*-class carriers. The USS *Abraham Lincoln* was laid down in November 1984 and the USS *George Washington* in August 1988. The *Abraham Lincoln* was commissioned in February 1988, and the *George Washington* is expected to be commissioned in 1992.

Above: The USS Dwight D. Eisenhower *was the second aircraft carrier of the* Nimitz *class to be commissioned.*

Cost is a major consideration in the construction of such massive and sophisticated ships as a *Nimitz*-class aircraft carrier. The *Roosevelt* was completed for $80 million less than the original estimates and 16 months ahead of schedule. Even so, the *Lincoln* and the *Washington* together are expected to cost $8.8 billion.

Nimitz-class carriers displace 81,600 tons when fully loaded, provisioned, and armed for sea. They are powered by four steam turbines that develop a total of 280,000 horsepower (SHP) and which are driven by two pressurized-water Westinghouse A4W nuclear generators with fuel cores estimated to have a life of 13 years or 800,000 to 1,000,000 miles. They are 1,040 feet in length at the waterline and are 134 feet wide (beam). They have flight decks that average 1,089 feet long and 250 feet wide, with hangar decks 684 feet long by 108 feet wide by 26.5 feet high. Because they use nuclear engines, they have no smokestacks—a point of identification—and their island structures are boxy. The top speed of these carriers is classified information, but they are known to exceed 30 knots (34.5 miles per hour).

This class of carrier has a normal crew complement of between 3,100 to 3,200 officers and men plus an additional 2,800 members of the air wings when aboard. They also carry 72 officers and enlisted Marines, who provide for the vessel's security.

Each *Nimitz*-class carrier has about 85 aircraft aboard when on station. The usual complement is two fighter squadrons (VF) of F-14A Tomcat fighters, two attack squadrons (VA) of A-7E Corsairs, one attack squadron of A-6E Intruders; one electronic warfare squadron (VAQ) of EA-6B Prowlers, one squadron of early warning (VAW) E2C Hawkeyes; one

Left: *The USS* Nimitz *gives its name to the largest warships ever built.* Below: *The* Eisenhower, *like the rest of the* Nimitz *class, is powered by two Westinghouse A4W pressurized nuclear reactors.* Bottom: *The USS* Carl Vinson *on a visit to Australia.*

squadron of antisubmarine warfare (VS) S-3A Vikings, and one squadron of helicopter antisubmarine warfare (HS) SH-3H Sea Kings. Carrier Air Wing-8 (CVW) operates aboard the *Roosevelt,* CVW-7 aboard the *Eisenhower,* CVW-9 aboard the *Nimitz,* and CVW-15 aboard the *Vinson.* At present, CVWs have not been identified for the two new *Nimitz*-class carriers.

Nimitz-class carrier decks have two launching areas for simultaneous operations—a straight deck, referred to as the axial deck, and an angled deck. Each deck has two steam catapults and is served by two elevators operating at the deck edges. Each carrier also has surface search, air detection, and threat detection radars, depending on the specific ship. Three 20 millimeter Phalanx Close-In Weapons System three-barrel Gatling guns provide close-in protection in the four later ships, and all have three eight-tube Sea Sparrow missile launchers for longer-range protection. In the main, the *Nimitz*-class carriers depend on their escorts for air, surface, and submarine protection.

The *Nimitz*-class aircraft carriers are probably the largest that will ever be built. The expense of both their construction and maintenance has become untenable. And their vulnerability has never been tested in a shooting war. The Falkland Islands War held many unpleasant surprises for warships, though those ships did not have the threat-detection and countermeasures capabilities lavished on these supercarriers. The destructive power of modern conventional weaponry has increased fourfold since World War II, and extremely accurate sea-launched cruise missiles have made their appearance. Today it is possible to throw massive numbers of missile aircraft at a battle fleet, knowing that some will always get through the defensive screen—emulating the Japanese World War II kamikaze tactic. These, however, will be unmanned cruise missiles equipped to home in on specific vessels. Their very numbers will assure that some get through, and massive conventional, or even nuclear, warheads will assure major destruction.

NIMITZ-CLASS (CVN) AIRCRAFT CARRIERS

Operational (commissioned):	CVN 68 USS *Nimitz* (May 1975) CVN 69 USS *Dwight D. Eisenhower* (October 1977) CVN 70 USS *Carl Vinson* (March 1982) CVN 71 USS *Theodore Roosevelt* (October 1986) CVN 72 USS *Abraham Lincoln* (November 1989)
Building:	CVN 73 USS *George Washington*
Displacement:	81,600 tons
Dimensions:	
Length overall:	1,089 ft., 6 in.
Beam:	134 ft.
Draft:	37 to 38 ft., 6 in.
Propulsion:	Four steam turbines Two Westinghouse A4W pressurized-water nuclear reactors
Speed:	Classified
Armament:	Three 20mm Phalanx CIWS 3-barrel gun Three Sea Sparrow 8-tube Mk 29 launchers Small arms
Fire control:	Three Mk 91 missile systems
Aircraft:	F-14A Tomcats, F/A-18 Hornets, A-7E Corsair IIs, A-6E Intruders, EA-6B Prowlers, E-2C Hawkeyes, S-3A Vikings, SH-3H Sea Kings
Surveillance radar:	
All:	SPS-49 air search
CVN 68-70:	SPS-10F/28B search
CVN 71-73:	SPS-228E SPS-64 threat detection SPS-65 threat detection SPS-67(V) surface search
Sonar:	None
Crew:	
Navy:	3,105 to 3,219
Naval air wing:	Approximately 2,885
Marines:	72

Top: *The USS* Nimitz *is three and one half football fields long.* Center: *The two nuclear reactors and four steam turbines combine to drive* Nimitz-*class carriers at speeds of more than 30 knots.* Bottom: *Aircraft from the USS* Nimitz *give a demonstration of firepower.* Opposite: *A flight of F-14 Tomcats from 142 Squadron passes over the USS* Eisenhower.

BATTLESHIPS

Until January 1942, the battleship was the queen of the seas. Germany's *Bismarck* had proved that by sinking Britain's HMS *Hood* the year before. The threat of Germany's *Tirpitz* waiting in the Norwegian fjords for the British Home Fleet to enter the high seas had kept a large part of the British fleet tied up at Scapa Flow in Scotland.

Then, in January 1942, Japanese land-based aircraft sank the British battleship HMS *Prince of Wales.* A month earlier, Japanese carrier-based aircraft had wiped out a major part of the American Pacific battle fleet—including its battleships—at Pearl Harbor. From that time on, no battleship dared to venture into the open ocean without a strong escort of carrier-based aircraft for protection. The battleship, it seemed, was as dead as the wind-powered man-of-war.

But old ideas die hard. If he had his eye on flag rank, every naval officer in every navy in the world aspired to a battleship command. The proponents of the battleship fought hard to retain the behemoths. And in 1943, construction began on the last class of battleship to be built anywhere in the world.

The *Iowa*-class battleship had been on the drawing boards since 1938. They were to be faster and more powerful than the *South Dakota* class then in service. The *Iowa* battleships were armed with nine 16-inch rifles in three massively armored turrets, 20 five-inch rifles, and dozens of 20 millimeter and 40mm antiaircraft guns. There was not a capital ship (a big and important ship) in the world that could be expected to stand up against the *Iowa* ships. The threat to battleships from air power grew, and it was believed that adding more antiaircraft guns would meet this threat. By the time the *Iowa* ships were commissioned, they carried 80 40mm and 60 20mm guns. They were also armored with 17 inches of steel designed to survive a direct hit from the new 18-inch rifles the Japanese were installing on their latest battleship class.

By the time four ships of the *Iowa* class—*Iowa, Missouri, New Jersey,* and *Wisconsin*—were commissioned, the battleship had been relegated almost exclusively to the antiaircraft and shore bombardment roles. The last enemy battleship, the *Yamoto,* had been sunk by naval aircraft.

By the end of the 1940s, all four *Iowa* battleships were in the reserve fleet, and the last two, the *Illinois* and the *Kentucky,* had been canceled. The four battleships were reactivated for use during the Korean War as shore bombardment ships. The USS *New Jersey* was reactivated a second time for a 120-day cruise in 1968–69, again serving as a shore bombardment vessel—this time off the coast of South Vietnam.

The advent of antiship and land target cruise missiles gave the *Iowa* battleships a new lease on life in the early 1980s. As part of the American military buildup to match a similar Soviet buildup, the *Iowa*-class battleships were once again activated. The five-inch rifles were replaced by Harpoon and Tomahawk missiles. The remaining antiaircraft guns were replaced by 20mm Phalanx multibarrel guns.

The *Iowa*-class battleship now forms the centerpiece of its own task force. The USS *New Jersey* led the first such task force into action off the coast of Lebanon in the early 1980s. *Missouri* led the second into the Persian Gulf in 1987 as part of a multinational task force to keep that waterway open to international shipping. While not as versatile and capable as aircraft carriers, *Iowa*-class battleships carrying their missile armament are once again effective warships.

Above: *The USS* New Jersey *has been recommissioned three times since 1945.*

Above: *The USS* Iowa *is one of the most heavily armed and armored naval ships to ever sail.*

Iowa-Class (BB) Battleships

Above: *The USS* Iowa *was the first of the class of largest battleships ever built.*

The four battleships in the *Iowa* class are the only battleships in the world that remain in service. They were reactivated beginning in 1984 and modernized to serve as gun- and missile-launching platforms in battle areas having only moderate air and submarine threat. They are intended to fill the gap between carrier-led task forces and convoys shepherded by frigates.

All four ships carry three main turrets. The turrets are heavily armored, with 17 inches on the front surface. Each turret has three guns with bore diameters of 16 inches. They are 66.6 feet long and have 96 0.15-inch-deep grooves each. The rounds are propelled by a cordite composition known in the Navy as "black powder," which is packed in 110-pound bags. Three bags are loaded separately behind a shell, or warhead. Powder and warhead are stored in separate magazines.

The *Iowa*-class battleships fire three types of 16-inch rounds: the Mark 13 High Capacity Projectile (HICAP), which weighs 1,900 pounds and carries a high explosive payload; the Mark 19 submunition round which also weighs 1,900 pounds; and an armor-piercing round weighing 2,700 pounds. The Mark 13 HICAP projectiles have been fitted with a variety of fuses to achieve air bursts at varying levels as well as surface bursts. One fuse, the M72, produces an air burst at 20 feet over a target. The submunitions in the Mark 19 projectile are anti-armor and antipersonnel mines or bomblets. Muzzle velocity of the armor-piercing round is 2,425 feet per second; that of the HICAP round is 2,690 feet per second.

Iowa-class battleships also carry 12 five-inch, Mark 28 guns, which are mounted in six twin turrets along the ship's sides. This is four fewer than were carried during tours of duty in World War II, Korea, and Vietnam. The missing four turrets were sacrificed to make room for Tomahawk and Harpoon missile systems. The five-inch guns also use a separate shell; the 30-pound powder charge in a galvanized steel case is placed behind it. Muzzle velocity is 2,400 feet per second.

The main armament of *Iowa*-class battleships is now the Harpoon (RGM-84) surface-to-surface antiship missiles and the Tomahawk (BGM-109) land-attack and antiship cruise missiles. Missile complements include 16 Harpoons in four Mark 141 quadruple-tube launchers and 32 Tomahawk cruise missiles in armored-box launchers. The Harpoons have a range of 60 nautical miles (69 miles). The Tomahawk antiship cruise missiles have a range of 250 nautical miles (287.5 miles); the land-attack version has a range of 1,200 nautical miles (1,380 miles). In March 1983, the *New Jersey* became the second ship in the U.S. Navy to receive the Tomahawk missile.

Each operating as part of a battleship group, they make up the most powerful surface naval force in the world today. Each battleship leads a task force composed of one *Ticonderoga*-class Aegis antiaircraft missile cruiser (CG 47), one *Kidd*-class (DDG 993) or *Arleigh Burke*-class (DDG 51) guided-missile destroyer, one *Spruance*-class destroyer (DD 963), three *Perry*-class guided-missile frigates (FFG 7), and one support ship.

Iowa-class battleships are equipped with four Phalanx Close-In Weapons System (CIWS) 20 millimeter point defense weapons. Each CIWS fires at a nominal rate of 3,000 rounds per minute. Inclusion of the Sea Sparrow point defense missile system for anti-air warfare defense was proposed, but the proposal was dropped because the missiles could not withstand the concussion when the 16-inch guns were fired.

Four General Electric turbines (Westinghouse in the USS *New Jersey*) produce a total of 212,000 horsepower, providing a maximum top speed of 33 knots (37.95 miles per hour). The turbines are in turn powered by eight Babcock & Wilcox boilers.

IOWA-CLASS (BB) BATTLESHIPS

Operational (commissioned):	BB 61 USS *Iowa* (April 1984) BB 62 USS *New Jersey* (December 1982) BB 63 USS *Missouri* (May 1986) BB 64 USS *Wisconsin* (November 1988)
Displacement:	57,350 tons
Dimensions:	
Length:	887 ft., 3 in.
Beam:	108 ft., 2.4 in.
Draft:	38 ft.
Propulsion:	
All:	Eight Babcock & Wilcox 600-psi boilers
BB 61, 63, 64:	Four General Electric steam turbines
BB 62:	Four Westinghouse steam turbines
Speed:	33 knots (37.95 mph)
Armament:	Sixteen Harpoon SSMs in Mk 141 quadruple launchers Thirty-two Tomahawk sea- and land-attack cruise missiles in 8 armored-box quadruple launchers Nine 16-inch Mk 7 guns in triple mounts Twelve 5-inch dual-purpose Mk 28 guns in twin mounts
Fire control:	One SWG-2 Tomahawk weapon control system Four Mk 37 gun fire control systems Two Mk 38 gun directors with Mk 25 radar One Mk 40 gun director with Mk 27 radar
Aircraft:	None
Surveillance radar:	
All:	SPS-49 air search
BB 61, 63, 64:	SPS-67 surface search
BB 62:	SPS-10F
Sonar:	None
Crew:	
Navy:	1,515
Marines:	40

The *Iowa*-class battleships have never engaged another battleship, or any other major surface vessel, in a gun-to-gun confrontation, and they probably never will. Commissioned late in World War II, they served primarily as antiaircraft gunfire support ships with their original batteries of 80 40mm and 60 20mm guns. After the war, the USS *Missouri* was used as a training ship; the other three ships were mothballed. Since then, one battleship, the USS *New Jersey,* has been reactivated three times—during the Korean War, the Vietnam War, and the present recommissioning. The *New Jersey* was active off the Lebanese coast in late 1983 and early 1984 and fired guns at shore targets. The *Missouri* served in the Persian Gulf as part of the multinational task force to secure freedom of shipping in those international waters in 1987.

Top: *Recommissioned in 1984,* Iowa-*class battleships retained their 16-inch guns but their 20mm, 40mm, and many of their five-inch guns have been replaced by antiaircraft and cruise missiles.* Bottom: *The USS* Wisconsin *is the last of a long line of American battleships to put to sea.*

Iowa-*class battleships have 17 inches of steel armor protecting vital areas of the ship.*

CRUISERS

The cruiser class of warships was developed toward the end of the 19th century as "armored cruising ships." They were designed to act either alone as powerfully armed ships or as flagships for small fleets or task forces. During World War I, they served as escorts for battleships and, although still in the armored cruising role, as scouts for main battle fleets. By World War II, they had become the "utility" ships of fleets and operated alone, as task force leaders of other cruisers or smaller vessels, or as escorts for battleships and aircraft carriers. By the end of World War II, four different types of cruisers had evolved: large cruisers (CB) with 12-inch guns, heavy cruisers (CA) having main batteries of guns larger than six inches, light cruisers (CL) with guns of six inches and below, and antiaircraft defense cruisers (CLAA) with large batteries of antiaircraft guns. Only five CLAAs and two CBs were built.

Since the end of World War II, the cruiser class has slowly undergone a transformation and taken on a new significance. In 1945, more than 80 cruisers were in service. Today, not one of those ships survives; all have been replaced by modern designs in which missiles have been substituted for guns.

There are more than 35 cruisers in service today, divided into eight classes. They serve as escorts for task forces headed by aircraft carriers and provide heavy air-defense screens. All are fitted with antiaircraft missiles. Some are being fitted for the antiship role with Harpoon and Tomahawk cruise missiles and vertical launch missiles such as the ASROC. The cruiser force supports seven battle groups containing two aircraft carriers each, one carrier battle group with one aircraft carrier, and four surface action groups, each headed by a single battleship. Thus, the cruiser is once again fulfilling one of its oldest tasks.

Nine cruisers are nuclear-powered (CGN); the rest are powered by conventional oil-fired boilers (CG). In fact, the USS *Long Beach* (CGN 9) was the first American nuclear-powered surface ship when it was commissioned in 1961, as well as the first to be fitted with guided missiles, rather than guns, as its main battery. The nuclear-powered USS *Bainbridge* (CGN 25) followed the next year. No so-called "gun ships" remain in commission. The only two remaining eight-inch gun cruisers are in the mothball fleet. Thirteen cruisers are equipped with five-inch guns, and ten cruisers have no guns at all except for their Phalanx Close-In Weapons System multibarrel point defense units.

It is doubtful that any more nuclear-powered cruisers will be built. In the 1970s, when naval deployment plans required a large number of cruisers, the high cost of nuclear powerplants and related equipment made it impossible to build the desired force level. There are still several cruisers under construction, and these additions will be enough to provide sufficient escorts for the 15 aircraft carriers and four surface action groups into the next century.

Before World War II, United States cruisers were traditionally named for American cities. In the 1970s, they were given the names of states. Throughout the 1980s, they were named for famous battles, except for one cruiser that was named for a secretary of the Navy.

Left: *The USS* Leahy, *lead ship in its class, is the oldest nonnuclear cruiser in service with the Navy.* Opposite: *The USS* Bunker Hill *shows off one of its SPY-1A multifunction radar antennae on the forward face of its bridge structure. Above are the dish antennae of its SPG-62 radar and in between, the SPQ-9A radar antenna.*

The USS Arkansas *is a nuclear-powered guided-missile cruiser of the* Virginia *class.*

Long Beach-Class (CGN) Cruiser

Above: *The USS* Long Beach *was the world's first nuclear-powered warship.*

On September 9, 1961, the world's first nuclear-powered surface warship, the cruiser USS *Long Beach,* was commissioned into the United States Navy. It followed the world's first nuclear-powered vessel, the submarine USS *Nautilus,* by seven years, and the first nuclear-powered surface vessel, the Soviet icebreaker *Lenin,* by two years. The *Long Beach* was originally classed as a light guided-missile cruiser (CLGN) but was reclassified to a CGN even before the keel was laid down (marking the start of construction). Its original assigned number was CGN 160, but in July 1957, it was renumbered to CGN 9.

The USS *Long Beach* was the first surface warship to be completely furnished with guided-missile weapons rather than gun batteries. As might be expected of a ship that pioneered new technology, the *Long Beach* underwent a number of design changes even before construction began, and more afterward. It was originally designed to be a 7,800-ton frigate equipped with guided missiles. Before the keel was laid down, its size and displacement had doubled, and it was placed in the cruiser class.

Because its task was to provide an anti-air warfare and antisubmarine warfare screen for the aircraft carriers it would be escorting, the *Long Beach* was equipped with missiles. Terrier (RIM-2) guided missiles in two twin launchers were mounted forward, and one Talos (RIM-8) missile launcher was mounted at the stern. Terrier was a surface-to-air missile that had a solid-fuel motor and was equipped to ride a radar beam to its target. It was later fitted with a homing warhead and could carry nuclear or nonnuclear warheads. Talos was a surface-to-air missile with a solid-propellant rocket/ramjet engine that could also carry a nuclear or nonnuclear warhead. Both have been replaced by the far more capable and reliable Standard-Extended Range (RIM-67B), which has a range of 90 nautical miles (103.5 miles).

The *Long Beach* was also designated to fire the Regulus II surface-to-surface missile, an early cruise missile with a range of 1,000 nautical miles (1,150 miles). But the Regulus was never installed. Instead, the Polaris intercontinental ballistic missile was to be put aboard in eight launch tubes fitted amidships. But this plan was also canceled. Until the completion of its modernization (1980–83), *Long Beach* had no long-range surface-to-surface missiles. During refit, it was equipped with the Tomahawk (BGM-109) cruise missile, both sea-attack and land-attack versions, which are fired from two quadruple Mark 141 launchers located on the after deck. Shorter-range surface-to-surface missile capability is supplied by eight Harpoon (RGM-84A) missiles fired from two quadruple Mark 141 launchers, which are mounted on the after superstructure. Antisubmarine warfare weaponry includes 20 ASROC (RUR-5A) antisubmarine rockets fired from one Mark 16 eight-cell launcher.

For the ship's own protection, two five-inch dual-purpose single-barrel guns were installed for use against low-flying, subsonic aircraft or surface threats. Two Phalanx Close-In Weapons Systems have also been installed on the aft superstructure for point defense.

The *Long Beach*'s superstructure has the overlarge, boxy appearance that made the USS *Enterprise* so distinctive. This was due to the very large SPS-32 and SPS-33 phased-array antennae mounted on the four sides of the superstructure. These have now been replaced by paired SPG-55B missile-guidance radars and the SPS-48C 3D air search and SPS-67 surface search and navigation radars. The paired missile-guidance radars are mounted on the deckhouse forward of the bridge, and the air search and surface search radars are mounted on the bridge superstructure. All four radar antennae enhance the futuristic look of the ship.

In the late 1970s, installation of the Aegis weapon system was considered for the USS

Long Beach, including installation of the SPY-1 radar and two Mark 26 missile launchers for the Standard and ASROC missiles (for more information concerning the Aegis system, see Ticonderoga-Class Cruisers). But this was canceled because of costs and the possible effect on other cruiser construction underway or planned at that time. The *Long Beach* received the up-rated SPS-48C and SPS-49 radars instead.

The USS *Long Beach* is powered by two pressurized-water Westinghouse C1W nuclear reactors, which are very similar to the Westinghouse A2W nuclear reactors in the carrier *Enterprise.* The reactor provides steam to four General Electric turbines, which produce a total of 80,000 horsepower. The *Long Beach* is capable of more than 30 knots (34.5 miles per hour) and traveled 160,000 miles before its original fuel cores were changed.

In 1964, the USS *Long Beach*, in company with the aircraft carrier USS *Enterprise* (CVN 65) and the cruiser USS *Bainbridge* (CVN 25)—all nuclear-powered—sailed around the world without refueling to demonstrate their capability and range. Even though it has now been in service for nearly 30 years, there are no plans to retire the *Long Beach.*

Above: *The USS* Long Beach *was originally fitted with SPS-32/33 fixed antenna radars, which are the rectangles to the left and along the upper two thirds of the bridge structure. These radars were removed in 1980.*

Top: *Although the* Long Beach *is nuclear-powered, it still requires oil and other stores. Here the* Long Beach *(left) receives supplies from the oiler* Kansas City *(center) while the* Leftwich *(right) provides escort.* Bottom: *The USS* Long Beach, *seen here after its 1980 modernization, was the first U.S. Navy cruiser built after World War II. It was also the first to be armed with guided missiles as the main battery.* Opposite: *The* Long Beach *is armed with Harpoon and Tomahawk missiles.*

LONG BEACH-CLASS (CGN) CRUISER

Operational (commissioned):	CGN 9 USS *Long Beach* (September 1961)
Displacement:	17,100 tons
Dimensions:	
Length:	721 ft., 3.6 in.
Beam:	73 ft., 3.6 in.
Draft:	29 ft.
Propulsion:	Two General Electric pressurized-water C1W nuclear reactors Four General Electric steam turbines
Speed:	30 knots (34.5 mph)
Armament:	Twenty ASROC (RUR-5A) in one 8-tube Mk 16 launcher Approx. 120 Standard-ER (RIM-67B) missiles in two twin Mk 10 launchers Eight Harpoon (RGM-84A) missiles in two quadruple Mk 141 launchers Eight Tomahawk missiles in two quadruple Mk 141 launchers Two 5-inch dual-purpose Mk 30 guns Two 20mm Phalanx CIWS Mk 15 chain guns
Fire control:	One SWG-2(V)5 Tomahawk fire control system One Mk 14 weapon direction system Two Mk 56 gun fire control systems One Mk 76 missile fire control system One Mk 111 antisubmarine warfare fire control system Two SPG-49B radars Four SPG-55B radars Two SPW-2B radars
Aircraft:	None
Surveillance radar:	SPS-67 surface search SPS-49 air search SPS-48C 3D search
Sonar:	SQQ-23 PAIR keel mount
Crew:	985

Leahy-Class (CG) Guided-Missile Cruisers

Above: Leahy-*class cruisers, such as the USS* Halsey, *were designed and built as antiaircraft warfare escorts for large naval task forces.*

The ships of the *Leahy* class are the smallest vessels in the United States Navy to be classified as cruisers (CG). Like the later *Belknap* cruisers, the *Leahy*-class cruisers were originally designed and built as guided-missile frigates, but they were changed to cruisers in June 1975 during a Navy-wide reevaluation of ship classes to bring them in line with the capabilities and duties of the ships. As either frigates or cruisers, their task is to provide protection to the aircraft carriers that lead task forces.

This class of cruisers is referred to as "double-ended" because the ships are equipped with anti-air warfare (AAW) missiles on both the foredecks and afterdecks, in contrast to the later *Belknap*-class cruisers, which had AAW missiles on the foredecks only. The *Leahy* class also introduced the new "mack" superstructure, a combination of mast and smoke stack that was designed to lighten the superstructure. With less weight above the center of gravity, more capable radar installations could be added.

As originally built, the nine ships of the *Leahy* class had two three-inch antiaircraft guns amidships in twin mounts. These have since been removed to make way for the Harpoon (RGM-84A) missiles and their launchers. Because these ships were always intended for the AAW role, they never had five-inch guns fitted for surface warfare, nor did they carry helicopters for antisubmarine warfare. They do have a Vertical Replenishment (VERTREP) helicopter landing area on the stern that is capable of landing SH-2F Seasprites. They carry no maintenance facilities for helicopters.

Each ship is equipped with two Mark 10 twin launchers for the Standard-Extended Range (RIM-67B) surface-to-air missiles, which have a range of up to 90 nautical miles (103.5 miles). Point air-defense protection is provided by two 20 millimeter Phalanx Close-In Weapons System Mark 15 two-barrel point defense chain guns mounted on either side of the aft deckhouse. The eight Harpoon missiles are contained in two quadruple Mark 141 launchers amidships.

Antisubmarine warfare weaponry includes ASROC (RUR-5A) antisubmarine rockets fired from one Mark 16 launcher forward of the bridge. The ASROC is a rocket-propelled unit into which Mark 44 or Mark 46 homing torpedoes can be fitted for standoff (fired from a safe distance) launchings. The homing torpedo separates from the rocket carrier before entering the water. It circles until its passive radar picks up the enemy submarine. It then accelerates to 40 knots (46 miles per hour) and homes in on the submarine. In the final stages of its run, it uses its active sonar to correct its course. In addition, six 12.75-inch torpedoes are carried that can be fired from their two Mark 32 triple-tube launchers, which are located amidships on the rail near the aft end of the forward deckhouse.

The *Leahy* class of cruisers are all 533 feet long and displace 8,200 tons. They are powered by two General Electric, De Laval, or Allis-Chalmers steam turbines that develop 85,000 horsepower and drive two propeller shafts. Steam is supplied by four Babcock & Wilcox or Foster Wheeler boilers. Each cruiser is capable of making 32 knots (36.8 miles per hour), and can carry sufficient fuel to steam 8,000 nautical miles (9,200 miles).

Construction on the USS *Leahy* began in December 1959, launched in May 1961, and commissioned in August 1962. The last ship in this class, the USS *Reeves*, was commissioned in May 1964. Three of the nine *Leahy*-class cruisers are deployed to the Atlantic fleet, the rest to the Pacific fleet.

Having served in peace and war from the waters of the Gulf of Tonkin to the Gulf of Sidra, the *Leahy*-class cruisers have been the workhorse cruisers of the postwar Navy. At this time, the Navy has no plans to retire any ships of the Leahy class, even though they are nearing 30 years of service.

Top: *The USS* England *of the* Leahy *class fires a guided missile.* Center: Leahy *cruisers are called double-ended because they carry main armament fore and aft.* Bottom: Leahy-*class cruisers are armed with Standard antiaircraft missiles, Harpoon antiship missiles, and ASROC antisubmarine missiles.*

LEAHY-CLASS (CG) GUIDED-MISSILE CRUISERS

Operational (commissioned):	CG 16 USS *Leahy* (August 1962) CG 17 USS *Harry E. Yarnell* (February 1963) CG 18 USS *Worden* (August 1963) CG 19 USS *Dale* (November 1962) CG 20 USS *Richmond K. Turner* (June 1964) CG 21 USS *Gridley* (May 1963) CG 22 USS *England* (December 1962) CG 23 USS *Halsey* (July 1963) CG 24 USS *Reeves* (May 1964)
Displacement:	8,200 tons
Dimensions:	
Length:	533 ft.
Beam:	55 ft.
Draft:	25 ft.
Propulsion:	
CG 16–18:	Two General Electric steam turbines
CG 19–22:	Two De Laval steam turbines
CG 23, 24:	Two Allis-Chalmers steam turbines
CG 16–18:	Four Babcock & Wilcox 1,200-psi boilers
CG 19–24:	Four Foster Wheeler 1,200-psi boilers
Speed:	32 knots (36.8 mph)
Armament:	ASROCs (RUR-5A) in one 8-tube Mk 16 launcher Approx. 80 Standard-ER (RIM-87B) missiles in two twin Mk 10 launchers Eight Harpoon (RGM-84A) missiles in two quadruple Mk 141 launchers Six 12.75-inch torpedoes in two triple Mk 32 launchers Two 20mm Phalanx CIWS Mk 15 chain guns
Fire control:	Mk 14 weapon direction system Mk 76 missile fire control system with SPG-53F radar One Mk 114 antisubmarine warfare fire control Four SPG-55B radars
Aircraft:	None
Surveillance radar:	SPS-10F or 67 surface search SPS-49(V)3 air search SPS-48A 3D search
Sonar:	
All:	SQS-23 bow mount
CG 17:	SQQ-23B PAIR
Crew:	423

The USS Halsey*'s eight-round ASROC launcher is located just forward of the bridge structure.*

Bainbridge-Class (CGN) and Truxtun-Class (CGN) Cruisers

Although these are two distinct classes of nuclear-powered cruisers, they will be described together, since they are both one-ship classes and because the USS *Truxtun* was a follow-on to the USS *Bainbridge*. They were the third and fourth nuclear-powered vessels built for the United States Navy.

Construction began on the USS *Bainbridge* in May 1959. It was launched in April 1961 and commissioned in October 1962. The USS *Truxtun* was laid down in June 1963, launched in December 1964, and commissioned in May 1967. Both *Bainbridge* and *Truxtun* were originally designated as nuclear-powered guided-missile destroyers (DLGN), but they were reclassified in June 1975 as nuclear cruisers (CGN). Each ship is powered by two pressurized-water General Electric D2G nuclear reactors that furnish steam to two 60,000 horsepower turbines. Top speed for both is 30 knots (34.5 miles per hour) or greater.

Bainbridge and *Truxtun* were originally fitted with the Terrier (RIM-2) antiaircraft missile system. The Terrier missile rides a radar beam to its target. This feature requires the radar to remain focused on the target during the missile's entire flight, which limits the number of targets that can be engaged at one time. The Terrier could also carry a nuclear warhead. The Terrier missile system has been replaced by the far more capable Standard-ER (Extended Range) surface-to-air missile (RIM-67B). The Standard-ER has a longer range—up to 90 nautical miles (103.5 miles)—and an inertial reference system and mid-course guidance correction. In addition, it does not require radar illumination of the target from the ship until the final phases of the missile's flight.

Both ships originally had three-inch guns, which were removed in the 1970s. In *Bainbridge*, 20 millimeter antiaircraft weapons were installed, but during modernization between 1983 and 1985 they were replaced with two 20mm Phalanx Close-In Weapons System Mark 15 point defense guns mounted on the aft deckhouse. *Truxtun* also received two Phalanx systems, which are mounted forward of the bridge.

Bainbridge and *Truxtun* are also equipped with ASROC antisubmarine missiles. *Bainbridge*'s ASROCs are contained in a single Mark 16 eight-cell launcher on the foredeck; *Truxtun*'s are housed in a Mark 10 launcher. Both ships are also equipped with eight Harpoon (RGM-84A) surface-to-surface missiles (SSM) in storage/launch containers on the quadruple Mark 141 launcher.

The USS *Truxtun* mounts a five-inch dual-purpose Mark 42 gun on the foredeck, but *Bainbridge* does not. *Truxtun* has Mark 32 torpedo launchers that fire the Mark 46 torpedo over the side from the aft deckhouse. The Mark 32 launcher replaced the original Mark 25 launcher that fired the heavy Mark 48 torpedo through a stern port. *Bainbridge* carries the Mark 46 12.75-inch torpedo, fired from two Mark 32 triple launchers located amidships. Radar, fire control, and sonar systems in the two ships are similar.

The major equipment difference between the two cruisers is the *Truxtun*'s helicopter hangar in the aft deckhouse. The hangar is 40.3 feet by 18.75 feet and can accommodate a Kaman SH-2F Seasprite Light Airborne Multipurpose System I (LAMPS I) helicopter. The *Bainbridge* has a landing area on the stern, but no hangar or maintenance facilities.

The *Bainbridge* was originally assigned to the Pacific fleet but after modernization in 1985, it was transferred to the Atlantic fleet in 1987. *Truxtun* serves with the Pacific fleet.

Above: *The cruiser USS* Bainbridge *was the third nuclear-powered surface warship built for the Navy.* Opposite: *The USS* Truxtun *was the fourth nuclear-powered surface warship built for the Navy.*

BAINBRIDGE-CLASS (CGN) AND TRUXTUN-CLASS (CGN) CRUISERS

Operational (commissioned):	CGN 25 USS *Bainbridge* (October 1962) CGN 35 USS *Truxtun* (May 1967)
Displacement:	
CGN 25:	8,580 tons
CGN 35:	8,800 tons
Dimensions:	
Length:	
CGN 25:	550 ft.
CGN 35:	564 ft.
Beam:	58 ft.
Draft:	
CGN 25:	29 ft.
CGN 35:	31 ft.
Propulsion:	Two steam turbines Two General Electric pressurized-water D2G nuclear reactors
Speed:	30 knots (34.5 mph)
Armament:	
All:	Standard-ER (RIM-67B) missiles in two Mk 13 launchers Eight Harpoon (RGM-84A) missiles in two quadruple Mk 141 launchers Two 20mm Phalanx CIWS Mk 15 chain guns
CGN 25:	ASROCs (RUR-5A) in one 8-tube Mk 16 launcher Six 12.75-inch torpedoes in two triple Mk 32 launchers

Armament continued	
CGN 35:	Twenty ASROC (RUR-5A) in one twin Mk 10 launcher Four 12.75-inch torpedoes in two twin Mk 32 launchers One 5-inch Mk 45 single-barrel gun
Fire control:	
All:	Mk 14 weapon direction system Mk 76 fire control system Two SPG-55B radars
CGN 25:	One Mk 111 antisubmarine warfare fire control system
CGN 35:	Mk 68 gunfire control system One Mk 114 antisubmarine warfare fire control system
Aircraft:	
CGN 25:	None
CGN 35:	One SH-2F Seasprite LAMPS I helicopter
Surveillance radar:	
CGN 25:	SPD-48C surface search SPS-49 air search SPS-67 surface search
CGN 35:	SPS-40D air search SPS-48C 3D search SPS-67 surface search
Sonar:	
CGN 25:	SQQ-23
CGN 35:	SQS-26BX
Crew:	
CG 25:	558
CG 35:	591

The USS Bainbridge *is currently in service with the Atlantic fleet.*

Belknap-Class (CG) Guided-Missile Cruisers

The *Belknap* class of cruisers was built with one purpose in mind: to screen (protect from attack) aircraft carriers. Originally designed as guided-missile frigates (DLG), these ships were improvements on the smaller *Leahy*-class frigates, which are now designated as cruisers. The *Leahy* class has two missile launchers, one at either end of the ship. The *Belknap*-class ships have one Mark 10 launcher on the forward deck ahead of the bridge; in place of the second launcher, they have a five-inch dual-purpose Mark 42 gun mounted on the rear deck.

The task of each cruiser in the *Belknap* class is to provide heavy anti-air warfare (AAW), antiship, and antisubmarine warfare (ASW) screens for the aircraft carrier(s) it is escorting. Construction began on the first of the nine ships in this class, the USS *Belknap*, in February 1962. It was launched in July 1963 and commissioned in November 1964. The last, the USS *Biddle*, was commissioned in January 1967. Four ships are attached to the Atlantic fleet and five to the Pacific fleet. The USS *Belknap* was refitted as a fleet flagship during 1985 and 1986 and took its place as flagship of the Sixth Fleet in the Mediterranean in July 1986.

The Mark 10 launcher was originally for the Terrier (RIM-2) surface-to-air missile. These missiles have been discarded in favor of Standard-Extended Range (RIM-67B) surface-to-air missiles, which have a longer range—up to 90 nautical miles (103.5 miles). The Mark 10 Modification 7 missile launcher used aboard the *Belknap* class is magazine-fed. Each magazine holds 20 missiles in a ring configuration, and each launcher is equipped with three rings for a total of 60 Standard missiles.

When first built, the *Belknap* cruisers had two three-inch guns on antiaircraft mounts amidships. These were subsequently removed to make way for the Harpoon missile launchers. Additional air defense is now provided by the single five-inch dual-purpose Mark 42 gun and by two 20 millimeter Phalanx Close-In Weapons System Mark 15 point defense chain guns. The Phalanx guns are located outboard of the aft deckhouse and are staggered.

Antisubmarine warfare weaponry includes ASROC (RUR-5A) antisubmarine rockets fired from the Mark 10 launcher. The ASROC is a rocket-propelled unit into which Mark 44 or Mark 46 homing torpedoes can be fitted for standoff launchings. Six 12.75-inch torpedoes can be fired from Mark 32 triple-tube launchers. The torpedo tubes are located amidships along the rail between the forward and aft deckhouses. Each of the eight Harpoon (RGM-84A) antiship missiles are fired from their Mark 141 quadruple-mount launchers. One Harpoon launcher is located on the starboard side opposite the port side Phalanx, and the other is on the port side at the forward end of the aft deckhouse.

Each ship in the *Belknap* class carries one Kaman SH-2F Seasprite Light Airborne Multipurpose System I (LAMPS I) helicopter, which is housed in a hangar on the 01 deck of the superstructure. The USS *Belknap* has a landing area for an SH-3 Sea King helicopter but no hangar.

All ships in the *Belknap* class are powered by two steam turbines that develop 85,000 horsepower each. Four boilers provide steam. General Electric turbines and Babcock & Wilcox boilers are used in CG 26 through 28, CG 32, and CG 34; De Laval turbines and Combustion Engineering boilers are used in the others. All ships can make 33 knots (37.9 miles per hour). They have a range of 7,100 nautical miles (8,165 miles) at 20 knots (23 miles per hour).

Below: *The USS* Horne *was commissioned in 1967 and serves in the Pacific fleet.* Opposite: *The mack structure, which combines the functions of mast and smokestack, can be clearly seen on this* Belknap *cruiser, the USS* Jouett.

BELKNAP-CLASS (CG) GUIDED-MISSILE CRUISERS

Operational (commissioned):	CG 26 USS *Belknap* (November 1964) CG 27 USS *Josephus Daniels* (May 1965) CG 28 USS *Wainwright* (January 1966) CG 29 USS *Jouett* (December 1966) CG 30 USS *Horne* (April 1967) CG 31 USS *Sterett* (April 1967) CG 32 USS *William H. Standley* (July 1966) CG 33 USS *Fox* (May 1966) CG 34 USS *Biddle* (January 1967)
Displacement:	7,930 tons
Dimensions:	
Length:	547 ft.
Beam:	54 ft., 9 in.
Draft:	
Over sonar dome:	28 ft., 9 in.
Over hull:	19 ft., 4 in.
Propulsion:	
CG 26–28, 32, 34:	Two General Electric steam turbines Four Babcock & Wilcox 1,200-psi boilers
CG 29–31, 33:	Two De Laval steam turbines Four Combustion Engineering 1,200-psi boilers
Speed:	33 knots (37.9 mph)
Armament:	Twenty ASROC (RUR-5A) in one Mk 10 Mod 7 launcher Approx. 120 Standard-ER missiles in one Mk 10 Mod 7 launcher
Armament continued	Eight Harpoon (RGM-84A) missiles in two quadruple Mk 141 launchers Six 12.75-inch torpedoes in two triple Mk 32 launchers One 5-inch Mk 42 single-barrel gun Two 20mm Phalanx CIWS Mk 15 chain guns
Fire control:	
All:	Mk 14 weapon direction system Mk 68 gunfire control system with SPG-53F radar Two SPG-55B radars
CG 26:	One Mk 116 antisubmarine warfare fire control system
CG 27–34:	One Mk 114 antisubmarine warfare fire control system
Aircraft:	
CG 26:	None
CG 27–34:	One SH-2F Seasprite LAMPS I helicopter
Surveillance radar:	
All:	SPS-10 or SPS-67 surface search SPS-48D 3D search
CG 26–30:	SPS-49 air search
CG 31–34:	SPS-40 air search
Sonar:	
CG 26:	SQS-53A
CG 27:	SQS-26AXR
CG 28–34:	SQS-26BX
Crew:	
CG 26 (flagship):	111
CG 27–34:	477

The Mk 10 launcher for antiaircraft missiles is visible on the foredeck of the USS Josephus Daniels.

27

California-Class (CGN) Guided-Missile Cruisers

The two *California*-class cruisers, USS *California* and USS *South Carolina*, were built in the early to mid-1970s as nuclear-propelled versions of the conventionally powered guided-missile cruisers that had been proposed in the early 1960s.

The *California* class was first funded in fiscal year 1967 and ordered in calendar year 1968. Secretary of Defense Robert McNamara was opposed to the nuclear-powered ships because of high costs, and construction did not start until 1970, following McNamara's tenure in office. Although the *California* was launched in September 1971, it was not commissioned until February 1974. The *South Carolina* was launched in July 1972, but it was not commissioned until January 1975. These ships were intended to be the first of a new class of nuclear-powered escorts, but because of their cost and minimal armament, they were dropped in favor of the cheaper and more capable *Virginia* class of nuclear-powered surface escorts.

The *California*-class ships have a helicopter landing area at the stern but no hangar or maintenance facilities. While resembling the later *Virginia*-class cruisers, they are distinguished by the ASROC Mark 16 launcher and the aft five-inch Mark 45 dual-purpose gun, which is mounted on the aft deckhouse rather than on the deck itself. In addition, the *California*-class masts are rounded rather than squared off in cross section as in the *Virginia* class.

Although *California*-class cruisers are slightly longer than the *Virginia*-class cruisers, they displace 770 tons less. The two engines produce 60,000 horsepower each, and top speed is more than 30 knots (34.5 miles per hour).

Both *California* cruisers carry minimal armament for their antisubmarine warfare (ASW), antiship warfare, and anti-air warfare escort roles. They were originally armed with Tartar guided missiles for air defense. The Tartars have been replaced by the more capable Standard-MR (RIM-66C) housed in two single Mark 13 launchers. Since the Mark 13 launcher is not capable of firing other missiles, ASROC missiles are fitted in the Mark 16 launcher, which is located on the main deck just forward of the deckhouse but behind the forward five-inch dual-purpose Mark 45 gun. Two 20 millimeter Phalanx Close-In Weapons System Mark 15 twin-barrel chain guns are carried as well, one on either side of, and forward of, the aft mast.

For the anti-surface warfare role, eight Harpoon (RGM-84A) missiles are carried in two quadruple storage/launch canisters on Mark 141 launchers. The port launcher is mounted on the superstructure 01 deck behind the aft five-inch Mark 42 gun. The starboard launcher is mounted amidships between the fore and aft deckhouses.

The two *California*-class cruisers are equipped for ASW as well. In addition to the ASROCs and their Mark 16 launcher on the forward deck, these ships also are armed with 12.75-inch Mark 48 torpedoes, which are launched from Mark 32 torpedo tubes.

The *California* and *South Carolina* each carry the appropriate radar, sonar, and fire control systems to perform their escort and ASW roles. Both ships are scheduled for upgrades but, neither ship is scheduled to receive the Tomahawk (BGM-109) missile system.

Above: *The* California-*class cruisers were the first nuclear-powered cruisers approved for series production. Only two were built; further production was deferred to the* Virginia *class.*

CALIFORNIA-CLASS (CGN) GUIDED-MISSILE CRUISERS

Operational (commissioned):	CGN 36 USS *California* (February 1974) CGN 37 USS *South Carolina* (January 1975)
Displacement:	10,530 tons
Dimensions:	
Length:	596 ft.
Beam:	61 ft.
Draft:	31 ft., 6 in.
Propulsion:	Two steam turbines Two General Electric pressurized-water D2G nuclear reactors
Speed:	30 knots (34.5 mph)
Armament:	ASROCs (RUR-5A) in one 8-tube Mk 16 launcher Approx. 80 Standard-MR (RIM-66C) missiles in two Mk 13 launchers Eight Harpoon (RGM-84A) missiles in two quadruple Mk 141 launchers Four 12.75-inch torpedoes in two twin Mk 32 launchers Two 5-inch Mk 45 single-barrel guns Two 20mm Phalanx CIWS Mk 15 chain guns
Fire control:	Mk 11 weapon direction system SPG-80 and SPQ-9A radar with Mk 86 gun fire control system Mk 74 fire control system Mk 114 antisubmarine warfare fire control system
Aircraft:	None
Surveillance radar:	Two SPG-10 surface search SPS-40B air search SPS-48C 3D search
Sonar:	SQS-28CX
Crew:	
CGN 36:	603
CGN 37:	595

Top: *Although the bridge of the USS* California *appears conventional, ships of this class are really high-tech escort cruisers.* Bottom: *The USS* South Carolina *is attached to the Atlantic fleet.* Right: *The boxlike structure on the main deck ahead of the* South Carolina's *bridge is the Mk 16 launcher system for the ASROC missiles.*

The nuclear-powered California*-class cruisers were originally intended to provide escort for nuclear-powered aircraft carriers.*

Virginia-Class (CGN) Guided-Missile Cruisers

Once a promising means of providing high-speed, long-endurance propulsion for U.S. naval vessels, nuclear power has literally priced itself out of business. The four *Virginia*-class cruisers are probably the last nuclear-powered warships that will be built for the Navy, at least as a class.

Larger than the gas turbine-powered *Ticonderoga*-class cruiser, the four ships of the *Virginia* class were specifically designed to provide nuclear-powered escort for the nuclear-powered carriers in the Atlantic, Pacific, and Mediterranean fleets. These ships were originally classed as frigates, but the classification was changed to cruiser in 1975 to reflect their actual role and capability. At least two proposals have been made to build either additional *Virginia*-class cruisers or modified versions. But the proposals were rejected in favor of building the more capable, if nonnuclear-powered, *Ticonderoga*-class cruiser.

Although *Virginia*-class cruisers lack the integrated SPY-1 system that is the heart of the Aegis air-defense system, they are nevertheless a real threat to enemy ships and aircraft attacking a task force. *Virginia* ships are equipped with solid-state, digital SPS-40B air search and SPS-48A 3D search in the CGN 38 and CGN 39 versions. The improved SPS-48C was installed in CGN 40 and CGN 41 versions, which have automatic detection and tracking capability.

Virginia-class cruisers use the Mark 26 missile launcher, which has a continuous-feed belt system for reloading. The launcher can handle a variety of missiles, including the ASROC and the Standard SM-2 Medium Range missile, which requires guidance from the ship's radar only in the terminal stage of its flight. Harpoon (RGM-84A) surface-to-surface missile launchers are located forward of the deckhouse. *Virginia*-class ships are also equipped with two Mark 45 dual-purpose guns effective against airborne and surface targets, and two 40 millimeter Mark 11 guns for saluting purposes. For point defense, each *Virginia* cruiser also carries two 20mm Phalanx Close-In Weapons System Mark 15 rapid-firing guns.

One Kaman SH-2F Seasprite Light Airborne Multipurpose System I (LAMPS I) helicopter is carried in a below-decks hangar at the stern. The hangar is covered by a telescoping deck, and the helicopter is raised by an elevator. Problems with the elevator mechanism and trouble with maintaining a watertight seal on the elevator doors have led to the decision to remove the helicopter and substitute two quadruple-mount Mark 143 Tomahawk missile launchers in that deck space. The retrofit is now being carried out.

The Tomahawk launchers will carry eight Tomahawk (BGM-109) antiship missiles for longer-range work. Harpoon missiles have a range of up to 80 nautical miles (92 miles) and carry a warhead containing 510 pounds of high explosive. Tomahawks, however, have a range of more than 250 nautical miles (287.5 miles) and carry 1,000 pounds of high explosive. One SWG-2 Tomahawk fire control system is being installed along with the missiles.

The *Virginia* class has proved very capable at antisubmarine warfare (ASW). The Mark 116 ASW fire control system has a digital interface with the SQS-53A sonar system that operates in the active/passive mode. The interface with the fire control system allows the ASROC missile to be aimed and launched at a faster rate than had been the case with the previous SQS-26 system.

The nuclear-powered cruisers USS *Virginia* and USS *Mississippi* are in service with the Atlantic fleet; the USS *Texas* and the USS *Arkansas* serve with the Pacific fleet.

Above: Virginia-*class nuclear-powered cruisers like the USS* Texas *incorporate significant improvements over* California *cruisers.*

Top: Virginia-*class cruisers, such as the USS* Arkansas, *include an internal helicopter hangar and more reliable solid-state sonar and digital radars.* Center: *The USS* Mississippi, *like all* Virginia *cruisers, carries two 5-inch Mk 45 guns and two 20mm Phalanx guns for close-in defense.* Bottom: *The USS* Virginia *provides the namesake for the class.* Virginia *cruisers were the last nuclear-powered surface warships built for the Navy.*

VIRGINIA-CLASS (CG) GUIDED-MISSILE CRUISERS

Operational (commissioned):	CGN 38 USS *Virginia* (September 1976) CGN 39 USS *Texas* (September 1977) CGN 40 USS *Mississippi* (August 1978) CGN 41 USS *Arkansas* (October 1980)
Displacement:	11,300 tons
Dimensions:	
Length:	585 ft.
Beam:	63 ft.
Draft:	29 ft., 6 in.
Propulsion:	Two steam turbines Two General Electric pressurized-water D2G nuclear reactors
Speed:	30 knots (34.5 mph)
Armament:	ASROCs (RUR-5A) in two twin 8-tube Mk 26 launchers Standard-MR (RIM-66C) missiles in two twin Mk 26 launchers Eight Tomahawk (BGM 109) missiles in two quadruple Mk 143 launchers Eight Harpoon (RGM-84A) missiles in two quadruple Mk 141 launchers Two 5-inch Mk 45 single-barrel guns Two 20mm Phalanx CIWS Mk 15 chain guns
Fire control:	Mk 13 weapon direction system SPG-60 and SPQ-9A radar with Mk 86 gun fire control system Mk 74 fire control system Mk 116 antisubmarine warfare fire control system One SWG-2 Tomahawk fire control system
Aircraft:	One SH-2F Seasprite LAMPS I (being replaced with the Tomahawk missile launchers)
Surveillance radar:	
All:	SPS-55 surface search
CG 38, 39:	SPS-40B air search SPS-48A 3D search
CG 40, 41:	SPS-48C 3D search
Sonar:	SQS-53A
Crew:	
CGN 38:	565
CGN 39:	572
CGN 40:	613
CGN 41:	582

Originally classed as frigates, the Virginia *ships were redesignated to the cruiser class on June 30, 1975.*

38

Ticonderoga-Class (CG) Guided-Missile Cruisers

Above: *The* Ticonderoga *class of cruisers is equipped with the sophisticated Aegis system to counter saturation missile attacks on aircraft carrier task forces. Seen here is the USS* Bunker Hill.

The *Ticonderoga* class of cruisers will be the most numerous cruiser class in U.S. naval service when the 25 authorized ships in that class are completed. Of this class, 13 are currently in commission, and nine are under construction. The Navy's original objective was to provide three *Ticonderoga*-class cruisers for every two carrier battle groups and one for every four surface action groups headed by battleships.

The task of *Ticonderoga*-class cruisers is anti-air warfare (AAW) defense. They were developed in response to the Soviet naval tactic of saturation missile attacks on a carrier task force. Heavy concentrations of antiship missiles would be launched from aircraft, submarines, and surface craft in an attempt to overwhelm the task force's air defense. The *Ticonderoga*-class cruisers are well suited to counter this tactic. All vessels in this class carry the Standard-MR SR-2 surface-to-air missile. Ships CG 47 through 51 have two twin Mark 26 launchers, originally for the Standard-MR (RIM-66C) but now containing the ASROC (RUR-5A); later ships have Mark 41 launchers. MR indicates medium range—40 nautical miles (46 miles). The Standard replaced the earlier Talos, Terrier, and Tartar missiles. Standard has a semiactive radar homing system and a high-explosive warhead. All vessels have eight Harpoon ship-to-ship missiles (RGM-84) launched from the Mark 141 quadruple box launcher. For point defense, all *Ticonderoga* cruisers mount two 20 millimeter Phalanx Mark 15 two-barrel chain guns and two five-inch Mark 45 single-barrel guns that can be used to engage surface or air targets. These latter two weapons are especially comforting since the boxy configuration of these ships gives them a large radar cross section, making them inviting targets.

All are equipped for the antisubmarine warfare (ASW) role as well. The first five *Ticonderoga*-class cruisers carry the ASROC (RUR-5A) antisubmarine rocket, which can be fitted with the Mark 44 or Mark 46 torpedo, or with a nuclear depth charge. Later vessels use the Vertical Launch ASROC with the Vertical Launch System (VLS), which also permits them to launch the Tomahawk (BGM-109) cruise missile. Beginning with CG 52 USS *Bunker Hill*, this class is being, or has been, fitted with the VLS system. All *Ticonderoga* cruisers are also equipped with six 12.75-inch Mark 32 torpedo tubes, which can launch the Mark 46 or Mark 50 lightweight torpedo, both of which use active/passive acoustical homing. The *Ticonderoga*-class cruisers carry either two SH-2F Airborne Multipurpose System I (LAMPS I) or two SH-60B Seahawk LAMPS III helicopters.

But the heart of the *Ticonderoga*'s ability to provide air defense for carrier and battleship task forces is its radar and fire control system. To handle dozens of incoming missiles and aircraft, conventional radars using rotating antennae are simply not fast enough. Instead, four planar arrays—flat plates—were developed, each holding thousands of mini-radar transmitters and receivers in a fixed position. Being fixed in position, the individual transmitters can scan only a small portion of the sky at one time. When four such planar arrays are mounted to point in four different directions, the entire sky is covered. The entire system of radar detection and control, missile and gun aiming, and guidance is referred to as Aegis.

Each ship is equipped with an Aegis AAW system. The heart of that system is the SPY-1 radar system, which provides 360-degree coverage

around the ship out to 200 nautical miles (230 miles). Four fixed antennae operate in the F-band frequency, and each antenna contains 4,480 radiating elements arranged in an octagon 12.5 feet across. Two antennae are mounted on the deckhouse facing ahead and to starboard, and two more on the after deckhouse facing astern and to port. Four UYK-7 digital computers control the radar beams, which are projected by the hundreds in pencil-thin streams. As soon as a target is detected by even one beam, the computer aims several more beams at the target within one second. The computer can then measure the azimuth (the arc the target is traveling through the sky), distance, and height; identify the target; initiate a tracking sequence; and, if necessary, provide command guidance to ship-launched missiles. And the computer can do this for hundreds of targets simultaneously. If the Standard missile is fired, the SPY-1 tracks both missile and target and updates the missile's course continuously. Up to 20 missiles can be directed to separate targets at the same time. The SPY-1 system can also detect enemy jamming and shift frequencies.

When first designed, the *Ticonderoga*-class ships were intended to be guided-missile destroyers. Because of their size and capabilities, they were up-rated to cruisers before construction began. They are based on the design of the *Spruance* destroyers but have larger deckhouses to accommodate the SPY-1 radar system. *Ticonderoga* ships are powered by four General Electric LM2500 gas turbine engines (modified TF39 aircraft turbofan engines) and can generate a total of 86,000 horsepower.

The *Ticonderoga* ships were designed to serve as task force flagships and are equipped with sophisticated combat information centers. They are designed to accept and integrate data from other ships and aircraft in the task force.

The destruction of British destroyers by air-launched missiles during the Falkland Islands War in 1982 and the near loss of the USS *Stark* in the Persian Gulf have prompted internal changes, including the addition of armor plate to the magazine and other critical areas of the ship. The *Ticonderoga* class of cruisers is expected to remain in service well into the next century. These cruisers are capable of being up-rated as more powerful engines and more effective weapons and detection systems become available.

Above: *The USS* Valley Forge *fires a Standard missile from its aft Mk 26 launcher.*

TICONDEROGA-CLASS (CG) GUIDED-MISSILE CRUISERS

Operational (commissioned):	CG 47 USS *Ticonderoga* (January 1983)
	CG 48 USS *Yorktown* (July 1984)
	CG 49 USS *Vincennes* (July 1985)
	CG 50 USS *Valley Forge* (January 1986)
	CG 51 USS *Thomas S. Gates* (August 1987)
	CG 52 USS *Bunker Hill* (September 1986)
	CG 53 USS *Mobile Bay* (February 1987)
	CG 54 USS *Antietam* (June 1987)
	CG 55 USS *Leyte Gulf* (September 1987)
	CG 56 USS *San Jacinto* (January 1988)
	CG 57 USS *Lake Champlain* (July 1988)
	CG 58 USS *Philippine Sea* (March 1989)
	CG 59 USS *Princeton* (February 1989)
Building:	CG 60 USS *Normandy* (1990)
	CG 61 USS *Monterey* (1990)
	CG 62 USS *Chancellorsville* (1991)
	CG 63 USS *Cowpens* (1990)
	CG 64 USS *Gettysburg* (1990)
	CG 65 USS *Chosin* (1991)
	CG 66 USS *Hue City* (1991)
	CG 67 USS *Shiloh* (1991)
	CG 68 USS *Anzio* (1991)
Displacement:	
CG 47, 48:	9,530 tons
CG 49, 50, 51:	9,400 tons
CG 52–68:	9,500 tons
Dimensions:	
Length:	565 ft.
Beam:	55 ft.
Draft:	31 ft., 6 in.
Propulsion:	Four General Electric LM2500 gas turbines
Speed:	30 + knots (34.5 mph)
Armament:	
All:	Eight Harpoon (RGM-84A) missiles in two quadruple Mk 141 launchers
	Six 12.75-inch torpedoes in two triple Mk 32 launchers
	Two 5-inch Mk 45 single-barrel guns
	Two 20mm Phalanx CIWS Mk 15 chain guns
CG 47–51:	Approx. 68 Standard-MR (RIM-66C) missiles in two twin Mk 26 launchers
	Twenty ASROC (RUR-5A) 8-tube Mk 26 launchers
CG 52–68:	Approx. 122 Standard-MR (RIM-66C) missiles in two Mk 41
	Tomahawk (BGM 109) missiles in two Mk 41 vertical launchers
Fire control:	
All:	Mk 7 Aegis weapon system
	Mk 86 gun fire control system with SPQ-9A radar
	Mk 99 missile directors with SPG-62 radar
	Mk 116 antisubmarine warfare fire control system
CG 52–68:	SWG-3 Tomahawk fire control system
Aircraft:	
CG 47, 48:	Two SH-2F Seasprite LAMPS I helicopters
CG 49–68:	Two SH-60B Seahawk LAMPS III helicopters
Surveillance radar:	
All:	SPS-49(V)6 air search
CG 47, 48:	SPS-55 surface search
CG 47–58:	SPY 1A multifunction radar
CG 59–68:	SPY 1B multifunction radar
Sonar:	
CG 47–55:	SQS-53A
CG 54–68:	SQR-19 tactical towed array
CG 58–68:	SQS-53B
Crew:	364

Left: *The USS* Ticonderoga *fires a Standard missile from its forward Mk 26 launcher.* Opposite: *This view of the USS* Ticonderoga *shows the SPY-1A radar phased-array antenna on the face of its forward superstructure.*

47

DESTROYERS

Until the end of World War II, destroyers were medium-sized, high-speed warships, displacing between 2,000 and 3,000 tons. Their purpose was to support strike and amphibious forces. Since the end of World War II, however, the destroyer's weight and armament have changed, and so has the definition of a destroyer's duties.

Destroyers were put to sea at the turn of the 20th century as torpedo carriers whose targets were the armored cruisers and battleships of the day. Destroyers saw their first major action during the Russo-Japanese War (1904–05) without any noteworthy successes. By the eve of World War I, in July 1914, Great Britain had some 270 destroyers armed with up to three four-inch guns and four 21-inch torpedo tubes. Germany had 140 destroyers, which were classed as torpedo boats. Using destroyers as torpedo-firing warships against other warships in grand fleets began to decline; the destroyer's new role was as a convoy escort and antisubmarine vessel.

The development of the hydrophone—underwater microphone—to listen for audible sound frequencies emitted by submarines led to the development of "searchlight" sonar in 1918. Searchlight sonar was developed under the oversight of the Allied Submarine Devices Investigating Committee, from whose initials came the British term for sonar, ASDIC, which endured into World War II. The combination of the piezoelectric transducer, which uses vibrating crystals to impart ultrasonic pressure waves into the water, and the electronic amplifier made it possible for destroyers to effectively measure underwater distance by sound.

In 1917, Great Britain slowly began to organize its merchant ships, which were essential to Britain's existence, into convoys escorted by destroyers. But not until 1918, when the United States Navy was fully into World War I, did enough destroyers become available to allow the widespread development of convoys. The use of hydrophones and destroyer-escorted convoys caused German submarine losses to mount at an astounding rate. In 1918, 132 German submarines were sunk, far beyond the number that German money or manpower could afford. During World War II, the destroyer expanded its antisubmarine warfare role, particularly as smaller frigates and corvettes took on more convoy duty.

By the end of the war, it was clear that antiaircraft defense was growing in importance, even as the advent of the nuclear-powered submarine increased the threat of submarines. The guided missile proved to be more accurate and more destructive to enemy aircraft than the gun, and it quickly replaced the gun as the destroyer's main weapon. The guided missile also had application in antisubmarine warfare (ASW). The guided missile was developed to carry antisubmarine rockets (ASROC) and torpedoes as far as six nautical miles (6.9 miles) out from the ship. The Harpoon cruise missile provided a means of attacking enemy ships 80 nautical miles (92 miles) distant; the Tomahawk, up to 480 nautical miles (552 miles) distant. Today, a single destroyer can pack the punch of an entire World War II task force, even without the use of nuclear warheads.

The United States Navy today has some 68 destroyers in service, divided into six classes. Around 37 have surface-to-air missiles (SAM) and are classified as guided-missile destroyers (DDG). The remainder may carry SAMs but are considered general-purpose destroyers with emphasis on antisubmarine warfare.

The mainstay of the United States destroyer fleet in the 1990s will be the *Spruance* class, gradually giving way to the new *Arleigh Burke* class. The *Spruance* ships are specialists in ASW. They are supplemented by the four ships of the *Kidd* class, which were designed and built for the Iranian Navy. When the Shah was deposed in 1979, delivery of these ships was suspended, and they were purchased by the U.S. Navy. Older ships, such as those of the *Forrest Sherman* class, will gradually be retired or reassigned as the new ships are commissioned through the first decade of the next century. No World War II-era destroyers are still in service, not even with the reserve fleet.

Destroyers are traditionally named for naval heroes and famous leaders—Dewey, Turner Joy, Farragut, and so on. Names for this type of ship also include the names of secretaries of the Navy who are no longer living, and one famous admiral, Arleigh Burke, the Chief of Naval Operations from 1955 to 1961.

Left: *The USS* Barney *is a* Charles F. Adams-*class destroyer equipped with guns, guided missiles, torpedoes, and antisubmarine missiles.* Opposite: *The* Spruance-*class destroyer USS* Oldendorf *is seen here during commissioning ceremonies on March 4, 1978.*

972
972

The USS Preble, *a* Farragut-*class destroyer, is equipped for anti-air, anti-surface, and antisubmarine warfare.*

Forrest Sherman-Class (DD) Destroyers

The *Forrest Sherman*-class destroyers were the first to be wholly designed and built after World War II. They were constructed as three-gun destroyers and were armed with the five-inch .54 caliber Mark 42. They also carried two pairs of three-inch antiaircraft guns and had superstructures of aluminum to reduce weight.

Their major departure from previous classes of destroyers designed during the war, aside from the reduction in gunnery, was the exchange of antiship torpedoes for the new Mark 32 "long" antisubmarine warfare (ASW) torpedo. Initially, all ships of the class had four fixed Mark 25 torpedo tubes and two Hedgehog depth charge launchers. These have all been replaced by the two Mark 32 triple-tube launchers that fire the 12.75-inch Mark 46 homing torpedo.

At present, *Forrest Sherman*-class destroyers have no antiaircraft missiles. Four ships of the class were initially fitted with the Tartar (RIM-24) missile system, but the costs involved precluded the rest of the class from being so fitted. No ships of this class are fitted with the Phalanx or Vulcan point defense systems. Antiaircraft protection is provided only by the five-inch guns, since the three-inch guns were removed by the mid-1970s.

Six ships in the class—USS *Davis*, USS *Manley*, USS *Dupont*, USS *Blandy*, USS *Morton*, and USS *Richard S. Edward*—are well suited to the escort and antisubmarine warfare role. In addition to the homing torpedoes and ASROC missiles that all *Forrest Sherman* destroyers carry, these six ships have been fitted with the Mark 114 ASW fire control system and the SQS-35 Independent Variable Depth Sonar (IVDS) system. The IVDS uses a special submersible capsule that contains the sonar transmitter and is towed behind and below the ship. The IVDS did not prove as effective as expected and is being replaced throughout the entire fleet by a tactical towed array system.

Sherman destroyers are powered by a conventional steam boiler and turbine system developing a total of 70,000 horsepower for a top speed of 32.5 knots (37.4 miles per hour). They have a cruising range of 4,500 nautical miles (5,175 miles).

All ships in this class have now been decommissioned, and most are now in fleet reserve. The USS *Edson* is being used as a National Reserve Fleet training ship to train officer candidates in ship-handling techniques. Four other ships—USS *Decatur* (DD 936), USS *John Paul Jones* (DD 932), USS *Parsons* (DD 949), and USS *Somers* (DD 947)—were converted to DDG-class ships and reclassified as missile destroyers for use against enemy aircraft and missiles. Other numbers missing from the sequence had earlier been assigned to the ex-Japanese *Hanazuki*, which became DD 934, and two ex-German destroyers, the T.35, which became DD 935, and Z.39, which became DD 939.

Above: *The USS* Davis, *like all* Forrest Sherman-*class destroyers, is now assigned to the reserve fleet.* Opposite: Forrest Sherman *destroyers were the first class of destroyers built after World War II.*

FORREST SHERMAN-CLASS (DD) DESTROYERS

Operational:	None
Fleet reserve (commissioned):	DD 931 USS *Forrest Sherman* (November 1955) DD 937 USS *Davis* (February 1956) DD 940 USS *Manley* (February 1957) DD 941 USS *Dupont* (July 1957) DD 942 USS *Bigelow* (November 1957) DD 943 USS *Blandy* (November 1957) DD 944 USS *Mullinix* (March 1958) DD 946 USS *Edson* (November 1958) DD 948 USS *Morton* (May 1959) DD 950 USS *Richard S. Edward* (February 1959) DD 951 USS *Turner Joy* (August 1959)
Displacement:	4,050 tons
Dimensions:	
Length:	407 ft.
Beam:	45 ft.
Draft:	22 ft.
Propulsion:	
DD 931:	Two Westinghouse steam turbines
DD 937–951:	Two General Electric steam turbines
DD 931, 940–942, 946, 950, 951:	Four Foster Wheeler 1,200-psi steam boilers
DD 937, 943, 944, 948:	Four Babcock & Wilcox 1,200-psi steam boilers
Speed:	32.5 knots (37.4 mph)
Armament:	ASROC (RUR-5A) missiles in one 8-tube Mk 16 launcher Six 12.75-inch torpedoes in two triple Mk 32 launchers Three 5-inch dual-purpose Mk 42 guns
Fire control:	
All:	One Mk 5 target designator One Mk 56 gun fire control system with Mk 35 radar One Mk 68 gun fire control system with SPG-53A radar
DD 937, 940, 941, 943, 948, 950:	One Mk 114 ASW fire control system
Aircraft:	None
Surveillance radar:	
All:	SPS-10 surface search
DD 931, 937, 941, 943, 944, 948, 950:	SPS-40 air search
DD 940, 942, 946, 951:	SPS-37 air search
Sonar:	
All:	SQS-23 keel-mounted
DD 937, 940, 941, 943, 948, 950:	SQS-35 IVDS
Crew:	
DD 931–944, 948–951:	319–332
DD 946:	233 active, 125 reserve

The USS Barry, *a* Forrest Sherman *destroyer, lies in dock with the USS* Gemini, *a* Pegasus*-class patrol boat.*

933

Charles F. Adams-Class (DDG) Guided-Missile Destroyers

The *Charles F. Adams* class of destroyers was based on the design used for the *Forrest Sherman* class of three-gun destroyers. Designed primarily to provide anti-air war defense (AAW) for large aircraft carriers, they were the most heavily armed ships of their type at the time of their construction in the early 1960s. The design proved so successful that the Australian and West German navies each purchased three ships.

The first eight ships in this class were designed as three-gun destroyers with five-inch guns, two mounted forward and one aft. In 1966, the design and classification were changed and only two guns were mounted, one forward and the other aft. In place of the third gun, the new Tartar (RIM-24) missile system was installed on the afterdeck.

The Tartar missile is the most successful of the "3-T" (Terrier, Talos, and Tartar) missiles. It is half the size of the Terrier and far more capable. It uses a semiactive guidance system that requires a much less sophisticated radar suite aboard the ship. It also uses a two-stage motor. The first stage launches the missile from its container and drives it to cruising speed; the second stage provides power for terminal maneuvers. The effect reduced the size of the missile and its supporting launch facilities, permitting more missiles to be carried.

Three launchers were developed for the Tartar. The Mark 22 carries 16 reloads and is used on vessels smaller than those of the *Adams* class. The Mark 11 twin-rail missile launcher carries 42 reloads. The Mark 13 single-rail carries 40 reloads and can fire eight missiles per minute from its single launcher rail. The missile system is mounted aft on the main deck above its distinctive round reloader facility. AAW defenses are supplemented by the two five-inch Mark 42 single-barrel dual-purpose guns.

Both the Mark 11 and the Mark 13 missile launchers are used in the *Adams* class. These launchers can also launch the Harpoon (RGM-84) surface-to-surface missile. And the five-inch guns supplement the missiles for surface actions. *Adams*-class ships do not carry either the Phalanx or Vulcan defense gun systems.

Antisubmarine capabilities include the one eight-cell Mark 16 ASROC (RUR-5A) launcher mounted amidships between the stacks. The ASROC is a propulsion unit attached to the Mark 46 lightweight torpedo that enables the ship to stand off as far as six nautical miles (6.9 miles) and attack enemy

Above: *Although small for a destroyer, the USS* Sampson *is well armed with two 5-inch guns and anti-air, anti-surface, and antisubmarine missiles.*

submarines. The *Adams*-class destroyers can also launch the 12.75-inch Mark 46 lightweight torpedo from Mark 32 torpedo tubes mounted on the bridge wings.

The ships are powered by four boilers built by either Babcock & Wilcox, Combustion Engineering, or Foster Wheeler. They provide steam to two turbines built by either Westinghouse or General Electric. The turbines develop a total of 70,000 horsepower. Top speed for this class is nominally 31.5 knots (36.2 miles per hour), but in 1979, the USS *Joseph Strauss* set a speed record of 35.2 knots (40.5 miles per hour).

After more than 25 years of service, the *Adams*-class destroyers are nearing the end of their service lives. In the early 1980s, there were plans to modernize all ships in the class, but those plans were rejected by Congress as being too costly and liable to interfere with the construction of the new *Arleigh Burke*-class destroyers. A more moderate plan to modernize only the last ten *Adams*-class ships was also rejected. To date, only three—the USS *Tatnall*, USS *Goldsborough*, and USS *Benjamin Stoddert*—have been upgraded. All ships, however, will receive the new and more capable SQQ-23A PAIR sonar.

Above: Adams *destroyers, such as the* Benjamin Stoddert, *were originally intended to serve as antisubmarine destroyers. Their armament was changed and they were reclassified as guided-missile destroyers in 1956.*

CHARLES F. ADAMS-CLASS (DDG) GUIDED-MISSILE DESTROYERS

Operational (commissioned):	DDG 2 USS *Charles F. Adams* (September 1960) DDG 3 USS *John King* (February 1961) DDG 4 USS *Lawrence* (January 1962) DDG 5 USS *Claude Ricketts* (May 1962) DDG 6 USS *Barney* (August 1962) DDG 7 USS *Henry B. Wilson* (December 1960) DDG 8 USS *Lynde McCormick* (June 1961) DDG 9 USS *Towers* (June 1961) DDG 10 USS *Sampson* (June 1961) DDG 11 USS *Sellers* (October 1961) DDG 12 USS *Robison* (December 1961) DDG 13 USS *Hoel* (June 1962) DDG 14 USS *Buchanan* (February 1962) DDG 15 USS *Berkeley* (December 1962) DDG 16 USS *Joseph Strauss* (April 1963) DDG 17 USS *Conyngham* (July 1963) DDG 18 USS *Semmes* (December 1962) DDG 19 USS *Tatnall* (April 1963) DDG 20 USS *Goldsborough* (November 1963) DDG 21 USS *Cochrane* (March 1964) DDG 22 USS *Benjamin Stoddert* (September 1964) DDG 23 USS *Richard E. Byrd* (March 1964) DDG 24 USS *Waddel* (August 1964)
Displacement:	3,380 tons
Dimensions:	
Length:	420 ft.
Beam:	47 ft.
Draft:	22 ft.

Propulsion:	
DDG 2, 3, 7, 8, 10–13, 15–22:	Two General Electric steam turbines
DDG 4–6, 9, 14, 23–24:	Two Westinghouse steam turbines
DDG 2, 3, 7, 8, 10–13, 20–24	Four Babcock & Wilcox 1,200-psi steam boilers
DDG 4–6, 9, 14:	Four Foster Wheeler 1,200-psi steam boilers
DDG 15–19:	Four Combustion Engineering 1,200-psi steam boilers
Speed:	31.5 knots (36.2 mph)
Armament:	ASROC (RUR-5A) missiles in one 8-tube Mk 16 launcher Harpoon and either Tartar or Standard-MR (RIM-66C) missiles in Mk 11 twin-rail launcher or Mk 13 single-rail launcher Six 12.75-inch torpedoes in two triple Mk 32 launchers Two 5-inch dual-purpose Mk 42 guns
Fire control:	
All:	One Mk 4 or Mk 13 weapon director system One Mk 68 gun fire control system with SPG-53A radar or Mk 86 with SPG-60 and SPQ-9A radars system Two Mk 74 missile fire control system
DDG 2–15:	One Mk 111 ASW fire control system
DDG 16–24:	One Mk 114 ASW fire control system
Aircraft:	None
Surveillance radar:	SPS-10F or SPS-10D surface search SPS-4OB/D air search SPS-52 surface search
Sonar:	SQS-23A or SQQ-23A PAIR
Crew:	360

Opposite: *The USS* Joseph Strauss *set a speed record of 35.2 knots in 1979.*

16

Farragut-Class (DDG) Guided-Missile Destroyers

Above: *The USS* Luce *is a* Farragut-*class destroyer.*

The *Farragut* class was designed in the early 1950s as light destroyers (DL). The complicated history of their classification reflects the turmoil in the Navy during the 1950s and 1960s as it sought to redefine its role in naval warfare and consolidate its resources against the growing threat of enemy air and submarine attack.

The first three ships in the class were built originally as all-gun, light destroyers (DL 6 though 8). In November 1956, their classification was changed to guided-missile frigates (FFG). But by the time the first ship had completed fitting-out and was commissioned in December 1960, the three had been designated light guided-missile destroyers (DLG). Then in June 1975, in line with a Navy-wide redesignation program, they were reclassified as guided-missile destroyers (DDG), the classification they still retain. Finally, as if that were not complicated enough, this class is also sometimes referred to as the *Coontz* class, because ship DDG 40 (USS *Coontz*, ex-DLG 9) was the first in the class to be ordered as a light guided-missile destroyer. Officially, the *Coontz* and the ships that came after it are considered *Farragut*-class ships.

The *Farragut*-class ships were the first of the so-called anti-air war frigates built for the Navy in the late 1950s. They have flush deck hulls and latticework masts, unlike the larger *Belknap*-class guided-missile cruisers that came later. They are powered by four steam boilers manufactured by either Foster Wheeler or Babcock & Wilcox, which provide power to two turbines built by either De Laval or Allis-Chalmers. The propulsion system develops a total of 80,000 horsepower and enables these ships to run at 33 knots top speed (37.95 miles per hour), but their range is limited to only 4,500 nautical miles (5,175 miles) at 20 knots (23 miles per hour). As a consequence, all but the USS *Preble* were assigned to the Atlantic fleet, where range is not as important as in the Pacific. This lack of range was also instrumental in the Navy's decision to classify them as destroyers rather than cruisers, even though they are armed very much like the *Belknap* and *Leahy* classes of cruisers.

The ten ships of the *Farragut* class were ordered with two Mark 33 three-inch twin antiaircraft (AA) gun mounts and two five-inch guns. The second five-inch gun was located on the afterdeck; it has since surrendered its place to a Mark 16 eight-cell ASROC (RUR-5A) missile launcher. Only the first gun, on the main deck forward, has been retained. The two three-inch AA guns were also removed.

The *Farragut* class carries the Mark 10 twin-arm launcher for the Terrier and Standard-Extended Range (RIM-67B) surface-to-air missiles; the latter has a range of 90 nautical miles (103.5 miles). The Terrier is no longer in use. Only the USS *Coontz* (DDG 40) has been fitted with the 20mm Vulcan Gatling gun system for evaluation. The *Farragut* class cannot be fitted with the 20 millimeter Phalanx Close-In Weapons System because of weight and space limitations.

Antisubmarine warfare weaponry includes the ASROC (RUR-5A) antisubmarine rocket fired from the eight-cell Mark 16 launcher and six 12.75-inch torpedoes fired from triple Mark 32 torpedo tubes. Surface warfare capability includes the five-inch gun and eight Harpoon (RGM-84) anti-surface ship missiles fired from the Mark 141 quadruple-mount launchers. The Harpoon launchers are located on either side of the aft deckhouse.

All *Farragut*-class ships have a Vertical Replenishment (VERTREP), or landing area for helicopters, but no hangar or maintenance facilities.

Top: Farragut*-class ships were originally classified as frigates.* Center: *The USS* Coontz *was the first* Farragut*-class destroyer to be fitted with the 20mm Vulcan Gatling gun system for close-in defense.* Bottom: Farragut*-class destroyers, such as the* USS MacDonough, *can land helicopters but have no hangar facilities.*

FARRAGUT-CLASS (DDG) GUIDED-MISSILE DESTROYERS

Operational (commissioned):	DDG 37 USS *Farragut* (December 1960) DDG 38 USS *Luce* (May 1961) DDG 39 USS *MacDonough* (November 1961) DDG 40 USS *Coontz* (July 1960) DDG 41 USS *King* (November 1960) DDG 42 USS *Mahan* (August 1960) DDG 43 USS *Dahlgren* (April 1961) DDG 44 USS *William V. Pratt* (November 1961) DDG 45 USS *Dewey* (December 1959) DDG 46 USS *Preble* (May 1960)
Displacement:	4,700 tons
Dimensions:	
Length:	512 ft., 6 in.
Beam:	52 ft., 6 in.
Draft:	25 ft.
Propulsion:	
DDG 37–39, 45, 46:	Two De Laval steam turbines
DDG 40–44:	Two Allis-Chalmers steam turbines
DDG 37–39:	Four Foster Wheeler 1,200-psi steam boilers
DDG 40–46:	Four Babcock & Wilcox 1,200-psi steam boilers
Speed:	30 knots (34.5 mph)
Armament:	
All:	ASROC (RUR-5A) missiles in one 8-tube Mk 16 launcher Standard-ER (RIM-67B) missiles in one twin Mk 10 launcher Eight Harpoon (RGM-84A) missiles in two quadruple Mk 141 launchers Six 12.75-inch torpedoes in two triple Mk 32 launchers One 5-inch dual-purpose Mk 42 gun
DDG 40:	One 20mm Vulcan Gatling gun
Fire control:	One Mk 11 weapon director One Mk 68 gun fire control system Two Mk 76 missile fire control system One Mk 111 ASW fire control system
Aircraft:	None
Surveillance radar:	SPS-10B/C surface search SPS-48 3D search SPS-53 surface search
Sonar:	SLQ-23 PAIR
Crew:	400

Farragut *destroyers serve primarily as escorts to large aircraft carrier task forces.*

37

Spruance-Class (DD) Destroyers

Above: *The USS* Caron *is a* Spruance*-class destroyer;* Spruance *destroyers were built as more capable replacements for the aging* Sumner *and* Gearing *classes of destroyers.*

The *Spruance*-class ships were designed to be twice as large, twice as heavy, and twice as capable as the World War II-era destroyers they were replacing—primarily the *Sumner* (DD 692) and the *Gearing* (DD 710) classes. This class of 30 destroyers (plus one subsequently added by Congress) was destined to be a major player in the antisubmarine warfare (ASW) role. The basic design was so successful that it has spun off two other classes of ships—*Kidd* (destroyer) and *Ticonderoga* (cruiser).

The 31 *Spruance*-class destroyers were carefully designed and built in the 1970s with a great deal of attention to future up-rating. They were built in modular fashion as weapons platforms on which new weapons and electronic devices could easily be mounted as they became available during the expected 30-year lifetime of the class. The Ingalls Shipbuilding yards in Mississippi built a new facility to turn out all the *Spruance*-class destroyers.

Although the same size as most postwar cruisers, *Spruance*-class destroyers are powered by gas turbine engines instead of steam turbine—the first ships that large to be so operated. The General Electric LM 2500 gas turbine engines produce a total of 80,000 horsepower, which enables these ships to run at 32.5 knots (37.4 miles per hour). They have an unrefueled range of 6,000 nautical miles (6,900 miles) at 20 knots (23 miles per hour) and 3,300 nautical miles (3,795 miles) at 30 knots (34.5 miles per hour), a far greater operating range than the earlier steam-driven *Farragut*-class destroyers. The two gas turbine engines are paired to turn two controllable-pitch propellers. Even the electrical generators are run by a small gas turbine engine. The use of gas turbine engines minimizes noise. When *Spruance*-class destroyers are running ASW operations, they are quieter than any other surface ship in the U.S. Navy or any other navy in the world.

When first launched, *Spruance* destroyers seemed too lightly armed for warships. This perceived deficiency was the subject of a long hue and cry from the media and Congress. But the lack of armament is merely a perception. Unlike *Charles F. Adams*-class and *Farragut*-class destroyers, *Spruance*-class ships were not designed as anti-air war (AAW) defense ships, but as ASW ships. For self-protection, however most ships in the class do carry one eight-cell Mark 29 launcher for the short-range Sea Sparrow (RIM-7) AAW missile and two 20 millimeter Phalanx Close-In Weapons System guns. And their two five-inch dual-purpose Mark 45 guns can also be used in the air-defense role.

For surface and antisubmarine warfare, they are heavily armed. They carry eight Harpoon (RGM-84A) surface-to-surface missiles fired from Mark 141 launchers and eight Tomahawk (BGM-109) sea- and land-attack cruise missiles. The Tomahawks are fired from two quadruple-mount Mark 143 missile launchers in some of the ships and from the 61-cell Mark 41 Vertical Launch System (VLS) launcher in the rest. *Spruance*-class destroyers are also armed with ASROC (RUR-5A) antisubmarine torpedoes, fired from the Mark 16 launcher or from the VLS in those ships equipped with it. The Mark 16 launcher and its reloader have a total capacity of 24 ASROC missiles. The launchers are removed when the VLS system is installed in the deck forward of the bridge.

Six Mark 46 12.75-inch torpedoes can be fired from two triple Mark 32 launchers behind sliding hatches in the hull. The torpedo launchers are mounted on the enclosed main deck directly below the helicopter deck.

The USS *Merrill* was fitted with the Tomahawk missile in its Armored Box Launcher (ABL) in October 1982 and served as the test ship for the system. The Tomahawks in their ABLs are mounted in front of the bridge on either side of the ASROC Mark 16 launcher and behind the five-inch gun. So many different launchers can be fitted on the *Spruance*-

Above: *All* Spruance-*class destroyers were built by the Litton/Ingalls Shipyard at Pascagoula, Mississippi, between 1972 and 1983.* Right: Spruance *destroyers were originally intended as antisubmarine warfare ships.*

class destroyers, and so many combinations and varieties of missiles can be launched from them, that the designers achieved their aim in building a weapons platform on which various weapons can be interchanged. Despite the initial criticism, when the VLS launch system, Harpoons, and Phalanx gun systems are installed on all ships of the class, the *Spruance* destroyers will be the most heavily armed destroyers in any of the world's navies.

To attain their full ASW capability, the *Spruance* class is being fitted with the SQR-19 Tactical Towed Array Sonar in addition to the highly successful SQS-53A bow-mounted sonar. All ships of the class are slated to be refitted with the more capable SQS-53B sonar system.

Given the Service Life Extension Program system that seems to be able to add from 15 to 20 years to a ship's life, it is conceivable that *Spruance*-class destroyers will be in service into the second decade and possibly the third decade of the 21st century.

SPRUANCE-CLASS (DD) DESTROYERS

Operational (commissioned):

DD 963 USS *Spruance* (September 1975)
DD 964 USS *Paul F. Forester* (February 1976)
DD 965 USS *Kinkaid* (July 1976)
DD 966 USS *Hewitt* (September 1976)
DD 967 USS *Elliot* (January 1976)
DD 968 USS *Arthur W. Radford* (April 1977)
DD 969 USS *Peterson* (July 1977)
DD 970 USS *Caron* (October 1977)
DD 971 USS *David R. Ray* (November 1977)
DD 972 USS *Oldendorf* (March 1978)
DD 973 USS *John Young* (May 1978)
DD 974 USS *Comte De Grasse* (August 1978)
DD 975 USS *O'Brien* (December 1977)
DD 976 USS *Merrill* (March 1978)
DD 977 USS *Briscoe* (June 1978)
DD 978 USS *Stump* (August 1978)
DD 979 USS *Conolly* (October 1978)
DD 980 USS *Moosbrugger* (December 1978)
DD 981 USS *John Hancock* (March 1979)
DD 982 USS *Nicholson* (May 1979)
DD 983 USS *John Rodgers* (July 1979)
DD 984 USS *Leftwich* (August 1979)
DD 985 USS *Cushing* (October 1979)
DD 986 USS *Harry W. Hill* (November 1979)
DD 987 USS *O'Bannon* (December 1979)
DD 988 USS *Thorn* (February 1980)
DD 989 USS *Devo* (March 1980)
DD 990 USS *Ingersoll* (April 1980)
DD 991 USS *Fife* (May 1980)
DD 992 USS *Fletcher* (July 1980)
DD 997 USS *Hayler* (March 1983)

Displacement: 8,040 tons
Dimensions:
Length: 529 ft.
Beam: 55 ft.
Draft: 29 ft.
Propulsion: Four General Electric LM 2500 gas turbine engines
Speed: 32.5 knots (37.4 mph)
Armament:
All:
Sea Sparrow missiles in one 8-tube Mk 29 launcher
Eight Harpoon (RGM-84A) missles in two quadruple Mk 141 launchers
Six 12.75-inch torpedoes in two triple Mk 32 launchers
Two 20mm Phalanx CIWS Mk 15 chain guns
Two 5-inch dual-purpose Mk 45

DD 963–973, 975, 977, 978, 980–982, 985–988, 991, 992, 997: Mk 41 Vertical Launch System for Tomahawk and ASROC (RUR-5A) missiles

DD 974, 976, 979, 983, 984, 989, 990: Twenty-four ASROC (RUR-5A) missiles in one 8-tube Mk 16 launcher

DD 974, 976, 979, 983, 984, 989, 990: Eight Tomahawk missiles in two quadruple Mk 143 armored box launchers

Fire control:
One SWG-2 Tomahawk weapon control system in ships fitted with ABL
One SWG-3 Tomahawk weapon control system in ships fitted with VLS
One Mk 91 missile fire control system with SPG-80 and SPQ-9A radars
One Mk 86 gun fire control system with SPG-60 and SPQ-9A radars
One Mk 116 ASW fire control system

Aircraft: 2 SH-60B Seahawk LAMPS III helicopters

Surveillance radar:
SPS-4OB/C/D surface search
SPS-55 surface search

Sonar:
All: SQS-53A bow mount
DD 980: SQR-19 Towed Array Surveillance System

Crew: Approximately 334

Above: Spruance *destroyers have hangar facilities for two SH-60B Seahawk LAMPS III helicopters.* Left: *This view of the USS* Spruance *clearly shows its forward 5-inch gun and, just behind the gun, the Mk 16 ASROC missile launcher.*

Kidd-Class (DDG) Guided-Missile Destroyers

During the 1970s, the United States government closely supported the government of the Shah of Iran. The U.S. assisted in the construction of Iranian armed forces to act as a significant power in the Persian Gulf region to counterbalance Iraqi and Soviet intentions. A great deal of sophisticated military equipment was sold to the Shah's government, and the sale of a great deal more was pending at the time of the Islamic Revolution in 1979. Among the military equipment then being discussed were four extremely capable guided-missiles destroyers (*Karuroosh*, *Daryush*, *Ardeshir*, and *Nader*) based on an improved *Spruance*-class design. When the new Iranian government proved hostile to the United States, the sale of these destroyers was suspended and they were subsequently purchased by the U.S. Navy.

These destroyers comprise the *Kidd* class. Although they lack the Aegis SPY-1 anti-air war (AAW) system, they have extensive AAW as well as antisubmarine warfare (ASW) capabilities. Because the Iranian government wanted significant AAW and ASW capabilities in their new destroyers, the original version of the *Spruance*-class destroyers (called DGX) was resurrected and the *Kidd* class built to those specifications.

On a helicopter deck aft of the stern deckhouse, these destroyers have a closed hangar capable of housing two SH-60B Seahawk Light Airborne Multipurpose System III (LAMPS III) helicopters. At this time, however, only a single SH-2F Seasprite LAMPS I helicopter is carried aboard.

In addition to a full complement of AAW missiles, two five-inch Mark 45 dual-purpose guns are also carried, one on the main deck forward and the other on the main deck aft. These ships also carry two 20 millimeter Phalanx Close-In Weapons System Mark 15 chain guns. AAW missiles include the Standard-ER (RIM-67B) surface-to-air missile in two Mark 26 twin launchers with a complement of 68 missiles in the launcher and reloader. The forward missile launcher has a capacity of 24 missiles instead of the usual 44. The Mark 26 missile launchers are located forward on the main deck ahead of the bridge and on the 01 level of the aft deckhouse. Eight Harpoon (RGM-84A) missiles in two Mark 141 quadruple-mount launchers are also carried. The Harpoon launchers are mounted on either side of the aft deckhouse.

ASW weaponry includes the ASROC (RUR-5A) missile, which is also fired from the Mark 26 launchers, and six Mark 46 12.75-inch torpedoes in two Mark 32 triple-tube launchers. These launchers are mounted inside the ship and fire through ports below the helicopter deck. Plans have been made to install the SQR-19 Tactical Towed Array Sonar sleds at some future date.

The *Kidd* class is powered by four General Electric LM 2500 gas turbine engines that develop a total of 80,000 horsepower. They drive two shafts to produce speeds in excess of 30 knots (34.5 miles per hour). They have a range of 6,000 nautical miles (6,900 miles) at 20 knots (23 miles per hour) and 3,300 nautical miles (3,795 miles) at full speed.

Above: *The USS* Scott, *like all* Kidd *ships, was originally built for the Iranian Navy.*

KIDD-CLASS GUIDED-MISSILE (DDG) DESTROYERS

Operational (commissioned):	DDG 993 USS *Kidd* (July 1981) DDG 994 USS *Callaghan* (August 1981) DDG 995 USS *Scott* (October 1981) DDG 996 USS *Chandler* (March 1982)
Displacement:	9,574 tons
Dimensions:	
Length:	563 ft., 5 in.
Beam:	55 ft.
Draft:	30 ft.
Propulsion:	Four General Electric LM 2500 gas turbine engines
Speed:	30 knots (34.5 mph)
Armament:	Sixteen ASROC (RUR-5A) missiles in two twin Mk 26 launcher Approx. 68 Standard-ER (RIM-67B) missiles in two twin Mk 26 launchers Eight Harpoon (RGM-84A) missiles in two quadruple Mk 141 launchers Six 12.75-inch torpedoes in two triple Mk 32 launchers Two 20mm Phalanx CIWS Mk 15 chain guns Two 5-inch dual-purpose Mk 45 guns
Fire control:	Two Mk 74 missile fire control systems with SPG-51D radar One Mk 86 gun fire control system with SPG-60 and SPQ-9A radars One Mk 116 ASW fire control system
Aircraft:	One SH-2F Seasprite LAMPS I helicopter
Surveillance radar:	SPS-53 surface search SPS-55 surface search SPS-48C 3D air search
Sonar:	SLQ-25 Nixie SLQ-32(V)2
Crew:	339

Top: Kidd-*class destroyers are considered the most all-around capable destroyers in U.S. Navy service.* Bottom: *The USS* Callaghan, *like all of the* Kidd *class, was bought by the U.S. Navy after the fall of the Shah's government in Iran.*

Arleigh Burke-Class (DDG) Guided-Missile Destroyers

Above: *The USS* Arleigh Burke, *the name ship of the class, is the newest destroyer in the U.S. Navy.*

The *Arleigh Burke* series is a new class of guided-missile destroyer equipped for anti-air warfare (AAW). The series is intended to support Aegis-equipped cruisers and defend carrier task forces against enemy aircraft and missile attack. Once they are in service, they will be far more capable than any other class of destroyer and all cruisers as well, except those equipped with Aegis AAW systems.

This new class was first conceived in the late 1970s. The plans were for a 49-ship class. Under the Reagan administration, the class was first increased to 63 ships, but after the Department of Defense budget reductions of the mid-1980s, it was reduced to 29.

These ships will be built in two shipyards, Bath Iron Works in Maine and Ingalls Shipbuilding in Mississippi. A third source, Todd Pacific Shipyards in San Pedro, California, could not qualify and is closing operations. Construction of the first ship in this class, the *Arleigh Burke*, was started in July 1986 and launched in 1988. Since fitting-out is currently more than a year behind schedule, commissioning is not expected until 1990 at the earliest. The cost of these ships, which had a great deal to do with the reduction in numbers to be built, has risen from a per-ship price of $79 million in 1984 to $741.8 million in 1989.

The ships of the *Arleigh Burke* class were designed to be smaller and less expensive than the *Ticonderoga* Aegis-equipped vessels, which were finally classified as cruisers. Initially, the displacement of *Arleigh Burke*-class destroyers was not to be more than 6,000 tons. The decision to build the superstructure of steel rather than aluminum increased the displacement to more than 8,000 tons. Steel will provide additional strength against blast, fragment, and fire damage as well as increased protection against electromagnetic pulse weapons. This decision was based on a study of the collision between the *Belknap* (CG 26) and the *John F. Kennedy* (CV 67); the loss of HMS *Coventry* and HMS *Broadsword* during the 1982 Falkland Islands War later confirmed the decision. This class will also have additional Kevlar armor and nuclear-biological-chemical protection. The ships will be powered by four gas turbine engines that will develop a total of 100,000 horsepower at 30 knots (34.5 miles per hour).

Arleigh Burke-class ships will be equipped to land helicopters and provide minimal support to them. Currently, the Navy is following a congressional directive to determine if it is feasible to maintain a Light Airborne Multipurpose System III (LAMPS III) helicopter—the SH-60B Seahawk—aboard without jeopardizing the primary AAW mission and without increasing costs to unacceptable levels or delaying the construction program further. The Navy has determined that if the aft missile launcher facility were removed, two LAMPS III helicopters could be accommodated. But the loss of these 61 launching canisters would greatly reduce the ship's effectiveness as an AAW vessel.

The new destroyers will be equipped with one five-inch

ARLEIGH BURKE-CLASS (DDG) GUIDED-MISSILE DESTROYERS

Operational:	None
Launched:	DDG 51 USS *Arleigh Burke*
Building:	DDG 52 USS *John Barry*
Planned:	DDG 53 USS *John Paul Jones* DDG 54 USS *Curtis Wilbur* 23 additional
Displacement:	8,300 tons
Dimensions:	
Length:	466 ft.
Beam:	59 ft.
Draft:	37 ft., 7 in.
Propulsion:	Four General Electric LM 2500-30 gas turbine engines
Speed:	30 knots (34.5 mph)
Armament:	Two Mk 41 Mod 2 Vertical Launch Systems firing ASROC, Standard-MR (RIM-66C), and Tomahawk missiles Eight Harpoon (RGM-84A) missiles in two quadruple Mk 141 launchers Six 12.75-inch torpedoes in two triple Mk 32 launchers Two 20mm Phalanx CIWS Mk 15 chain guns One 5-inch dual-purpose Mk 75 gun
Fire control:	One SWG-3 Tomahawk fire control system Mk 99 Illuminators with SPG-62 radar One Mk 56 gun fire control system
Aircraft:	One SH-60B Seahawk LAMPS III (provisional)
Surveillance radar:	SQS-53C bow-mounted SPS-64 surface search SPS-67 surface search Four SPY-1D multifunction
Sonar:	SLQ-25 Nixie SLQ-32(V)2 SQR-19 tactical towed array sonar
Crew:	325

dual-purpose Mark 75 gun and two Phalanx Close-In Weapons System 20 millimeter twin-barrel point defense guns. They will carry two Mark 41 Vertical Launch System launchers for the Standard (RIM-67) surface-to-air missile and Tomahawk (BGM-109) cruise missile. The forward launcher will have 29 launching cells, the aft launcher 61. ASROC missiles will also be carried in the same launcher. Eight Harpoon missiles in two quadruple-mount Mark 141 launchers and six 12.75-inch torpedoes in Mark 32 launchers complete the armament of this class.

The electronic suite of the new destroyer class is only slightly less capable than that of the larger Aegis-equipped cruisers. These destroyers will carry four SPY-1D multifunction radars in addition to the usual air- and surface-search radars and fire control systems. In addition to the SQS-53C bow-mounted radar, they will also be equipped with the SQR-19 Tactical Towed Array Sonar sleds, which are pulled behind the ship during ASW operations.

At present, only four *Arleigh Burke*-class ships have actually been funded. At least 23 more ships are planned for funding. If these ships are actually built, the *Arleigh Burke*-class destroyer will be the Navy's mainstay well into the 21st century.

Above: *The USS* Arleigh Burke *under construction at Bath Iron Works, Maine.*

FRIGATES

Frigates in the United States Navy are primarily intended to serve as antisubmarine warfare (ASW) escorts, except for the *Oliver Hazard Perry* class, which provides limited anti-air warfare (AAW) protection as well.

The frigate class of ships dates to the 18th century, when they were introduced into the French Navy. The original frigates were two-decked ships that carried their armament on the top deck only. The British Royal Navy captured several French frigates in the 1740s and early 1750s, adopted the class, and even improved upon it. The chief attributes of the frigate were speed, excellent handling characteristics, and heavy armament for its size and displacement. Frigates were eagerly adopted by the new U.S. Navy because they were less complicated and thus quicker and cheaper to build. One of the most famous ships in American naval service is the frigate USS *Constitution,* built in the 1790s, still in commission today, and berthed in Boston Harbor.

When the steam engine replaced the sail, the frigate class of sailing ship declined and disappeared. The term was not used again until 1941, when the British Admiralty ordered a class of antisubmarine warfare escort vessels based on the Black Swan class of sloops. Although the new frigate class was larger than the sloop class, frigates carried fewer guns but more antisubmarine weapons in the form of Hedgehog depth charges and Squid mortars. By the end of World War II, the British had 105 frigates in service.

During World War II, the United States Navy also revived the frigate class to serve as convoy escorts. Two *Flower*-class ships were obtained from Canada to serve as prototypes, and a total of 100 *Ashville*-class and *Tacoma*-class frigates were built. All were retired immediately after the war ended.

In 1950, a second (*Dealy*) class of frigate was designed and built, but these ships were called ocean escorts rather than frigates. The *Dealy* ships have now all been turned over to friendly nations or stricken from the Navy list. Ten years later, at the urging of the Kennedy administration, the Navy revived the frigate class (FF) to serve as ASW escorts. They were to be fast enough to accompany carrier task forces; their main armament included 12.75-inch torpedoes fired from torpedo launchers or by rocket. They also carried one or more guns, either three-inch or five-inch, for antiaircraft protection. When the guns were replaced by guided missiles, the ships were known as guided-missile frigates (FFG).

At present, the U.S. Navy deploys 98 frigates, with 19 more in the Naval Reserve Fleet. The 19 Reserve ships have a combined active and reserve crew. No frigates are currently under construction, and none are planned until the late 1990s. A proposal to build an advanced-design frigate was canceled in 1986. The class with the most ships is the *Oliver Hazard Perry* class of frigates, which has 51 ships. In case of war, the *Perry*-class frigates will provide ASW and somewhat limited AAW protection to amphibious vessels, replenishment ships, and ships under convoy. They were also designed to provide ASW and AAW protection along the Sea Lanes of Communication (SLOC)—the shipping routes that were once known as trade routes. There is not a sufficient number of frigates to provide complete SLOC protection in case of an all-out war, but frigates constitute one of the few ship classes to have exceeded quotas in the quest for the 600-ship navy.

Left: Garcia-*class frigates are quite similar to* Brooke-*class frigates, but* Garcia *ships carry a second 5-inch gun rather than an antiaircraft missile launcher.* Opposite: *The USS* Schofield *is a* Brooke-*class guided-missile frigate.*

The USS Trippe *is a Knox-class frigate intended for surface warfare.*

Bronstein-Class (FF) Frigates

At the end of World War II, most destroyer escorts had top speeds between 20 and 25 knots (23 to 29 miles per hour). The development of the high-speed nuclear submarine in the United States, the Soviet Union, Great Britain, and France rendered all existing antisubmarine escorts too slow to keep pace with the new submarines. To increase speed as well as capability, the *Bronstein*-class frigate was developed in the mid-to-late 1950s. The new class was to be quite different from previous escort designs and was intended to serve as a prototype for later classes of escort vessels. Only two ships in this class were built. In June 1975, in the Navy-wide reorganization of ship classes, the *Bronstein* vessels were reclassified as frigates (FF).

In the *Bronstein* class, steam propulsion replaced the diesel propulsion of World War II vessels. The De Laval company developed a steam turbine that could produce a total of 20,000 horsepower from the output of two Foster Wheeler boilers. The combination turned a single propeller and drove the new ship at 24 knots (27.6 miles per hour). At 15 knots (17.25 miles per hour), *Bronstein* ships had a range of 4,000 nautical miles (4,600 miles). But this speed and range proved insufficient as high-speed submarine technology continued to develop.

Two other radical features of the *Bronstein*-class frigates were the raked stem design (angled bow support inside the hull) and, beneath it, the bow-mounted sonar. The raked stem design remained constant in all subsequent classes of frigates built by the U.S. Navy. The bow-mounted sonar was used in subsequent frigate classes until replaced by a keel-mounted unit in the *Oliver Hazard Perry* class.

Armament included two Mark 33 three-inch antiaircraft deck guns in a forward twin mount. These guns were the last three-inch guns to be installed on frigates until the *Perry* class. A single-mount three-inch gun was installed aft; it was later removed to make way for the Towed Array Surveillance System, which was installed only in the USS *McCloy.* For antisubmarine warfare, the *Bronstein* class was later equipped with an eight-tube Mark 16 ASROC launcher. There is no room in this class for the reloader. The two ships also carry two Mark 32 triple-tube launchers for the wire-guided Mark 46 homing torpedo. Both vessels had the capability to carry the DASH (Drone Antisubmarine Helicopter). When the project was canceled, that area on the afterdeck was converted to a helicopter landing pad. But neither ship has facilities for housing or maintaining a helicopter.

Both ships were built in the Avondale Shipyards, New Orleans, Louisiana. Both began construction in 1961, were launched the following year, and commissioned in 1963. The two *Bronstein*-class frigates can be identified by their distinctive mack (combined mast and smokestack). The round smokestacks jut from the structure at a sharp angle.

Although they pioneered several unique concepts in frigate escort design, the *Bronstein*-class frigates lacked the speed and range to successfully guard against Soviet nuclear submarines. No other ships of this class were built.

Right: Bronstein-*class frigates, such as the USS* McCloy, *were equipped with sophisticated antisubmarine warfare capabilities.*

BRONSTEIN-CLASS (FF) FRIGATES

Operational (commissioned):	FF 1037 USS *Bronstein* (June 1963) FF 1038 USS *McCloy* (October 1963)
Displacement:	3,560 tons
Dimensions:	
Length:	371 ft., 6 in.
Beam:	40 ft., 6 in.
Draft:	23 ft.
Propulsion:	One De Laval steam turbine Two Foster Wheeler 600-psi boilers
Speed:	24 knots (27.6 mph)
Armament:	ASROCs (RUR-5A) in one 8-tube Mk 16 launcher Six 12.75-inch torpedoes in two triple Mk 32 launchers Two 3-inch Mk 33 antiaircraft guns
Fire control:	One Mk 1 target designator One Mk 114 ASW fire control system One Mk 56 gun fire control system with Mk 35 radar
Aircraft:	None
Surveillance radar:	SPS-20 surface search SPS-40 air search
Sonar:	
All:	SQS-26AXR bow mount
FF 1038:	SQR-15 TASS
Crew:	
FF 1037:	216
FF 1038:	218

Garcia-Class (FF) Frigates

The *Garcia* class of frigates was originally ordered as destroyer escorts. The design was developed from the earlier *Bronstein*-class design. *Garcia*-class frigates are intended strictly for antisubmarine warfare. Since they have only one propeller and therefore limited speed, *Garcia* ships were reclassified as frigates (FF) in June 1975.

The ten frigates of the *Garcia* class are bigger than the *Bronstein*-class vessels. They are powered by one Westinghouse steam turbine developing a total of 35,000 horsepower. Steam is supplied by two Foster Wheeler boilers that are fitted with an integrated supercharger and control system that automatically regulates the intake of air, water, and fuel. Use of Naval Distillate fuel (a more refined naval fuel than is normally used) simplifies maintenance. This type of pressure-fired boiler was also installed in *Brooke*-class frigates and in the experimental ship, USS *Glover.* Range at 20 knots (23 miles per hour) is 4,000 nautical miles (4,600 miles).

Originally, the ships were to mount two five-inch Mark 42 guns, which could be fired remotely or under local control. But to keep costs down, two five-inch Mark 30 guns were mounted instead, one forward of the bridge and one on the after superstructure forward of the helicopter hangar. The location of the after gun tends to restrict its field of fire. These two guns, with a rate of fire slower than the Mark 42, provide the only self-defense for *Garcia*-class ships. *Garcia* frigates carry no anti-air warfare missiles or point defense guns. For air defense, they usually depend on *Brooke*-class frigates for protection.

USS *Bradley* evaluated the Sea Sparrow (RIM-7) surface-to-surface missile for the class, but they were never installed in other ships. The *Bradley*'s Sea Sparrows were removed and reinstalled in the USS *Forrestal.*

The frigates of this class have a flush-decked hull, which means the main deck is flush with the top of the hull from bow to stern. In other words, the main deck does not rise above or fall below the top of the hull. A mack structure juts from amidships and carries a variety of antennae. The afterdeck has a hangar structure originally intended to house the DASH (Drone Antisubmarine Helicopter). When the DASH program was canceled, the hangar was enlarged to house the Light Airborne Multipurpose System I (LAMPS I) SH-2F Seasprite helicopter. The LAMPS I provides the *Garcia* class with its primary antisubmarine warfare capability.

In addition to the Seasprite helicopter, the *Garcia* class carries an eight-tube Mark 16 ASROC (RUR-5A) missile launcher. In FF 1047 to FF 1051, the launcher has a reload capability of 16; earlier ships have no reload capability. The ASROC launcher is mounted forward of the bridge and behind the forward five-inch gun. Two triple-tube Mark 32 torpedo launchers are also carried. They fire the 12.75-inch homing torpedo.

Above: *The* Garcia *class evolved from the* Bronstein *class. Such ships as the USS* Bradley *were larger and more heavily armed than their predecessors.*

GARCIA-CLASS (FF) FRIGATES

Operational (commissioned):	FF 1040 USS *Garcia* (December 1964) FF 1041 USS *Bradley* (May 1965) FF 1043 USS *Edward McDonnell* (February 1965) FF 1044 USS *Brumbey* (August 1965) FF 1045 USS *Davidson* (December 1965) FF 1047 USS *Voge* (November 1986) FF 1048 USS *Sample* (March 1968) FF 1049 USS *Koelsch* (June 1967) FF 1050 USS *Albert David* (October 1968) FF 1051 USS *O'Callahan* (July 1968)
Displacement:	3,560 tons
Dimensions:	
Length:	414 ft., 6 in.
Beam:	44 ft., 6 in.
Draft:	24 ft.
Propulsion:	One Westinghouse steam turbine Two Foster Wheeler 1,200-psi pressure-fired boilers
Speed:	27 knots (31 mph)
Armament:	ASROCs (RUR-5A) in one 8-tube Mk 16 launcher Six 12.75-inch torpedoes in two triple Mk 32 launchers Two 5-inch Mk 30 dual-purpose guns
Fire control:	One Mk 1 target designator One Mk 114 ASW fire control system One Mk 56 gun fire control system with Mk 35 radar
Aircraft:	One LAMPS I SH-2F Seasprite helicopter
Surveillance radar:	SPS-10 surface search SPS-40B air search
Sonar:	
FF 1040–1045:	SQS-26AXR bow mount
FF 1047–1051:	SQS-26BX bow mount
FF 1040, 43, 48, 50:	SQR-15 TACTAS
Crew:	273 (average)

Top: *The USS* O'Callahan *carries the Mk 16 ASROC launcher and two 5-inch guns, as do all* Garcia *frigates.* Center: Garcia *frigates were originally ordered as destroyer escorts, but the Navy reclassified them as frigates in 1975.* Bottom: *The* Brumbey *is a* Garcia-*class frigate; all these ships carry the SH-2F LAMPS I helicopter.* Opposite: *The* Garcia-*class frigates were the first to use pressure-fired boilers.*

Brooke-Class (FFG) Guided-Missile Frigates

The *Brooke*-class frigates were designed in the late 1950s to serve as antisubmarine warfare (ASW) escorts in theaters of low-intensity conflict. They were given minimal anti-air warfare (AAW) and anti-surface warfare defenses but somewhat better ASW capability. The last frigate in this class was commissioned in November 1967. They have been divided evenly between the Atlantic and Pacific fleets.

Originally, a large number of *Brooke*-class frigates were to be built, but the AAW missile fitted to the ship increased the price to $11 million more than the *Garcia*-class frigate, which had no AAW missile capability. Congress directed that no more *Brooke*-class frigates be built after FFG 6, USS *Julius A. Furer.*

Brooke-class frigates are powered by two high-pressure boilers supplying steam to a single turbine, which develops a total of 35,000 horsepower and drives one propeller shaft. The frigates have a top speed in excess of 27 knots (31 miles per hour) and a range of 4,000 nautical miles (4,600 miles).

Their AAW armament originally consisted of the Tartar (RIM-24) missile, which has since been replaced by the Standard-MR (RIM-67A) in the Mark 22 Modification 0 launcher. This launcher has a reload capacity of 16 missiles, compared with a reload capacity of 40 missiles standard on larger vessels carrying later modifications of the Mark 22. The launcher is mounted on the after superstructure behind the helicopter hangar and replaces the second five-inch gun used in the *Garcia* class. Neither the Phalanx nor Vulcan point defense gun systems are mounted in the *Brooke* class.

Surface warfare capability includes the Mark 30 dual-purpose five-inch gun mounted on the main deck forward of the bridge. Antisubmarine warfare weapons include the ASROC (RUR-5A) missile propulsion unit for the Mark 46 homing torpedo, as well as six additional Mark 46 torpedoes fired from two Mark 32 triple-tube launchers. Harpoon (RGM-84) missiles cannot be carried because of the limited capacity of the particular Mark 22 launcher installed.

Brooke-class frigates also carry one SH-2F Seasprite Light Airborne Multipurpose System I (LAMPS I) helicopter, which is housed in a hangar on the afterdeck. The hangar was originally designed for the DASH project (Drone Antisubmarine Helicopter), a remotely controlled vehicle that could be flown by an operator on the ship. This project has subsequently been canceled.

Sonar and radar capability, while limited in comparison with larger escorts, are sufficient for its escort role in limited conflict situations.

Above: *The USS* Julius A. Furer *is a* Brooke-*class frigate.*

BROOKE-CLASS (FFG) GUIDED-MISSILE FRIGATES

Operational (commissioned):	FFG 1 USS *Brooke* (March 1966) FFG 2 USS *Ramsey* (June 1967) FFG 3 USS *Schofield* (May 1967) FFG 4 USS *Talbot* (April 1967) FFG 5 USS *Richard L. Page* (August 1967) FFG 6 USS *Julius A. Furer* (November 1967)
Displacement:	3,600 tons
Dimensions:	
Length:	390 ft.
Beam:	44 ft., 2.4 in.
Draft:	24 ft.
Propulsion:	One General Electric steam turbine Two Foster Wheeler 1,200-psi boilers
Speed:	27 knots (31 mph)
Armament:	ASROCs (RUR-5A) in one 8-tube Mk 16 launcher Standard-MR (RIM-67A) missiles in one Mk 22 Mod 0 launcher Six 12.75-inch torpedoes in two triple Mk 32 launchers One 5-inch Mk 30 dual-purpose gun
Fire control:	One Mk 4 weapon director One Mk 72 missile fire control system One Mk 114 ASW fire control system One Mk 56 gun fire control system One SPG-51C radar
Aircraft:	One SH-2F Seasprite LAMPS I helicopter
Surveillance radar:	SPS-49(V)214 surface search SPS-55 surface search
Sonar:	
FFG 1–3:	SQS-26AXR bow mount
FFG 4–6:	SQS-26BX bow mount
Crew:	277

Top: Brooke-*class frigates, such as the USS* Schofield, *share the same basic hull and propulsion system as the* Garcia *class.* Center: *The major difference between the* Garcia *class and the* Brooke *class is the substitution of a Mk 22 missile launcher for the second 5-inch gun, as seen here on the USS* Brooke. Bottom: *The* Julius A. Furer, *like all* Brooke *frigates, carries an SH-2F LAMPS I helicopter.* Right: Brooke-*class frigates, such as the USS* Talbot, *are fast anti-air and antisubmarine escorts.*

Only six Brooke*-class frigates were built because of the high cost of their missile systems.*

Knox-Class (FF) Frigates

The 46 ships of the *Knox* class were built between 1965 and 1973. *Knox*-class frigates are quite large for escort frigates, and they were the most numerous ship class to be built for the U.S. Navy prior to the *Spruance*-class destroyer.

Knox ships were originally classified as ocean escorts but were reclassified as frigates in 1975 in the Navy-wide reclassification program. *Knox* frigates are long, sleek ships with a round mack rising amidships that houses a latticework of radar and other antennae. The mack was built to house a more capable radar suite, but it was never built.

The powerplant used in the *Knox* class comprises two non-pressure boilers built by Combustion Engineering driving a Westinghouse steam turbine that develops a total of 35,000 horsepower. The powerplant provides *Knox*-class frigates with a top speed of more than 27 knots (31 miles per hour). The new powerplant required that the hull be built on a larger scale than in previous classes. One ship of this class was to have been built with a gas turbine powerplant for evaluation, but the order was canceled.

Designed primarily to escort convoys, amphibious task forces, and replenishment ships, *Knox* ships have only limited anti-air warfare and antisubmarine warfare capability. But in recent years their surface warfare capability has grown. Most of the ships in this class were originally equipped with a Sea Sparrow (RIM-7) point defense missile system fired from an eight-tube Mark 25 launcher to provide protection against enemy ships also equipped with surface-to-surface missile launchers. The Mark 25 launcher was mounted on the stern and gave the ships a surface-to-surface missile capability up to ten nautical miles (11.5 miles). However, the Mark 25 launcher did not have a reload capability; once all eight missiles were fired, the launcher was useless until a replenishment ship supplied more missiles.

The Sea Sparrow missile system was removed and replaced by the Phalanx Close-In Weapons System 20 millimeter point defense gun to deal with close-in surface and airborne threats. Each *Knox*-class frigate also mounts a five-inch Mark 42 dual-purpose gun that is effective against low-flying attack aircraft and surface threats. *Knox*-class frigates also carry an eight-cell ASROC (RUR-5A) launcher equipped to fire the Harpoon (RGM-84A) missile. The launcher is mounted ahead of the bridge but behind the five-inch gun. The Harpoon is a longer-range missile—up to 90 nautical miles (103 miles)—than the Sea Sparrow. This combination of close-in and long-range striking power makes the *Knox* frigates formidable opponents in the surface warfare role.

Antisubmarine warfare capability is also quite good. All ships in the class are equipped with bow-mounted sonars, and of the 46 ships, 32 are equipped with the Tactical Towed Array System sonar. Each *Knox*-class frigate carries a Light Airborne Multipurpose System I (LAMPS I) SH-2F Seasprite helicopter, which is housed in a telescoping hangar on the rear deck. When the Seasprite lands, it is tied down, its blades folded, and a part of the hangar is moved to cover it. As with the *Brooke* class, *Knox* ships were originally fitted to carry the DASH (Drone Antisubmarine Helicopter), which is now defunct. This class of frigate fires the Mark 46 homing torpedo from the same launcher used for the Harpoon missile. *Knox* frigates also carry two twin-tube Mark 32 launchers for additional Mark 46 torpedoes.

The *Knox*-class vessels were known for shipping water over their low bow in rough seas. All have been, or are being, fitted with raised bow extensions that solve the problem. The Pacific fleet has 19 *Knox*-class frigates, 17 are assigned to the Atlantic fleet, and seven are with the Naval Reserve fleet. Naval Reserve fleet *Knox* frigates are manned by combined active and reserve crews.

Above: *Until the advent of the* Oliver Hazard Perry *class of frigates, the* Knox *class was the most numerous in the U.S. Navy. Seen here is the USS* Whipple. Opposite: *The USS* Roark, *the second* Knox-*class frigate built, shows its exceptional lines.*

1053

Left: *The USS* Ainsworth*'s 5-inch gun and SPS-40 air search radar on the mack can be clearly seen.*

KNOX-CLASS (FF) FRIGATES

Operational (commissioned):

- FF 1052 USS *Knox* (April 1969)
- FF 1053 USS *Roark* (November 1969)
- FF 1054 USS *Gray* (April 1970)
- FF 1055 USS *Hepburn* (July 1969)
- FF 1056 USS *Connole* (August 1969)
- FF 1057 USS *Rathburne* (May 1970)
- FF 1058 USS *Meyerkord* (November 1969)
- FF 1059 USS *W.S. Sims* (January 1970)
- FF 1060 USS *Lang* (March 1970)
- FF 1061 USS *Patterson* (March 1970)
- FF 1062 USS *Whipple* (August 1970)
- FF 1063 USS *Reasoner* (July 1971)
- FF 1064 USS *Lockwood* (December 1970)
- FF 1065 USS *Stein* (January 1972)
- FF 1066 USS *Marvin Shields* (April 1971)
- FF 1067 USS *Francis Hammond* (July 1970)
- FF 1068 USS *Vreeland* (June 1970)
- FF 1069 USS *Bagley* (May 1972)

Operational continued

- FF 1070 USS *Downes* (August 1971)
- FF 1071 USS *Badger* (December 1970)
- FF 1072 USS *Blakely* (July 1970)
- FF 1073 USS *Robert E. Peary* (September 1972)
- FF 1074 USS *Harold E. Holt* (March 1971)
- FF 1075 USS *Trippe* (September 1970)
- FF 1076 USS *Fanning* (July 1971)
- FF 1077 USS *Ouellet* (December 1970)
- FF 1078 USS *Joseph Hewes* (February 1971)
- FF 1079 USS *Bowen* (May 1971)
- FF 1080 USS *Paul* (August 1971)
- FF 1081 USS *Aylwin* (September 1971)
- FF 1082 USS *Elmer Montgomery* (October 1971)
- FF 1083 USS *Cook* (December 1971)
- FF 1084 USS *McCandless* (March 1972)
- FF 1085 USS *Donald B. Beary* (July 1972)
- FF 1086 USS *Brewton* (July 1972)
- FF 1087 USS *Kirk* (September 1972)

Left: *The hangar for the LAMPS I helicopter is clearly visible near the stern of the USS* Sims, *a* Knox-*class frigate.*

KNOX-CLASS (FF) FRIGATES

Operational continued	FF 1088 USS *Barbey* (November 1972) FF 1089 USS *Jesse L. Brown* (February 1973) FF 1090 USS *Ainsworth* (March 1973) FF 1091 USS *Miller* (June 1973) FF 1092 USS *Thomas C. Hart* (July 1973) FF 1093 USS *Capodanno* (November 1973) FF 1094 USS *Pharris* (January 1974) FF 1095 USS *Truett* (June 1974) FF 1096 USS *Valdez* (July 1974) FF 1097 USS *Moinester* (November 1974)
Displacement:	4,250 tons
Dimensions:	
Length:	438 ft.
Beam:	44 ft., 2.4 in.
Draft:	24 ft., 9 in.
Propulsion:	One Westinghouse steam turbine Two Combustion Engineering 1,200-psi boilers
Speed:	27 knots (31 mph)
Armament:	One 8-tube Mk 16 launcher for ASROC (RUR-5A) and Harpoon (RGM-84A) missiles and Mk 46 torpedoes Four 12.75-inch torpedoes in two twin Mk 32 launchers

Armament continued:	One 5-inch Mk 42 dual-purpose gun One Phalanx CIWS Mk 15 gun
Fire control:	One Mk 1 target designator One Mk 114 ASW fire control system One Mk 68 gun fire control system
Aircraft:	One LAMPS I SH-2F Seasprite helicopter
Surveillance radar:	SPS-10 surface search SPS-40B air search SPS-58 threat warning (in some ships)
Sonar:	
FF 1052, 1056, 1063–1071, 1073–1076, 1078–1097:	SQS-35 IVDS SQR-18A TACTAS
FF 1053–1055, 1057–1062, 1072, 1077:	SQS-26CX bow mount SQR-18V
Crew:	
FF 1052, 1054, 1056–1059, 1062–1071, 1073–1090, 1092–1095, 1097:	282
FF 1053, 1055, 1060, 1061, 1072, 1091, 1096:	175 active, 127–155 reserve

Oliver Hazard Perry-Class (FFG) Guided-Missile Frigates

After the Vietnam War, when military budgets and commitments were contracting, a new, cheap class of frigate was created, using the latest management and manufacturing procedures coupled with computerized planning, scheduling, design, and assembly techniques. The chief purpose of these ships—the *Oliver Hazard Perry* class—was to escort merchant ships, replenishment ships, and amphibious task forces. They were not intended to perform antisubmarine warfare (ASW), anti-air warfare (AAW), or surface warfare protection for large aircraft carrier-led task forces, but they have capabilities in all three areas. The *Perry*-class frigates are primarily escort ships. Their initial designation was patrol frigate.

A total of 75 such frigates were planned, but even as planning continued, the number began to decrease as enthusiasm for the now-defunct FFX small-frigate program increased. During the late 1970s and early 1980s, the planned number of *Perry*-class frigates fluctuated until the program settled at 51 vessels. Four additional ships were built by the Todd Shipyards in Seattle, Washington, and sold to Australia (FFG 17, 18, 35, and 44). Spain purchased two frigates. Additional ships of this design are being built in Australia and Spain.

The hulls were built as prefabricated sections in a number of shipyards around the country and then shipped to the Bath Iron Works in Maine, the Todd Shipyards in California, or the Todd Shipyards in Washington for assembly and fitting out. Flat panels and uncomplicated bulkheads were used as much as possible.

Ships of the *Perry* class are propelled by gas turbine engines, the same power suite used in *Spruance*-class destroyers, but *Perry* ships drive only one screw. Even so, some *Perry*-class ships have reported attaining speeds of 36 knots (41.4 miles per hour) during trials. The propulsion system produces a total of 40,000 horsepower at 28 knots (32.2 miles per hour). *Perry*-class ships also have auxiliary propellers mounted amidships in retractable pods; the propellers are powered by 350 horsepower electric drives. These auxiliary propellers increase *Perry*-class ships' maneuvering ability and provide an emergency power source should the main engines fail or be damaged.

The *Perry*-class frigates are lightly armed, in keeping with their status as "low-end" frigates, as opposed to the more costly and specialized *Spruance*-class destroyers and *Ticonderoga*-class cruisers whose task is to protect large carrier task forces. *Perry*-class frigates are equipped with one Mark 13 twin launcher capable of loading and firing the Standard-MR (RIM-67A) AAW or Harpoon (RGM-84) surface-to-surface missile. The launcher is mounted above the

Above: *The USS* Jack Williams *of the* Oliver Hazard Perry *class of frigates was launched in August 1980.*

circular reloader (which holds 40 rounds) on the main deck forward of the bridge. The *Perry* class is also armed with the new single-barrel Mark 75 76 millimeter rapid-firing gun developed by the Italian firm of Oto Melara. The gun is used for defense against air and surface attack. It is housed in a unmanned turret on top of the superstructure, facing aft. The *Perry* class carries a single 20mm Phalanx Close-In Weapons System point defense gun, which is mounted atop the helicopter hangar, aft of the 76mm gun.

Each *Perry* frigate is equipped with two triple-tube Mark 32 launchers for the 12.75-inch Mark 46 homing torpedo. They also carry two ASW Light Airborne Multipurpose System (LAMPS) helicopters, either the SH-2F Seasprite (LAMPS I) or the SH-60B Seahawk (LAMPS III), as their principle antisubmarine warfare weapon. The helicopters are housed in hangars at the rear of the superstructure. The Recovery, Assistance, Securing, and Traversing system, which allows helicopters to hover above a ship in rough seas and be winched down to a safe landing, is also being installed.

The 51 frigates of the *Oliver Hazard Perry* class are divided between the active Atlantic and Pacific fleets (39 ships) and the reserve Atlantic and Pacific fleets (12 frigates). The latter are manned by a combination of active and reserve crews. These frigates were all built between 1977 and 1987. Given the standard lifetime of 30 years for a ship, *Perry*-class ships can expect to be serving past the first decade of the 21st century.

Above: *The USS* Klakring *is one of many* Oliver Hazard Perry*-class frigates.*

OLIVER HAZARD PERRY-CLASS (FFG) GUIDED-MISSILE FRIGATES

Operational (commissioned):

- FFG 7 USS *Oliver Hazard Perry* (December 1977)
- FFG 8 USS *McInerney* (December 1979)
- FFG 9 USS *Wadsworth* (April 1980)
- FFG 10 USS *Duncan* (May 1980)
- FFG 11 USS *Clark* (May 1980)
- FFG 12 USS *George Philip* (November 1980)
- FFG 13 USS *Samuel Eliot Morison* (October 1980)
- FFG 14 USS *Sides* (May 1981)
- FFG 15 USS *Estocin* (January 1981)
- FFG 16 USS *Clifton Sprague* (March 1981)
- FFG 19 USS *John A. Moore* (November 1981)
- FFG 20 USS *Antrim* (September 1981)
- FFG 21 USS *Flatley* (June 1981)
- FFG 22 USS *Fahrion* (January 1982)
- FFG 23 USS *Lewis B. Puller* (April 1982)
- FFG 24 USS *Jack Williams* (September 1981)
- FFG 25 USS *Copeland* (August 1982)
- FFG 26 USS *Gallery* (December 1981)
- FFG 27 USS *Mahlon S. Tisdale* (November 1982)
- FFG 28 USS *Boone* (November 1982)
- FFG 29 USS *Stephen W. Groves* (April 1982)
- FFG 30 USS *Reid* (February 1983)
- FFG 31 USS *Stark* (October 1982)
- FFG 32 USS *John L. Hall* (June 1982)
- FFG 33 USS *Jarrett* (July 1983)
- FFG 34 USS *Aubrey Fitch* (October 1982)
- FFG 36 USS *Underwood* (January 1983)
- FFG 37 USS *Crommelin* (June 1983)
- FFG 38 USS *Curts* (October 1983)
- FFG 39 USS *Doyle* (May 1983)
- FFG 40 USS *Halyburton* (January 1984)
- FFG 41 USS *McClusky* (October 1983)
- FFG 42 USS *Klakring* (August 1983)
- FFG 43 USS *Thach* (March 1984)

Operational continued

- FFG 45 USS *De Wert* (November 1983)
- FFG 46 USS *Rentz* (June 1984)
- FFG 47 USS *Nichols* (March 1984)
- FFG 48 USS *Vandegrift* (November 1984)
- FFG 49 USS *Robert G. Bradley* (August 1984)
- FFG 50 USS *Taylor* (December 1984)
- FFG 51 USS *Gary* (November 1984)
- FFG 52 USS *Carr* (July 1985)
- FFG 53 USS *Hawes* (September 1985)
- FFG 54 USS *Ford* (June 1985)
- FFG 55 USS *Elrod* (July 1985)
- FFG 56 USS *Simpson* (November 1985)
- FFG 57 USS *Reuben James* (March 1986)
- FFG 58 USS *Samuel B. Roberts* (April 1986)
- FFG 59 USS *Kauffman* (February 1987)
- FFG 60 USS *Rodney M. Davis* (May 1987)
- FFG 61 USS *Ingraham* (August 1989)

Displacement: 3,650 tons

Dimensions:
- **Length:**
  - **FFG 7, 9–35:** 445 ft.
  - **FFG 8, 36–61:** 453 ft.
- **Beam:** 45 ft.
- **Draft:** 24 ft., 6 in.

Propulsion: Four General Electric LM 2500 gas turbine engines

Speed: 28+ knots (32.2+ mph)

Armament:
- One twin Mk launcher for Standard-MR (RIM-67A) or Harpoon (RGM-84A) missiles
- Six 12.75-inch torpedoes in two triple Mk 32 launchers
- One 76mm Mk 75 gun
- One 20mm Phalanx CIWS Mk 15 gun

Fire control:
- One Mk 13 weapon director
- One Mk 92 fire control system
- One STIR radar

Aircraft:
- **FFG 7, 9–35:** Two SH-2F Seasprite LAMPS I helicopters
- **FFG 8, 36–61:** Two SH-60B Seahawk LAMPS III helicopters

Surveillance radar:
- SPS-49(V)214 surface search
- SPS-55 surface search

Sonar: SLQ-56 keel mount

Crew:
- **FFG 7, 9–20, 23:** 114 active, 76 reserve
- **FFG 8, 21, 22, 24–61:** 205

Above: *The* Oliver Hazard Perry *frigate* John L. Hall *was constructed at Bath Iron Works, Maine.*

The USS Crommelin, *an* Oliver Hazard Perry-*class frigate, sails past the aircraft carrier* Constellation.

37
10
NK

AMPHIBIOUS SHIPS

Much of the deterrent capacity of United States armed forces depends on the quick movement of troops and supplies to a potential zone of conflict. Although the United States Air Force is responsible for airlifting the initial cadres of ground forces and some light equipment, the majority of troops and equipment still must be transported by sea. The complexity of such a task and the amount of shipping involved can be shown when moving one Marine division. To transport the 15,000 troops plus their equipment—personal arms, rations, tanks, artillery—requires 58 ships.

Today's amphibious ships are not amphibious in the World War II sense of the term, when "amphibious" landing craft could actually beach themselves to allow troops to come ashore. Amphibious ships now keep well offshore under the close air and antisubmarine protection of their escorts. Their cargo of troops and equipment are put ashore in a variety of other craft.

The United States Navy presently has 58 amphibious-class ships in commission. But it would be misleading to say the Navy has 58 amphibious ships available. First, the ships are evenly divided between the Atlantic and Pacific oceans. Second, at any given time, some are moving to or from their fleet assignments or home ports, while others are either on detached duties or are being serviced or modernized. At best, the Navy currently has the capability to move half a division. The Navy's goal is to have 72 amphibious ships. This number would provide enough ships to make up for those ships in transit, in dry dock, or on detached duty and still maintain sufficient ships to move a Marine Corps division.

The Marine Corps is the U.S. combat force that makes all initial landings on defended beachheads. To accomplish this task, the Marines have developed three tiers of organization. The smallest combat unit the Marines would use in an amphibious landing is the Marine Expeditionary Unit (MEU), which consists of about 1,900 Marines. The MEU also has a helicopter squadron attached to it. The MEU requires between three and five amphibious ships, depending on the capacity of the individual ships.

The next tier up is the Marine Expeditionary Brigade (MEB), comprising about 15,000 troops. The MEB contains between two and five infantry battalions. It will also have a reinforced artillery battalion; a company each of Light Armored Vehicles, tanks, combat engineers, reconnaissance vehicles, and amphibious landing craft; and a TOW antitank missile platoon. To move a MEB requires 20 or more amphibious ships.

Finally, there is the Marine Expeditionary Force (MEF), which contains nearly 50,000 troops. Normally included in an MEF is a full combat division, an artillery regiment, and a battalion of the same support elements that are in company strength in the MEB. An MEB would be used only in a conflict of major proportions, such as an attack by Warsaw Pact forces on NATO forces in Europe.

The carriers, battleships, destroyers, and frigates may seem more glamorous than amphibious ships, but the efforts of these bigger ships would be largely worthless without amphibious ships to bring in the troops to take and hold ground. And this is the essential element of Navy strategy.

The Navy's amphibious ships currently in service are divided into seven classes. These class designations are somewhat confusing: LPH is a helicopter amphibious assault ship; LHA is a general-purpose amphibious assault ship; LHD is a multipurpose amphibious assault ship; LSD is a dock landing ship; LPD is an amphibious transport dock for loading and unloading where there are no port facilities; LST is a tank landing ship; and LKA is an amphibious cargo ship. Amphibious assault ships are named for battles fought by the U.S. Marines.

Opposite: *The USS* Duluth *is an* Austin-*class amphibious transport dock ship.* Above: *The USS* El Paso, *an amphibious cargo ship of the* Charleston *class, is shown here before being recently fitted with two 20mm Phalanx guns.*

Iwo Jima-Class (LPH) Amphibious Assault Ships

Above: *The USS* Tripoli *is an* Iwo Jima-*class amphibious assault ship.*

In the late 1940s, the U.S. Marine Corps began experimenting with "vertical envelopment." This concept involved using helicopters to fly lightly armed marines well behind enemy lines via helicopter to attack vital command and control installations and other targets during amphibious landings. In the mid-1950s, the USS *Thetis Bay,* a World War II escort carrier, was converted to carry helicopters. The concept was so successful that a second escort carrier was scheduled for conversion. Instead, the second conversion was dropped, and a new class of amphibious assault ship—the *Iwo Jima* class—was developed.

The *Iwo Jima* class does not carry surface landing craft. Instead, it carries seven CH-46 Sea Knights, 11 CH-53D Sea Stallions or CH-53E Super Stallions, and other utility and attack helicopters to convey the landing parties ashore. The helicopters are housed in a large hangar deck and lifted to the flight deck by two elevators mounted at the deck's edge. The starboard elevator is mounted aft of the island and the port side elevator forward of the island. The main deck, which is more than 600 feet long, has room for five helicopters on the port side and two on the starboard side. No provisions, such as catapults or arresting gear, have been made for fixed wing aircraft, although AV-8A Harriers were operated aboard the USS *Guam* in the early 1970s.

The *Iwo Jima* class is powered by a single steam turbine producing 22,000 horsepower and driving one propeller shaft. Steam is furnished by two boilers. Top speed is 22 knots (25.3 miles per hour), and the cruising range is 16,600 nautical miles (18,975 miles) at 11.5 knots (13.2 miles per hour).

Since the *Iwo Jima* class, like all assault landing ships, operates in combat zones only as part of an amphibious task force, the ships are lightly armed. This class carries two eight-cell Mark 25 missile launchers for the Sea Sparrow (RIM-7) missile (only one in the USS *Okinawa*) and two 20 millimeter Phalanx Close-In Weapons System point defense gun systems for defense against attacking aircraft or small craft. Originally, the *Iwo Jima* class mounted four three-inch antiaircraft guns. Two were removed to make way for the Mark 25 launchers, and the remaining three-inch guns are fired under local control by their crew.

The *Iwo Jima* class was the first type of ship in any of the world's navies to be designed specifically to carry helicopters. They are basically World War II escort carriers that have been modernized and redesigned for helicopter operations. The *Iwo Jima* class can carry a fully equipped battalion of marines plus supporting elements; the helicopter complement can lift the battalion ashore.

Left: *The USS* Iwo Jima, *the class namesake, can carry 25 CH-46 Sea Knight helicopters and 2,000 fully equipped troops.* Below: *The* Iwo Jima-*class ships, such as the USS* Inchon, *were the first in any navy to be designed specifically to carry helicopters.*

IWO JIMA-CLASS (LPH) AMPHIBIOUS ASSAULT SHIPS

Operational (commissioned):	LPH 2 USS *Iwo Jima* (August 1961) LPH 3 USS *Okinawa* (April 1962) LPH 7 USS *Guadalcanal* (July 1963) LPH 9 USS *Guam* (January 1985) LPH 10 USS *Tripoli* (August 1966) LPH 11 USS *New Orleans* (November 1968) LPH 12 USS *Inchon* (June 1970)
Displacement:	18,300 tons
Dimensions:	
Length:	602 ft., 3 in.
Beam:	106 ft.
Draft:	26 ft.
Propulsion:	One steam turbine
Speed:	22 knots (25.3 mph) Two 600-psi boilers
Armament:	
All:	Two twin 3-inch Mk 33 antiaircraft guns Two 20mm Phalanx CIWS point defense guns
LPH 2, 7–12:	Sea Sparrow missiles in two 8-tube Mk 25 launchers
LPH 3:	One 8-cell Mk 25 launcher for Sea Sparrow missiles
Fire control:	Mk 115 missile fire control system
Aircraft:	25 helicopters
Surveillance radar:	SPS-10 surface search SPS-40 air search
Sonar:	None
Crew:	
Navy:	685
Combat troops:	2,000

Tarawa-Class (LHA) Amphibious Assault Ships

Above: *The* Tarawa *is the lead ship of its class of amphibious assault ships, which are the largest amphibious ships ever built.*

The origin of this class of ships lies in the island campaigns of the Pacific during World War II. After transporting troops and equipment to the scene of an amphibious landing, these ships had to be put ashore under fire. To handle the thousands of troops and tons of equipment and supplies, specialized ships were required. A series of landing craft was developed; these craft ranged from little more than powered barges (Landing Craft Infantry) to amphibious tractors to larger craft able to land tanks and artillery pieces (Landing Craft Tank).

The *Tarawa* and its related classes—the *Wasp* and *Iwo Jima*—represent the epitome of this development. The *Tarawa* class combines the capabilities of an amphibious command ship, a general-purpose amphibious assault ship, an amphibious cargo ship, an amphibious transport dock, a helicopter amphibious assault ship, and a tank-landing ship. It also has an aircraft carrier deck for landing fixed wing Vertical/Short Takeoff and Landing aircraft and helicopters. This class of ship is fitted with the Tactical Amphibious Warfare Data System (TAWDS) and other command facilities, enabling an amphibious commander to make a *Tarawa*-class ship a command flagship. The TAWDS system keeps track of every element—troop units, vehicles, helicopters, landing craft, and supplies—belonging to the task force.

Five *Tarawa*-class amphibious assault ships were built and commissioned between 1971 and 1980. Nine ships were originally planned, but four were canceled in the military procurement retrenchment that followed the end of the Vietnam War.

Tarawa-class ships are 820 feet long and 107 feet wide; they are fitted with both a hangar deck for aircraft and helicopters and a landing well for specialized landing craft. The hangar deck, which is 820 feet long, 78 feet wide, and 20 feet high, can accommodate every type of helicopter in Marine Corps or Navy inventory. The usual aircraft deployment aboard a *Tarawa*-class ship might include 12 CH-46 Sea Knights, six CH-53D/E Sea Stallions or Super Stallions, four AH-1 SeaCobra assault helicopters, and two UH-1N Huey utility helicopters. Such fixed wing aircraft as the AV-8B Harrier II and the OV-10 Bronco can also operate from the landing deck.

The docking well in the stern is 268 feet long and 78 feet wide and can dock a wide variety of landing craft. Up to eight AAVP7A1 (formerly the LVTP-7) amphibious tractors can be launched at the same time. Up to four Utility Landing Craft (LCUs)—which can carry three M-60 tanks, two M-1 Abrams tanks, or 150 tons of other cargo—can be docked in the well. Two Landing Craft Mechanized (LCMs), each able to carry up to 80 fully equipped troops, can also be accommodated. The docking well can hold only one Landing Craft Air Cushion (LCAC) vehicle because of the interior arrangement. At least 34 additional amphibious tractors can be carried on a third deck.

The interior arrangement of *Tarawa* ships is specifically designed to handle vast quantities of cargo. A central support structure, dividing the docking well into two parts, houses a conveyor belt. The conveyor belt runs to the vehicle decks, which can hold up to 200 tanks, artillery pieces, and trucks, and up to 40 AAVP7A1 amphibious tractors. The vehicle decks are all connected by ramps. The conveyor belt is served by five elevators—three at the forward, or vehicle deck, end and two at the docking well. Up to 2,000 pounds of cargo can be stored on pallets in holds deeper in the ship. Cargo can be transferred to the landing craft in the docking well by a monorail system or lifted directly onto the hangar deck via the rear elevators. Cargo can also be moved onto the flight deck in transporters that drive up a sloping ramp and emerge at the forward base of the island.

Tarawa-class ships can carry 2,000 troops and a naval crew of more than 900. Forward in the hull is a 5,000 square foot acclimatization section, which also contains a gymnasium so troops can exercise. Temperature and humidity in this area can be controlled to ready the troops for the climate in which they will be fighting. Behind this area is an extensive, fully equipped hospital.

Tarawa-class assault ships are powered by two steam turbines that develop a total of 70,000 horsepower. The turbine is fed by two steam boilers. Each ship also has a 900 horsepower "through tunnel thruster," which is a propeller encased in a tunnel in the forward part of the hull that assists in maneuvering. Top speed is 24 knots (27.6 miles per hour); range at 20 knots (23 miles per hour) is 10,000 nautical miles (11,500 miles).

For close-in defense, these ships are equipped with two eight-cell Mark 25 launchers for the Sea Sparrow missile (only one on the USS *Tarawa*) for use against surface threats. The USS *Saipan* and the USS *Nassau* carry one Phalanx Close-In Weapons System Mark 15 point defense gun system to deter airborne threats. *Tarawa* ships are armed with three five-inch Mark 45 dual-purpose guns and six 20 millimeter Mark 67 antiaircraft guns. The Mark 67 guns are the last such crew-served antiaircraft guns in U.S. Navy service.

TARAWA-CLASS (LHA) AMPHIBIOUS ASSAULT SHIPS

Operational (commissioned):	LHA 1 USS *Tarawa* (May 1976) LHA 2 USS *Saipan* (October 1977) LHA 3 USS *Belleau Wood* (September 1978) LHA 4 USS *Nassau* (July 1979) LHA 5 USS *Peleliu* (May 1980)
Displacement:	39,400 tons
Dimensions:	
Length:	820 ft.
Beam:	107 ft.
Draft:	26 ft.
Propulsion:	Two steam turbines driving two propeller shafts Two 600-psi boilers
Speed:	24 knots (27.6 mph)
Armament:	
All:	Three 5-inch Mk 45 dual-purpose guns Six 20mm Mk 67 antiaircraft guns
LHA 1:	Sea Sparrow missiles in one 8-tube Mk 25 launcher
LHA 2–5:	Sea Sparrow missiles in two 8-tube Mk 25 launchers
LHA 2, 4:	One 20mm Phalanx CIWS point defense gun
Fire control:	Mk 86 gun fire control system Mk 115 missile fire control system
Aircraft:	40 helicopters or 35 V/STOL aircraft
Surveillance radar:	SPS-10 F surface search SPS-52B 3-D search SPS-53 surface search SPS-40B air search
Sonar:	None
Crew:	
Navy:	940
Combat troops:	2,000

Left: Tarawa *assault ships, such as the USS* Nassau, *can carry 35 AV-8B Harrier II aircraft.*

Wasp-Class (LHD) Amphibious Assault Ships

Recently developed classes of amphibious assault ships often resemble World War II aircraft carriers that have been mated to cargo container ships. *Wasp*-class ships, along with the slightly smaller *Tarawa*-class ships, are the world's largest amphibious ships. The *Wasp* class is designed to be a helicopter carrier and is intended to be less expensive than the earlier *Tarawa* class. Five ships have been planned; one has been launched, and two are presently under construction.

Wasp-class ships can carry up to 40 helicopters of any type now in Marine Corps or Navy inventory—CH-46 Sea Knights, CH-53D Sea Stallions, and CH-53E Super Stallions—as well as four or more AH-1 SeaCobras and two or more UH-1 Hueys. The helicopters are used to ferry troops and equipment. *Wasp*-class ships can also carry the AV-8B Harrier, a Vertical/Short Takeoff and Landing aircraft, and the V-22 Osprey, should it be completed. The flight deck is long enough that these fixed wing aircraft do not require the British-designed ramp deck for short takeoffs to conserve fuel.

The *Wasp* class has a large docking well inside the hull to carry three Landing Craft Air Cushion (LCAC) vehicles as well as landing craft with conventional hulls, such as the Landing Craft Mechanized (LCM). The LCAC is an air-cushion vehicle developed by Bell Textron for conducting amphibious landings. The LCAC skims four to five feet above the water; only the tips of its rubber surface are in contact with the water.

One LCAC can carry up to 70 tons of payload at speeds in excess of 40 knots (46 miles per hour). Fully loaded vehicles can be driven directly onto an LCAC's cargo deck and then driven directly onto the beach when the landing area is reached. Since they travel on a cushion of air, LCACs can traverse 70 percent of the world's beaches compared with only 17 percent for landing craft with conventional hulls. The Navy currently has 16 LCACs in service—nine with Assault Craft Unit Five (ACU-5) at Camp Pendleton, California, and seven with ACU-4 at Little Creek, Virginia.

Above: *The USS* Wasp *is the lead ship in a new class of amphibious assault ships that have slightly longer carrier decks than the* Tarawa *class.*

Wasp-class ships displace 40,530 tons. They are 844 feet long and 140 feet wide. They are powered by two steam turbines that produce a total of 71,000 horsepower to turn two propeller shafts. Two boilers provide the steam. Top speed for the *Wasp* class is 22 knots (25.3 miles per hour). Cruising range is 9,500 nautical miles (10,925 miles).

For close-in defense against surface attack, the *Wasp* ships carry two eight-cell Mark 29 launchers for the Sea Sparrow missile. The Mark 29 launcher and Sea Sparrow missile provide *Wasp* ships with a surface-to-surface missile capability of up to 10 nautical miles (11.5 miles). For protection against air attack, the five ships of this class are being fitted with three 20 millimeter Phalanx Close-In Weapons System point defense guns. They also carry eight .50 caliber machine guns.

Marine Corps and Navy engineers and planners designed this new class of multipurpose amphibious assault ship specifically for the deployment, landing, and support of Marine Corps assault forces. Each ship of this class has 22,000 square feet of storage space for vehicles alone, and a total of 101,000 cubic feet has been devoted to cargo storage space.

WASP-CLASS (LHD) AMPHIBIOUS ASSAULT SHIPS

Operational (commissioned):	None
Launched:	LHD 1 USS *Wasp* (August 1987)
Building:	LHD 2 USS *Essex* (1992) LHD 3 USS *Kearserge* (1993)
Planned:	LHD 4 USS (unnamed) (1994) LHD 5 USS (unnamed) (1996)
Displacement:	40,530 tons
Dimensions:	
Length:	844 ft.
Beam:	107 ft.
Draft:	26 ft., 7 in.
Propulsion:	Two steam turbines driving two propeller shafts Two 600-psi boilers
Speed:	22+ knots (25+ mph)
Armament:	Sea Sparrow missiles in two 8-tube Mk 29 launchers Three 20mm Phalanx CIWS point defense guns Eight .50 caliber machine guns
Fire control:	Mk 23 tactical air search Two Mk 91 missile fire control systems
Aircraft:	40 helicopters or V/STOL aircraft
Surveillance radar:	SPS-64 surface search SPS-52C 3-D search SPS-49(V)5 air search
Sonar:	None
Crew:	
Navy:	1,081
Combat troops:	1,875

Top: *Overall, the* Wasp *class will be slightly smaller than the* Tarawa *class and have less vehicle space.* Bottom: *This photo of the USS* Wasp *in dry dock during construction provides an excellent view of the stern gate and stern elevator on the starboard side.*

Dock Landing-Class (LSD/LPD) Amphibious Ships

The World War II amphibious assault concept called for separate ships to carry troops (Attack Transports, APA), cargo (Attack Cargo Ships, AKA), and tanks and landing craft (Dock Landing Ships, LSD). By the end of the Pacific campaign in 1945, this was recognized as inefficient.

The USS *Thomaston* Dock Landing Ships (LSD) were the first of the new postwar class to be built. Their construction was spurred by the success of amphibious operations during the Korean War (1950–53). The *Thomaston* ships had large docking wells in the aft part of the ship and could carry up to 50 LVTP-7 amphibious tractors, three Utility Landing Craft, or nine Mechanized Landing Craft. For protection against air attack, they were heavily armed with 16 three-inch and 12 20 millimeter antiaircraft guns. Today, they carry only 12 three-inch guns.

In the early 1960s, a new class of LSD—the *Anchorage*—was built to increase the number of amphibious landing ships and to supplement the LPDs then under construction. *Anchorage*-class ships were given larger docking wells that had a removable helicopter deck above them. And *Anchorage* ships had 15,800 square feet of storage space.

In the early 1980s, after a long political battle, Congress agreed to fund a new class of LSD to replace the aging *Thomaston* class. The *Whidbey Island* class has large docking wells that can accommodate four Landing Craft Air Cushion (LCAC) vehicles. The *Whidbey Island* class is also able to land all helicopters and Vertical/Short Takeoff and Landing aircraft in the inventory of the Marine Corps or Navy.

A new class of ship was designed in the mid-1950s to combine the carrying of troops, cargo, and equipment. The result was the amphibious transport dock class (LPD). Essentially, these ships were designed to provide docking facilities where either no ports exist or none are available.

The *Raleigh* class of amphibious transport dock ships was commissioned in the early 1960s. The two *Raleigh*-class ships have docking wells in the aft part of the ship only; the forward part contains a large area for troops and vehicles. The docking well is large enough to contain two LCAC vehicles or a variety of smaller landing craft. Although a helicopter landing deck covers the docking well, these ships have no hangars or maintenance facilities.

The *Raleigh* class was followed by the *Austin* class, which was basically an enlarged version of the *Raleigh* ship. During construction, a 50-foot section was inserted forward of the docking well. This provided sufficient space to build a telescoping helicopter hangar behind the superstructure. Troop and vehicle capacity, and even the size of the well deck, are the same as in the *Raleigh* class.

All five classes of ships are roughly similar in size. They vary no more than 100 feet in length but range from 11,270 tons (*Thomaston* class) to 16,900 tons (*Austin* class) in displacement. All except the *Whidbey Island* class are equipped with two steam turbines that produce a total of 24,000 horsepower; the turbines are powered by two boilers. The *Whidbey Island* class carries four diesel engines that develop a total of 33,600 horsepower through two propellers. All have helicopter landing areas, but except for the *Austin* class, no class has helicopter hangars or maintenance facilities.

Above: *The USS* Duluth, *an* Austin-*class ship, was launched in August 1965.* Opposite, left: *The USS* Speigel Grove *is a* Thomaston-*class dock landing ship.* Opposite, right: *The USS* Pensacola, *shown here landing an LCAC air-cushion vehicle, is an* Anchorage-*class dock landing ship.*

THOMASTON-CLASS (LSD) DOCK LANDING SHIPS

Operational (commissioned):	LSD 28 USS *Thomaston* (September 1954) LSD 29 USS *Plymouth Rock* (November 1954) LSD 30 USS *Fort Snelling* (January 1955) LSD 31 USS *Point Defiance* (March 1955) LSD 32 USS *Spiegel Grove* (June 1956) LSD 33 USS *Alamo* (August 1956) LSD 34 USS *Hermitage* (December 1956) LSD 35 USS *Monticello* (March 1957)
Displacement:	11,270 tons
Dimensions:	
Length:	510 ft.
Beam:	84 ft.
Draft:	19 ft.
Propulsion:	Two steam turbines driving two propeller shafts Two 600-psi boilers
Speed:	22.5 knots (25.9 mph)
Armament:	Twelve 3-inch Mk 33 antiaircraft guns
Fire control:	None
Aircraft:	None
Surveillance radar:	SPS-10B surface search SPS-6 air search
Sonar:	None
Crew:	
Navy:	348
Combat troops:	325

ANCHORAGE-CLASS (LSD) DOCK LANDING SHIPS

Operational (commissioned):	LSD 36 USS *Anchorage* (March 1969) LSD 37 USS *Portland* (October 1970) LSD 38 USS *Pensecola* (March 1971) LSD 39 USS *Mount Vernon* (May 1972) LSD 40 USS *Fort Fisher* (December 1972)
Displacement:	14,000 tons
Dimensions:	
Length:	553 ft.
Beam:	85 ft.
Draft:	19 ft.
Propulsion:	Two steam turbines driving two propeller shafts Two 600-psi boilers
Speed:	20 knots (23 mph)
Armament:	Twelve 3-inch Mk 33 antiaircraft guns Two 20mm Phalanx CIWS point defense guns
Fire control:	None
Aircraft:	None
Surveillance radar:	SPS-10 surface search SPS-40 air search
Sonar:	None
Crew:	
Navy:	358
Combat troops:	330

WHIDBEY ISLAND-CLASS (LSD) DOCK LANDING SHIPS

Operational (commissioned):	LSD 41 USS *Whidbey Island* (February 1985) LSD 42 USS *Germantown* (February 1986) LSD 43 USS *Ft. McHenry* (August 1987)
Building:	LSD 44 USS *Gunston Hall*
Planned:	LSD 45 USS *Comstock* LSD 46 USS *Tortuga* LSD 47 USS *Rushmore* LSD 48 USS *Ashland* LSD 49 USS *Harpers Ferry*
Displacement:	15,704 tons
Dimensions:	
Length:	610 ft.
Beam:	84 ft.
Dimensions continued	
Draft:	20 ft.
Propulsion:	Four SEMT-Pielstick diesel engines driving two propeller shafts
Speed:	20 knots (23 mph)
Armament:	Two 20mm Phalanx CIWS point defense guns
Fire control:	None
Aircraft:	None
Surveillance radar:	SPS-67 surface search SPS-49 air search
Sonar:	None
Crew:	
Navy:	342
Combat troops:	500

Left: *Amphibious transport dock ships, such as the USS* Vancouver, *are basically dock landing ships built to accommodate greater numbers of troops and vehicles.*

RALEIGH-CLASS (LPD) AMPHIBIOUS TRANSPORT DOCK SHIPS

Operational (commissioned):	LPD 1 USS *Raleigh* (September 1962) LPD 2 USS *Vancouver* (May 1963)
Displacement:	14,650 tons
Dimensions:	
Length:	521 ft., 6 in.
Beam:	84 ft.
Draft:	22 ft.
Propulsion:	Two steam turbines driving two propeller shafts Two 600-psi boilers
Speed:	20 knots (23 mph)
Armament:	Four 3-inch Mk 33 antiaircraft guns
Armament continued	Two 20mm Phalanx CIWS point defense guns
Fire control:	None
Aircraft:	None
Surveillance radar:	SPS-10 surface search SPS-40 air search
Sonar:	None
Crew:	
LPD 1:	
Navy:	420
Combat troops:	930
LPD 2:	
Navy:	431
Combat troops:	930

AUSTIN-CLASS (LPD) AMPHIBIOUS TRANSPORT DOCK SHIPS

Operational (commissioned):	LPD 4 USS *Austin* (February 1965) LPD 5 USS *Ogden* (June 1965) LPD 6 USS *Duluth* (December 1965) LPD 7 USS *Cleveland* (April 1967) LPD 8 USS *Dubuque* (September 1967) LPD 9 USS *Denver* (October 1968) LPD 10 USS *Juneau* (July 1969) LPD 12 USS *Shreveport* (December 1970) LPD 13 USS *Nashville* (February 1970) LPD 14 USS *Trenton* (March 1971) LPD 15 USS *Ponce* (July 1971)
Displacement:	16,900 tons
Dimensions:	
Length:	583 ft.
Beam:	84 ft.
Draft:	23 ft.
Propulsion:	Two steam turbines driving two propeller shafts Two 600-psi boilers
Speed:	20 knots (23 mph)
Armament:	Four 3-inch Mk 33 antiaircraft guns Two 20mm Phalanx CIWS point defense guns
Fire control:	None
Aircraft:	None
Surveillance radar:	SPS-10F surface search SPS-40C air search
Sonar:	None
Crew:	
LPD 4–6, 14, 15:	
Navy:	425
Combat troops:	930
LPD 7–10, 12, 13:	
Navy:	425
Combat troops:	840

Top: *The USS* Shreveport *is an* Austin-*class amphibious transport dock ship. Note the two 20mm Phalanx guns mounted on its bridge structure.* Above: *The USS* Ponce, *like all* Austin *amphibious transport dock ships, was built to carry marines into forward embarkation areas.* Right: *The USS* Hermitage *is a* Thomaston-*class dock landing ship.*

Newport-Class (LST) Tank Landing Ships

Above: Newport-*class tank landing ships, such as the USS* San Bernardino, *can beach themselves to unload their cargo, but they generally use causeways.*

The design for the "landing ship tank" (LST) originated during the period between World War I and World War II. The design was prompted by the recognition that the Japanese Empire would be the United States' most likely enemy in the Pacific Ocean. After long years of war-gaming a Pacific conflict, the U.S. Navy decided the only way to effectively assault the Japanese home islands would be the sort of island-hopping campaign that actually ensued in World War II. Islands that could serve as air and naval bases for the final phase of the conflict had to be retrieved from Japanese military occupation forces. Troops, equipment, and particularly tanks and large artillery pieces had to be brought ashore during the attacks to capture those islands. The LST was one of many amphibious designs that moved quickly from the drawing board to the shipyard at the start of the Pacific phase of World War II. LSTs served extensively throughout the Pacific as well as in the China-Burma-India maritime theater, supporting successive invasions in that quarter. LSTs also proved decisive in putting Allied tanks, artillery, and other heavy equipment ashore during the invasions of North Africa, Sicily, Italy, Normandy, and southern France.

LSTs can beach themselves, lower a ramp, and unload their cargo directly into water shallow enough to wade ashore. LSTs then use their powerful engines to pull themselves free of the beach. Although the modern *Newport* class can still do this, these ships are more likely to unload their cargo onto specially built pontoon causeways that are carried on top of the LST's superstructure. The pontoon causeways can support the weight of a 63-ton M-1A1 Abrams Main Battle Tank. Each ship also carries four Landing Craft Vehicle and Personnel craft in davits (cranes that hold the craft over the side of the ship).

The *Newport* class bears only a slight resemblance to its World War II ancestors. The original boxy shape and flat bow/ramp have given way to rounded bow and stern ramps. The bow ramp is 12 feet long and set between two massive fixed booms that can lower the ramp to landing level or even with the landing pontoons. From the stern ramp, amphibious vehicles can debark directly into the water even while the ship is moving. The stern ramp can be attached to another amphibious vessel or to a pier, if necessary. Vehicles can be driven the length of the deck via a tunnel through the superstructure.

The *Newport* class was originally armed with four three-inch Mark 32 guns in open mounts. These World War II-era antiaircraft guns have almost all now been exchanged for two Phalanx Close-In Weapons System Mark 15 20 millimeter point defense guns.

Of the 20 ships in this class, 18 are in active service and two are in the Naval Reserve Fleet.

Top: *The USS* Newport *can carry 500 tons of vehicles and has 19,000 square feet of parking space.* Bottom: *The USS* Racine *is armed with two 20mm Phalanx guns in place of the four 3-inch antiaircraft guns with which it was originally equipped.*

NEWPORT-CLASS (LST) TANK LANDING SHIPS

Operational (commissioned):	LST 1179 USS *Newport* (June 1969) LST 1180 USS *Manitowoc* (January 1970) LST 1181 USS *Sumter* (June 1970) LST 1182 USS *Fresno* (February 1970) LST 1183 USS *Peoria* (November 1969) LST 1184 USS *Frederick* (February 1970) LST 1185 USS *Schenectady* (April 1970) LST 1186 USS *Cayuga* (August 1970) LST 1187 USS *Tuscaloosa* (October 1970) LST 1188 USS *Saginaw* (January 1971) LST 1189 USS *San Bernadino* (March 1971) LST 1190 USS *Boulder* (June 1971) LST 1191 USS *Racine* (July 1971) LST 1192 USS *Spartanburg County* (September 1971) LST 1193 USS *Fairfax County* (October 1971) LST 1194 USS *La Moure County* (December 1971) LST 1195 USS *Barbour County* (February 1972) LST 1196 USS *Harlan County* (April 1972) LST 1197 USS *Barnstable County* (May 1972) LST 1198 USS *Bristol County* (August 1972)
Displacement:	8,450 tons
Dimensions:	
Length:	522 ft., 2.4 in.
Beam:	69 ft., 6 in.
Draft:	17 ft., 6 in.
Propulsion:	One Arco diesel engine driving two propeller shafts
Speed:	20 knots (23 mph)
Armament:	Two 20mm Phalanx CIWS point defense guns
Fire control:	None
Aircraft:	None
Surveillance radar:	SPS-10F surface search
Sonar:	None
Crew:	
Navy:	253
Combat troops:	400

Charleston-Class (LKA) Amphibious Cargo Ships

The *Charleston*-class vessels were originally intended as attack cargo ships (AKA), but their designation was changed to amphibious cargo ships (LKA) in the Navy-wide reclassification of June 1975. All previous ships in the AKA or LKA classes had been converted from, or built according to, civilian merchant ship designs. The *Charleston* ships are the first built specifically for the amphibious cargo ship role.

The task of *Charleston* ships is to move heavy loads of equipment and supplies for troops participating in amphibious landing operations. They then serve in a cargo-carrying role for the duration of the conflict. *Charleston* ships are designed to permit the rapid loading of equipment into landing craft and helicopters. Although they do not have helicopters, hangars, or maintenance facilities of their own, *Charleston* ships do have a helicopter landing area built over the rear deck. The original set of four three-inch Mark 33 twin antiaircraft guns has been replaced by two Mark 15 Phalanx Close-In Weapons System 20 millimeter point defense guns.

The *Charleston* class has an estimated 33,000 square feet of storage area for vehicles and 70,000 cubic feet of cargo space. The distinctive features of the *Charleston* class are the two cargo booms before the bridge and the single boom aft. The forward booms have a capacity of 48 tons each, the aft boom, 78 tons. Each ship also has eight booms of 15-ton capacity.

Charleston-class ships are powered by a single Westinghouse steam turbine producing 22,000 horsepower. The turbine is driven by two boilers built by Combustion Engineering. Top speed for this class is 20 knots (23 miles per hour). Of the five ships in the *Charleston* class, four were placed in the Naval Fleet Reserve between 1979 and 1981. As tensions rose around the world in the mid-1980s, these ships were brought back into active service. All *Charleston* ships are currently in the active fleet; the USS *Charleston* and the USS *El Paso* serve with the Atlantic fleet, the other three with the Pacific fleet.

Below: *The USS* Charleston *is the first of a class of five amphibious cargo ships.*

Above: *The USS* Durham, *a* Charleston-*class ship, is designed to carry heavy equipment and supplies for amphibious assaults.* Below: *The USS* St. Louis *was commissioned November 22, 1969.*

CHARLESTON-CLASS (LKA) AMPHIBIOUS CARGO SHIPS

Operational (commissioned):	LKA 113 USS *Charleston* (December 1968) LKA 114 USS *Durham* (May 1969) LKA 115 USS *Mobile* (September 1969) LKA 116 USS *St. Louis* (November 1969) LKA 117 USS *El Paso* (January 1970)
Displacement:	18,600 tons
Dimensions:	
Length:	578 ft.
Beam:	62 ft.
Draft:	25 ft., 6 in.
Propulsion:	One Westinghouse steam turbines driving one propeller shaft Two Combustion Engineering 600-psi boilers
Speed:	20 knots (23 mph)
Armament:	Two 20mm Phalanx CIWS point defense guns
Fire control:	None
Aircraft:	None
Surveillance radar:	SPS-10 surface search
Sonar:	None
Crew:	
Navy:	360
Combat troops:	225

PATROL AND SPECIAL WARFARE CRAFT

Since the end of World War II, the United States Navy has evinced a great deal of interest in specialized coastal patrol boats but has had little success developing them. Several types, notably the Sea Viking concept, have collapsed for various reasons. Historically, the Navy has been more interested in fulfilling the needs of the oceangoing navy. As in World War II and Vietnam, the Navy remains confident of its ability to develop and procure the needed small craft in the event of war.

But the requirements for coastal patrol craft have changed drastically. Today's patrol craft fulfill multiple roles: a high-speed, agile missile launching boat; a coastal interdiction boat; and a special warfare operations mission boat. In the first role, the boat would carry sea-skimming missiles for use against enemy military and commercial shipping. The second role would involve assisting in patrolling the coastal waters of the United States to prevent drug smuggling. The third role would provide the Navy's SEAL teams with a fast and stealthy means of infiltrating an enemy coast.

The only patrol boat class presently in service with the U.S. Navy is the *Pegasus* class. All previous Navy patrol gunboats and fast gunboats, as well as the hovercraft and riverine warfare boats used with such success in South Vietnam, have been removed from service. A new class of six patrol boats, currently referred to as Patrol Missile Craft: PXM Type, are planned for procurement beginning in federal fiscal year 1990. These boats are expected to be armed with the Harpoon antiship missile and a 30 millimeter or 57mm defensive gun system, but they are not expected to have antisubmarine warfare capability.

Above: *The USS* Hercules *is a* Pegasus-*class patrol combatant.*

Pegasus-Class Missile Patrol Boats

The *Pegasus*-class patrol boats are high-speed, heavily armed hydrofoil craft designed for antiship warfare in coastal or restricted waters. They are the first and thus far only class of surface craft to utilize the hydrofoil hull in a nonexperimental vessel.

The history of the *Pegasus* class is typical of small boat development in the U.S. Navy. The class was championed by Admiral Elmo Zumwalt when he was Chief of Naval Operations in the early 1970s. Planning called for the construction of 30 small craft to carry antiship missiles. When Admiral Zumwalt retired, the program was downgraded. Congress revived the program in 1976, and six craft were approved and designated PHM (Patrol, Hydrofoil, Missile). The first PHM, the *Pegasus,* was completed in 1977. In November 1982, PHM 6 *Gemini* was commissioned, and the construction program ended.

This class of boat rides on submerged, canard-shaped foils that lift the hull completely out of the water. The forward foil provides about 32 percent of lift and is mounted on a single strut. The rear foil provides the remaining lift and is mounted on a double strut, which is needed to carry the extra load. Both foils retract—the forward foil lifts even with and sticks out in front of the bow, the rear foil, up and beyond the stern. Step flaps fitted into the trailing edge of both foils serve as control surfaces.

Above: *All* Pegasus-*class patrol craft are water-jet-powered hydrofoils.*

When the hull is in the water, propulsion is provided by twin waterjet pumps that are powered by two diesel engines capable of developing 12 knots (13.8 miles per hour). When slow maneuvering is necessary, a bow thruster driven by the diesel engines is used. When riding on the hydrofoils, the craft is driven by a single waterjet powered by a General Electric LM 2500 gas turbine engine. This waterjet is mounted on the rear foil and can move the craft at speeds up to 50 knots (57.5 miles per hour). The waterjet pumps 141,000 gallons of water per minute. The *Pegasus*-class boats have a range of 1,400 miles at 11 knots (12.65 miles per hour) or, when using hydrofoils, 600 miles or more at 40 knots (46 miles per hour).

The PHMs are heavily armed. They carry eight Harpoon antiship missiles that are fired from two Mark 141 quadruple launchers. *Pegasus* boats also carry one 76 millimeter Mark 75 antiaircraft gun mounted on the bow. Since they are not intended for the antisubmarine warfare role, they have no antisubmarine capability. All *Pegasus*-class patrol craft are assigned to PHMS Squadron 2, based at Key West, Florida.

PEGASUS-CLASS MISSILE PATROL BOATS

Operational (commissioned):	PHM 1 USS *Pegasus* (July 1977) PHM 2 USS *Hercules* (January 1983) PHM 3 USS *Taurus* (October 1981) PHM 4 USS *Aquila* (June 1982) PHM 5 USS *Aries* (September 1982) PHM 6 USS *Gemini* (November 1982)
Displacement:	256 tons
Dimensions:	
Length:	
Overall:	118 ft., 1 in.
Foils retracted:	147 ft., 2 in.
Foils extended:	131 ft., 6 in.
Beam:	28 ft., 2 in.
Draft:	
Foils retracted:	6 ft., 2 in.
Foils extended:	3 ft., 2 in.
Propulsion:	
Foil-borne:	One General Electric LM 2500 gas turbine driving one waterjet
Hull-borne:	Two MTU 8V331 diesel engines driving two waterjets
Speed:	
Foil-borne:	50 knots (57.5 mph)
Hull-borne:	12 knots (13.8 mph)
Armament:	Eight Harpoon (RGM-84A) missiles in two quadruple Mk 141 launchers One 76mm Mk 75 antiaircraft gun
Fire control:	One Mk 92 weapons fire control system
Aircraft:	None
Surveillance radar:	SPS-63 surface search
Sonar:	None
Crew:	23

Top: *The USS* Pegasus *is armed with eight Harpoon missiles and one 76mm Mk 75 antiaircraft gun.* Above: *The water jet and the Harpoon missile canisters at the stern of the USS* Pegasus *are clearly visible.* Left: Pegasus*-class patrol craft can reach speeds of 57.5 miles per hour when foil-borne.*

Above: *The USS* Pegasus, *firing a Harpoon missile, demonstrates its deadly bite.*
Left: Pegasus-*class patrol craft carry a relatively large crew of four officers and 19 enlisted sailors.*

WEAPONS AND SURVEILLANCE SYSTEMS

From the time ships first sailed the high seas, the detection of a possible threat before the danger approached too close was an ongoing challenge. For hundreds of years, a sailor kept watch from the crow's nest high above the deck of the sailing ship. Although far from perfect, this method provided additional warning time to prepare for battle.

But while this surveillance system changed little over the centuries, the range and deadliness of naval firepower continued to increase. Bronze and iron cannons—fired at ranges of less than a quarter of a mile and designed to rip gaping holes in wooden ships—were replaced by long-range rapid-fire guns that were capable of hurling high-explosive projectiles many miles. Great gun battles conducted at long distances quickly became the norm of naval warfare.

The accuracy of guns increased immensely with the advent of radars, sonars, and sophisticated direct control systems. But when missiles were introduced after World War II, the armament emphasis shifted from deck guns to high-technology weaponry. Ships were still built with giant superstructures, but the crow's nest was replaced by more sophisticated surveillance systems.

Modern naval warfare uses long-range, highly accurate missiles; instant communication with satellites for targeting; reconnaissance aircraft that can direct the battle from long distances; and a host of jamming and self-defense measures to protect sophisticated and expensive ships. Sonar, radar, surveillance systems, and sophisticated fire control systems will receive even greater emphasis in the future. Ships will evolve from vessels with giant superstructures to ones that sit low in the water. And they will be loaded with the latest in high-technology weapons and surveillance systems.

Above: *The nine 16-inch rifles mounted by each of the four* Iowa*-class battleships are the largest such guns still in use today.*

Antiship Guns

Periodically, a new discovery or development in missile technology prompts Navy experts to call for ship designs that will carry the latest in high-technology weaponry while doing away with conventional naval gun systems. But almost as soon as the Navy starts to drop deck guns from ships under construction and ships in for retrofitting, a world event occurs that demonstrates the need for a continuous and directed firepower that modern missiles simply cannot supply. Recent examples of this include events off the coast of Lebanon in the early 1980s and Navy operations in the Persian Gulf against Iranian oil derricks that were used as staging areas for laying mines and directing attacks against oil tankers.

All four *Iowa*-class battleships carry the giant 16-inch guns that are the heavy artillery of the U.S. Navy. These guns can fire projectiles the weight of a subcompact car to a range of 16 miles. The high-explosive round can leave a crater the size of a football field. When firing a broadside with all nine 16-inch guns, the 58,000-ton battleship can be pushed laterally up to ten feet with each blast. Although the production lines for the 16-inch gun have long since been closed, the Navy has 34 extra barrels in inventory and nearly 18,000 rounds of stockpiled ammunition.

One of the most numerous guns in U.S. Navy inventory is the five-inch Mark 45 gun, which entered service in 1974. The compact Mark 45 replaced the aging and less reliable five-inch Mark 42 gun. The Mark 45's high level of automation increases overall safety of operation because none of the crew of six is required to be in the turret. The Mark 45 weighs 25 tons and is capable of a steady rate of fire of more than 20 rounds per minute. This gun can easily handle small to medium targets without being overly complex or cumbersome.

Larger in size than the Mark 45 is the 76 millimeter Mark 75 gun. The Mark 75 is produced under license from OTO Melara and is used on *Pegasus*-class patrol craft and *Oliver Hazard Perry*-class frigates. This gun is so dependable that it serves in 34 additional navies throughout the world. Variable rate of fire ranges from ten to 85 rounds per minute, and it can fire up to 80 rounds without reloading. At seven and a half tons, the Mark 75 is lightweight but is capable of firing a 14-pound shell to a maximum range of more than seven miles.

Other guns found in the Navy's inventory consist of those with old technology systems, as well as a hodgepodge of anti-boarding and area-suppression weaponry.

Although not necessarily in the forefront of modern weaponry, Navy guns nonetheless form the foundation that makes the U.S. Navy a world power and force on the high seas. Emphasis has certainly shifted to the more sophisticated weapons offered by missiles and rockets, but there are still countless examples where Navy guns are called in to do the job.

Above: *The Mk 45 5-inch gun was designed to engage either air or surface targets.*

ANTISHIP GUNS	
16-inch gun:	
Bore:	16 in.
Rate of fire:	2 rounds per minute
Range:	16 miles
Date of service:	1940
Mark 45:	
Caliber:	.54
Rate of fire:	20 rounds per minute
Range:	3 miles
Date of service:	1974
Mark 75:	
Caliber:	.62
Rate of fire:	85 rounds per minute
Range:	7 miles
Date of service:	1977

Above: *The crew of the radar-directed Mk 45 5-inch gun is stationed below decks and operates the turret from a remote station.* Opposite: *The USS* Iowa *fires a broadside from its massive 16-inch rifles.*

Antiship Missiles

Until the 1950s, the major aerial threat to ships came from aircraft that would dive in and unload a free-fall gravity bomb. The bomb was designed to either explode on impact or bury itself deep within the ship before detonating. But this is no longer the case. Today long-range attack aircraft, as well as ships hundreds of miles away, can launch devastatingly accurate explosive missiles equipped with conventional or nuclear devices. The two most deadly surface-to-surface antiship missiles in the U.S. Navy's modern inventory are the Harpoon Missile and the Tomahawk Sea Launched Cruise Missile (SLCM).

The Harpoon is a short- to medium-range, all-weather, antiship missile that can be launched from ships, submarines, or aircraft. It carries a high-explosive fragmentation warhead. The missile skims over the sea waves at a speed of Mach .75 to a range of more than 69 miles to find its target. In a standard launch, the Harpoon generally follows a ballistic path during its boost phase and then descends to a sea-skimming flight altitude controlled by the inertial autopilot and radar altimeter. When the missile nears the target, the active radar turns on and then searches for and acquires the target. After the target is acquired, the radar guides the missile to the target.

In the past, the Harpoon missile flew the same basic flight path but then performed a "terminal maneuver"; the missile would suddenly fly upward, or "pop-up," and then dive to the target. This maneuver has been discontinued because more sophisticated ship-borne defensive gun and missile systems made the Harpoon too vulnerable.

For long-range antiship attacks, the Tomahawk SLCM can be fired from ships equipped with either the armored box or vertical launch systems. Submarines can fire the Tomahawk from standard 21-inch-diameter torpedo tubes. The missile's wings flip into place after launch, and the booster provides direction control through the missile's jet vanes.

The Tomahawk is actually an entire family of cruise missiles that can be adapted to various strategic or tactical applications against ship or land targets. The Tomahawk can be used against land targets more than 1,500 miles away, but for the antiship role, the RGM/UGM 109B Tomahawk has a variant range of approximately 300 miles. The Tomahawk flies at speeds of more than 500 miles per hour. Using a modified Harpoon guidance system with inertial navigation plus a radar altimeter for midcourse correction, the Tomahawk uses an active radar system for its terminal approach. Like the Harpoon, the Tomahawk flies a ballistic trajectory during its initial launch and boost phase and then descends to sea-skimming level as it nears the target. After the target has been acquired and locked on, the 264-pound high-explosive warhead fuses with a delayed-detonation device that enables the missile to burrow deep into the vessel before exploding.

Nearly every missile-capable ship in the U.S. Navy is armed with either the Harpoon or Tomahawk or both. Any enemy ship within range of these missiles sails into harm's way.

Above: *When used in the antiship role, the Tomahawk cruise missile has a range of 300 miles.*

Above: *The Harpoon missile can be launched from a surface ship, submarine, or aircraft.*

ANTISHIP MISSILES	
Harpoon:	
Length:	15 ft., 1 in.
Diameter:	1 ft., 1 in.
Weight:	1,498 lbs.
Speed:	600 mph
Range:	92 miles
Warhead:	488-lb. high-explosive
Date of service:	1978
Tomahawk:	
Length:	20 ft., 5 in.
Diameter:	1 ft., 7 in.
Weight:	3,290 lbs.
Speed:	548 mph
Range:	552 miles
Warhead:	200-kt nuclear or 264-lb. high-explosive
Date of service:	1978

Antisubmarine Weapons

Few things strike more fear into a ship's crew than the threat of an undetected enemy submarine in their immediate vicinity. Submarines can float silently, scout, shoot, and disappear with a great deal of impunity. The U.S. Navy is investing billions of dollars in research and weaponry to counter the threat posed by these underwater warriors.

The first line of defense against a submarine has been and will continue to be another submarine. Barring that option, the defenses become more limited and the hunt more challenging, immediate, and critical. To protect the modern carrier battle group, a combination of fixed wing and rotary wing antisubmarine warfare (ASW) aircraft constitute a second line of defense. Such aircraft as the P-3 Orion and the Seahawk helicopter, equipped with sonobuoys, dipping sonars, and other devices to detect and attack submarines, try to locate, track, and then destroy an enemy submarine before it gets within range of the carrier battle group.

Depth charges are not the best way to attack today's submarine. Depth charges require the attacking ship to get very close to an enemy submarine. That submarine is equally capable of launching missiles or torpedoes that can destroy the attacking ship. The modern approach is to hunt, locate, and destroy the enemy submarine from afar. Aircraft armed with everything from depth charges to torpedoes are used.

The lightweight Mark 46 antisubmarine torpedo carries a 100-pound warhead. The Mark 46 would be pressed into service in situations where the Navy wanted to debilitate, but not necessarily destroy, an enemy submarine. The high-performance dual-purpose Mark 48 torpedo moves a step up the destructive scale. Carrying a warhead of nearly 600 pounds, the Mark 48 would be brought to bear on enemy submarines the Navy hoped to eliminate quickly and completely.

Besides torpedoes, the Navy uses missiles. The antisubmarine rocket system (ASROC) was developed as a short-range ballistic missile that could quickly transport an acoustic torpedo or nuclear depth charge to the vicinity of an enemy submarine. Using position information about the submarine, the ship's fire control system aims the ASROC launchers to attain the correct trajectory. The missile is launched, and the rocket motor is jettisoned after burning out. The missile continues on an unguided trajectory. Before hitting the water, the ASROC missile releases the torpedo, which descends via parachute. When the torpedo hits the water, the parachute is released, and the torpedo is activated. The radar searcher in the torpedo seeks for and acquires the target by using a combination of active and passive guidance systems. If the torpedo misses the target on the first pass, it has a reserve capacity to reacquire the target and attack again. The ASROC missile system has a range of 1.2 to 6 miles; the torpedo has a range of up to 7 miles after it enters the water.

The ASROC system has been in operation since 1961. The U.S. and 11 other nations employ the system. A total of

Above: *The ASROC missile system consists of a homing torpedo fitted with a rocket propulsion unit.*

ANTISUBMARINE WEAPONS

Mark 46:	
Length:	8 ft., 6 in.
Diameter:	1 ft., 0.75 in.
Weight:	508 lbs.
Speed:	45 knots (51.7 mph)
Range:	6.8 miles
Depth:	1,000 ft.
Warhead:	95-lb. high-explosive
Date of service:	1966
Mark 48:	
Length:	19 ft., 2 in.
Diameter:	1 ft., 9 in.
Weight:	3,450 pounds
Speed:	55 knots (63 mph)
Range:	23 miles
Depth:	2,500 ft.
Warhead:	PBNX-3 high-explosive
Date of service:	1967
ASROC:	
Length:	15 ft.
Diameter:	12 ft., 0.75 in.
Weight:	1,000 lbs.
Speed:	561 mph
Range:	6 miles
Warhead:	Mk 46 torpedo or W44 nuclear depth charge
Date of service:	1961

Top: *The Sea Lance missile was to replace the SUBROC, but budget considerations have delayed deployment for now.* Bottom: *The Mk 46 torpedo, shown here being loaded aboard the cruiser USS* Wainwright, *can home in on its target using on-board sonar.*

more than 2,000 ASROC missile systems are planned. Currently, a total of 127 U.S. Navy ships are equipped with ASROC, including all cruisers, destroyers, and frigates previous to the *Oliver Hazard Perry* class.

Over the past few years, the Navy has eliminated the Submarine Rocket system (SUBROC) from U.S. submarines. Similar to the ASROC system, SUBROC was the basis of an offensive nuclear punch for attack submarines operating against Soviet boats. The SUBROC's limited range, dated technology, and questionable readiness caused the system to be eliminated. The new Sea Lance missile, which was to replace the SUBROC, has been put on hold due to budget considerations.

Most submarines are equipped with sensors and detection devices that can detect and foil most surface, moored, and bottom-sitting mine systems in use today. A potentially much more effective development is the encapsulated torpedo. Rather than the traditional underwater mine, a Mark 46 or Mark 48 torpedo is laid by any aircraft or ship with mine-laying capability. As the torpedo sits passively on the ocean floor, its passive sonar monitors all traffic that passes within its specified range. When a submerged vessel—a submarine rather than a surface vessel—is detected, the active sonar turns on and the torpedo's launch time is calibrated and calculated. When the submarine comes into range, the torpedo is launched. Since the unit has no Identification, Friend or Foe system, friendly submarines must be warned to stay out of the area.

Submarines continue to develop stronger hulls and deeper diving capability, and they are becoming even more elusive and undetectable. More research and development will be needed to find weapons able to handle the threat of submarines.

The ASROC, here being fired from the frigate USS Brooke, *is carried and launched from the Mk 16 launcher.*

Surface-to-Air Weapons

Above: *The Sea Sparrow, here being launched from the aircraft carrier* America, *has been adapted from the air-launched Sparrow aircraft missile.* Opposite, top: *The Phalanx Close-In Weapons System fires 20mm bullets of depleted uranium.* Opposite, bottom: *The RIM-66C Standard antiaircraft missile on its Mk 13 Mod 4 launcher.*

Today's U.S. Navy warship must be able to protect itself from a host of aerial threats. Everything from slow, lumbering bombers armed with sea-skimming antiship cruise missiles to supersonic strike aircraft carrying high-speed attack missiles are all part of today's battlefield on the high seas. To meet this aerial threat, the Navy has developed a layered defense system that uses a variety of sophisticated weaponry, including aircraft with long-range missiles, short- to long-range surface-to-air missiles, and rapid-firing cannons/guns called Close-In Weapons Systems.

The first line of warship defense is to dispatch fighter interceptors to knock out the missile-carrying bomber aircraft. Any enemy bombers that get through this first line of defense would meet the second line of long-range defense: the family of Standard missiles developed by General Dynamics. The Standard I (SM-1) missile was developed as a replacement for the Talos, Tartar, and Terrier air-defense missiles. Although some Standard missiles are air-launched versions and some are surface-to-surface models, most of the nearly 5,000 Standard I and 3,500 Standard II (SM-2) missiles used by the U.S. and its allies are designed to seek out and destroy enemy aircraft and missiles.

The SM-1 initially entered service in 1969. It uses a solid-propellant rocket in two versions—Medium Range (11.2 miles) and Extended Range (40 miles). Both versions travel at speeds of more than twice the speed of sound and can reach an altitude of 65,000 feet or more.

The more advanced SM-2 entered service in 1978. Its range, speed, and electronic countermeasures capability are all much greater than those of the SM-1. The SM-2 can travel at speeds of more than Mach 2.5. Like the SM-1, the SM-2 comes in two versions—Medium Range (35 miles) and Extended Range (80 miles). An evolution of the SM-1, the SM-2 is a state-of-the-art, all-weather medium- to long-range air-defense missile that can be fired from rail or vertical launch systems.

The next line of defense is the Sea Sparrow RIM-7 missile. The Sea Sparrow first went into inventory in the early 1970s. Modernized RIM-7E, H, and M versions were introduced in 1973, 1982, and 1983, respectively. Built to take on attacking aircraft and cruise missiles, the Sea Sparrow carries either a 66- or 88-pound warhead. The Sea Sparrow has a range up to 28 miles, can engage targets at altitudes up to 50,000 feet, and travels at speeds of Mach 1.3. More than 8,000 Sea Sparrow missiles have been produced for the U.S. and its allies.

The fourth line of defense for missiles now rapidly approaching a ship is a system called Rolling Airframe Missile (RAM). RAM was originally a cooperative project among Denmark, West Germany, and the U.S. It is designed to be a fast-response, high-firepower missile defense system made from existing components. RAM combines the fuse, 20-pound high-explosive warhead, and solid-propellant rocket motor of the Sidewinder missile with the infrared seeker of the Stinger missile. The RAM missile has an effective maximum range of 5.6 miles and can travel at supersonic speeds toward targets up to 40,000 feet in altitude. The RAM missile has two canard (horizontal stabilizer) controls that work in conjunction with a new autopilot system to impart a high degree of maneuverability. RAM missiles can be launched from any standard NATO Sea Sparrow launcher or from special lightweight launchers.

If there are so many incoming enemy missiles that the first four lines of defense are unable to stop or destroy them, there is still the "last ditch" stopper. This final line of defense is known as the Phalanx Close-In Weapons System, built by General Dynamics. The Phalanx gun system became operational in 1980 and is fitted on more than 250 warships. Using a close-in radar system, the Phalanx can find, track, lock on, and destroy a target with its 20 millimeter fire.

Navy experts agree that the aerial threat will continue to challenge ship commanders with an increasing level of difficulty. Vigilance, technology, and sophisticated weaponry will remain the major factors in either staying in the battle or going completely out of action.

SURFACE-TO-AIR WEAPONS

Standard I Medium Range:	
Length:	14 ft., 7 in.
Diameter:	1 ft., 1 in.
Weight:	1,358 lbs.
Speed:	Mach 2+
Range:	11.2 miles
Altitude:	65,000 ft.
Guidance system:	Semi-active radar
Date of service:	1969
Standard I Extended Range:	
Length:	27 ft.
Diameter:	1 ft., 5 in.
Weight:	2,969 lbs.
Speed:	Mach 2+
Range:	40 miles
Altitude:	65,000 ft.
Guidance system:	Semi-active radar
Date of service:	1969
Standard II Medium Range:	
Length:	15 ft., 5 in.
Diameter:	1 ft., 1 in.
Weight:	1,558 lbs.
Speed:	Mach 2.5+
Range:	35 miles
Altitude:	65,000 ft.
Guidance system:	Semi-active radar
Date of service:	1978
Standard II Extended Range:	
Length:	26 ft., 2 in.
Diameter:	1 ft., 5 in.
Weight:	3,320 lbs.
Speed:	Mach 2.5+
Range:	80 miles
Altitude:	65,000 ft.
Guidance system:	Semi-active radar
Date of service:	1978
Sea Sparrow:	
Length:	12 ft., 1 in.
Diameter:	7 in.
Weight:	502 lbs.
Speed:	Mach 1.3
Range:	28 miles
Altitude:	50,000 ft.
Guidance system:	Semi-active radar
Date of service:	1973
RAM:	
Length:	9 ft., 2 in.
Diameter:	4 in.
Weight:	162 lbs.
Speed:	Mach 1+
Range:	5.6 miles
Altitude:	40,000 ft.
Guidance system:	Radio frequency seeker and passive infrared
Date of service:	1990
Phalanx:	
Caliber:	.76
Rate of fire:	3,000 rounds per minute
Range:	Close-in defense
Date of service:	1980

Above: *The radar-guided Sea Sparrow missile has a range of 28 miles.* Left: *The aircraft-borne version of the Sea Sparrow is the AIM-7 Sparrow III; it has a range of nearly 35 miles.*

Left: *Standard II Extended Range antiaircraft missiles, shown here mounted on their Mk 10 launcher, have a range of 80 miles.* Below: *A Standard missile is fired from the USS* California.

The Sea Sparrow, here being launched from the USS Kitty Hawk, *was originally developed to counter the threat of Soviet submarines that had to surface to fire their cruise missiles.*

NAVY
NAVY

Radars and Surveillance Systems

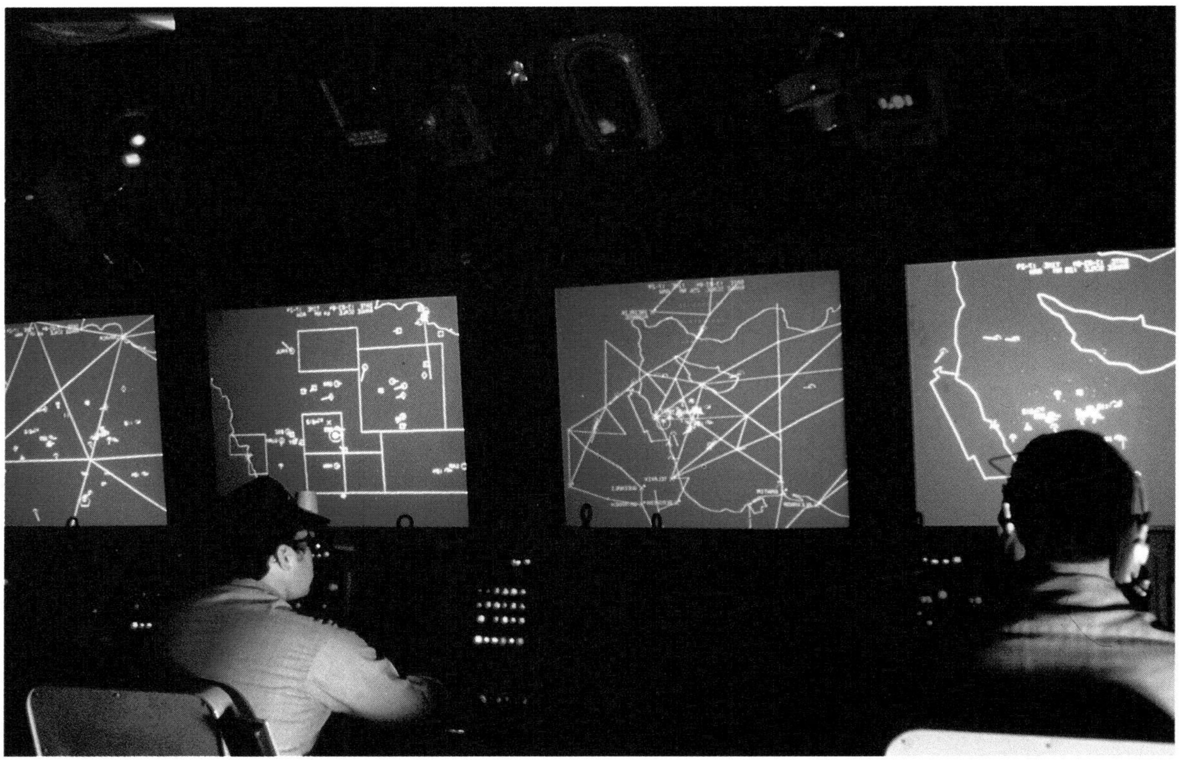

For hundreds of years, ships had to rely on the spotter in the crow's nest to watch for and report possible threats. The spotter was limited by what could be seen to the horizon. The advent of the airplane made this method of surveillance inadequate. By the time a flight of fighters reached the horizon, a ship had little if any time to prepare to defend itself.

The modern U.S. Navy ship relies on a variety of high-technology radars, sonars, and sensor systems to defend itself against possible attack from above, below, or on the water. Although the modern warship may pack a mighty offensive punch, without sophisticated sensors, it is nearly helpless.

To protect the modern carrier battle group, the Navy has built Aegis—the world's finest air-defense system. Its sole task is to provide a blanket-like shield of cover and coordination. This complicated system is based upon the SPY-1A phased-array radar system. SPY-1A can automatically keep track of, and coordinate the destruction of, multiple enemy missiles and aircraft while also handling a variety of submarine and surface threats. Through the Aegis radar system, the complete air battle can be controlled from one command ship. That command ship can control its own missiles as well as the missiles aboard other ships. The idea is to provide central coordination for all ships involved in a battle.

Since the air threat is such a major concern on the high seas, the Navy has developed a new and lighter derivative of the SPY-1A radar. Called the SPY-1D, it will be found on the *Arleigh Burke*-class frigates. Rather than the two transmitters and four illuminators found on the Aegis SPY-1A system, the 1D version has only one transmitter and three illuminators. The SPY-1D version will have the same defensive capabilities as the SPY-1A, but it will come in a smaller package.

Although air battle coordination will almost certainly be handled by either the Aegis system or *Arleigh Burke* frigates in the event of a major conflict, every ship in the Navy has some capability to watch out for and handle threats from above and below the surface. To increase the capability of these individual ships further, the modern carrier battle group would operate its fleet of Airborne Early Warning aircraft. One such aircraft is the E-2C Hawkeye, which is equipped with a distinctive 24-foot-diameter radome (housing for its antennae system) perched above its fuselage.

Enemy submarines also present a major threat to the carrier battle group. The carrier battle group's fleet of helicopters, equipped with sonobuoys and other sonar devices, tries to detect enemy submarines long before they get within range of the carrier group. Within the carrier battle group itself, each ship—equipped with its own hull-mounted sonar systems—remains the principal antisubmarine warfare sensor system. Each ship's sonars can be operated in the active or passive modes. Many ships also carry variable-depth sonar systems that can include the long towed array cable. This cable reels out several thousand feet behind the stern of a ship, greatly increasing the ship's ability to detect prowling enemy submarines.

Although radar and sonar remain the principal detection sensors in the Navy, other technologies are continuously being explored. Some of these technologies include infrared detectors and sensors, low-light television with computer video enhancement to sharpen the grainy thermal imagery, and laser designators and range finders. With threats coming so quickly from so many different areas, sensors, detection equipment, and threat warning systems are of paramount importance in order to fight and survive in the modern battlefield at sea.

Above: *Aegis is a sophisticated radar system that can search for enemy aircraft; measure their altitude and range; illuminate them for radar-guided missiles; and provide fire control data to guns, missiles, or aircraft.* Opposite: *The SPY-1 multifunction phased-array radar is the heart of the Aegis system.*

Above: *The SPY-49 radar system, shown here aboard the cruiser USS* Ticonderoga, *searches for hostile aircraft.* Left: *The Aegis system is central to the modern U.S. naval task force air-defense system.* Opposite: *A Standard missile, fired from a* Ticonderoga-*class cruiser, receives fire control data from the Aegis system.*

SUBMARINES

The submarine—with roots stretching back to the American Revolution and with limited application during the American Civil War—has been a tool of warfare throughout the history of the United States. Today, the modern U.S. Navy would be hard to imagine without submarines able to fire deadly long-range intercontinental ballistic missiles or submarines able to hunt and destroy other submarines or enemy ship convoys.

Today, we give little thought to submarines able to dive to depths of near hull-crushing pressure or submarines able to stay submerged for months at a time. But for the first 50 years of mass production of submarines, it was basically a vessel that traveled and fought most of its battles on the surface. When a submarine had to dive (usually only to hide or protect itself from surface attack), it rarely went much deeper than its own length. Even when submerged and waiting for an unsuspecting surface ship, one of the submarine's greatest drawbacks was its extremely slow speed. Most surface combatant vessels could easily overtake a retreating submarine. At that point, a combination of ordnance—including the lethal depth charge—often meant either the vessel's destruction or its being forced to the surface to fight or surrender.

The 1940s brought changes in the submarine's status; modern technology developed by the Allied and Axis powers enabled the submarine to become a much more effective attack vessel. By the mid-1950s, the U.S. Navy's submarines were some of the most effective ship sinkers to patrol the high seas. In the event of a conflict, the odds of virtually any surface warship or tanker/freighter surviving a submarine attack were not good. The submarine, for the most part, enjoyed a period of stealthy impunity from threats above, on, and below the surface.

Today, the advent of the nuclear-powered submarine missile boat (SSBN)—often referred to as the "boomer"—and the attack boat (SSN)—"hunter/killer"—has given the submarine an endurance that is limited only by the psychological and physiological needs of the crew. Both the East and the West have assembled an impressive array of submarines designed to be either long-range missile platforms or close-in attack boats. The modern submarine can carry a host of long- and short-range weaponry that can be used against land, sea, and air threats or targets. There is no spot on the globe that is not within range of a submarine-launched weapon.

Most technological shortcomings have been surmounted. The modern submarine can operate at speeds comparable with surface vessels and dive to depths that previously would have crushed the vessel's hull. Today's submarines operate so silently that detection is becoming increasingly difficult. While no submarine is "invisible" in the water environment, it is the first, and thus far only, proven stealth weapon system. The great deal of modern technology found on the U.S. Navy's submarines reflects a major investment to enable them to remain undetected in a variety of environments, as well as to fight and survive under diverse conditions. The modern submarine is difficult to locate, identify, track, and destroy.

As East and West learn more about the world the underwater warrior must operate in, changes in the submarine's design, function, and purpose are guaranteed. The boomer and hunter/killer—able to attack an enemy's homeland or destroy his convoys of ships—occupy a unique position in the world of sea power.

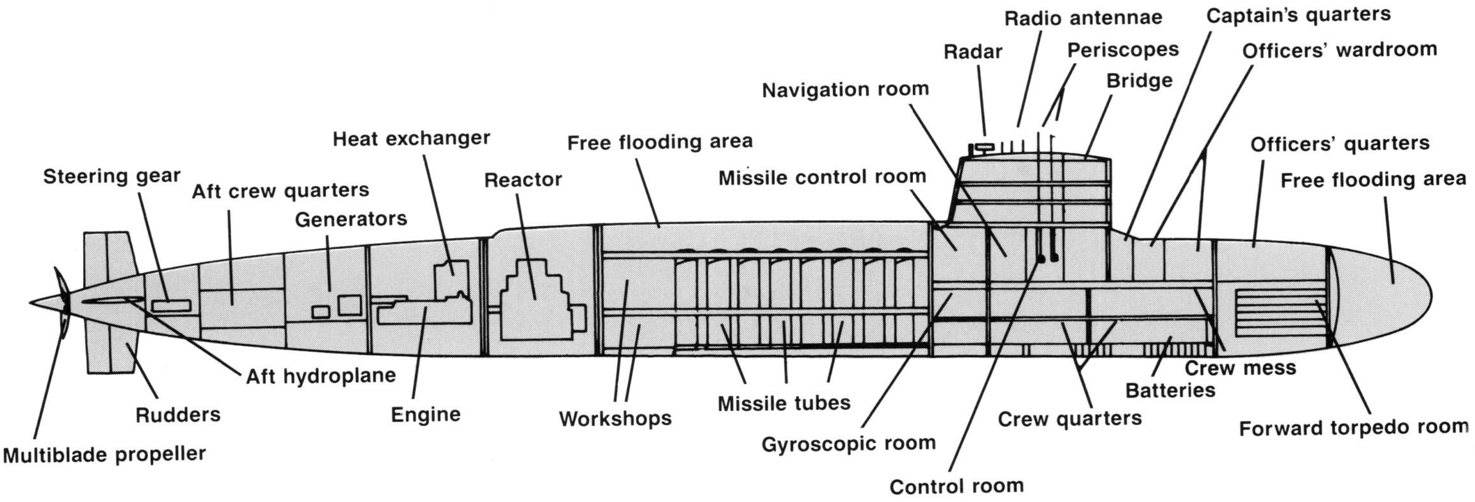

Opposite: *This rendering of a typical American submarine locates the major equipment and weaponry currently in use.* Above: *One part of America's nuclear deterrent is borne by the* Ohio-*class submarine fleet.*

Ohio-*class submarines, such as the USS* Henry M. Jackson, *carry 24 nuclear-tipped strategic missiles.*

Lafayette-Class (SSBN) and Benjamin Franklin-Class (SSBN) Ballistic Missile Submarines

Above: *The USS* Daniel Boone *is a* Lafayette*-class strategic submarine;* Lafayette *submarines carry 16 nuclear-tipped missiles.*

The *Lafayette*-class submarines were part of the first generation of ballistic missile boats built for the U.S. Navy. Among the early Ballistic Missile Submarines, Nuclear-Powered (SSBN) were *Skipjack*-class submarines that had been converted to *George Washington*-class boats by adding a 130-foot missile section welded aft of the fin. The *George Washington* boats were followed by the *Ethan Allen*-class submarines, which from the beginning were designed to be the first true "missile boats." The *Ethan Allen* boats formed the basis for an improved design that eventually became the *Lafayette* class.

Lafayette submarines are powered by one S5W water-cooled, pressurized nuclear reactor producing 15,000 horsepower. The submarine can move at speeds of 20 knots (23 miles per hour) or faster and can dive to depths nearly equal to the larger and more technologically advanced *Ohio*-class submarines. With a length of 425 feet and a displacement of just over 8,250 tons when submerged, the *Lafayette* boat is a rather small submarine in the world of modern boomers. In terms of general layout and weapon/sensor packages, *Lafayette* boats differ little from the earlier *Ethan Allen*-class submarines. The major difference between *Lafayette* boats and earlier submarines are the *Lafayette*'s larger missile tubes, which were intended to accommodate future ballistic missile designs of greater diameter, range, and power. The capacity to handle larger future missiles increased the submarine's hull length by nearly 15 feet over the *Ethan Allen*-class boats, but the rest of the dimensions stayed the same.

The first eight *Lafayette* boats went to sea with 16 Polaris A-2 missiles. Polaris A-2 missiles carried a single nuclear warhead and had a range of only 1,500 nautical miles (1,700 miles). The next 23 submarines in the *Lafayette* class headed out with the newer Polaris A-3 missile, which had three warheads and a range of nearly 2,500 nautical miles (2,800 miles). In 1970, *Lafayette* submarines were retrofitted with the more potent Poseidon missile. The Poseidon has a range similar to the older Polaris A-3, but carries up to ten 150-kiloton warheads.

To prolong the life of *Lafayette* boats, the Navy decided in 1979 to retrofit 12 of the submarines with quieter propulsion equipment that would further insulate the sub from detection. The Trident C-4

missile, more capable than the Poseidon, was also added. Work on these 12 boats was completed in 1982, and all 12 carry the designation of *Benjamin Franklin*-class missile boats.

The *Benjamin Franklin* submarines come equipped with two Mark 2 Ship's Inertial Navigation Systems, which update missile targeting via satellites. *Benjamin Franklin* boats also have upgraded commercial navigation systems/radars for surface operations and four forward torpedo tubes capable of firing the Mark 48 torpedo.

A total of 31 submarines of the *Lafayette* and *Benjamin Franklin* class were built at four different shipyards between 1963 and 1967. To comply with the provisions of the unratified SALT II treaty limits, some of these boats were decommissioned and removed from active inventory. Many others, still on active service, are slated for decommissioning and retirement as the United States plans further force reductions in the 1990s.

continued on page 468

Above: The Benjamin Franklin *class of submarines are equipped with quieter nuclear powerplants than the* Lafayette *submarines.*

Above: *All U.S. nuclear submarines have their diving planes mounted on the sail, as in the USS* Ulysses S. Grant. Left: *A Navy tug assists a* Lafayette-*class submarine at Pearl Harbor.* Opposite: *When surfaced, there is always a full watch. Here two officers and three enlisted sailors of the* John C. Calhoun *keep a sharp watch for other traffic.*

continued from page 465

LAFAYETTE-CLASS (SSBN) AND BENJAMIN FRANKLIN-CLASS (SSBN) BALLISTIC MISSILE SUBMARINES

Operational (commissioned):	SSBN 616 USS *Lafayette* (April 1963) SSBN 617 USS *Alexander Hamilton* (June 1963) SSBN 619 USS *Andrew Jackson* (July 1963) SSBN 620 USS *John Adams* (May 1964) SSBN 622 USS *James Monroe* (December 1963) SSBN 623 USS *Nathan Hale* (November 1963) SSBN 624 USS *Woodrow Wilson* (December 1963) SSBN 625 USS *Henry Clay* (February 1964) SSBN 626 USS *Daniel Webster* (April 1964) SSBN 627 USS *James Madison* (July 1964) SSBN 628 USS *Tecumseh* (May 1964) SSBN 629 USS *Daniel Boone* (April 1964) SSBN 630 USS *John C. Calhoun* (September 1964) SSBN 631 USS *Ulysses S. Grant* (July 1964) SSBN 632 USS *Von Steuben* (September 1964) SSBN 633 USS *Casimir Pulaski* (August 1964) SSBN 634 USS *Stonewall Jackson* (August 1964) SSBN 635 USS *Sam Rayburn* (December 1964) SSBN 636 USS *Nathaniel Greene* (December 1964) SSBN 640 USS *Benjamin Franklin* (October 1965) SSBN 641 USS *Simon Bolivar* (October 1965) SSBN 642 USS *Kamehameha* (December 1965) SSBN 643 USS *George Bancroft* (January 1966) SSBN 644 USS *Lewis and Clark* (December 1965)
Operational continued	SSBN 645 USS *James K. Polk* (April 1966) SSBN 654 USS *George C. Marshall* (April 1966) SSBN 655 USS *Henry L. Stimson* (August 1966) SSBN 656 USS *George Washington Carver* (June 1966) SSBN 657 USS *Francis Scott Key* (December 1966) SSBN 658 USS *Mariano G. Vallejo* (December 1966) SSBN 659 USS *Will Rogers* (April 1967)
Displacement:	
Surfaced:	7,350 tons
Submerged:	8,250 tons
Dimensions:	
Length:	425 ft.
Beam:	33 ft.
Draft:	29 ft.
Propulsion:	One S5W water-cooled, pressurized nuclear reactor
Speed:	20 + knots (23 + mph)
Diving depth:	984.25 ft.
Armament:	
SSBN 616–636:	Sixteen Poseidon C-3 long-range ballistic missiles Four Mk 48 torpedoes
SSBN 640–659:	Sixteen Trident I C-4 long-range ballistic missiles Four Mk 48 torpedoes
Fire control:	One Mk 88 missile fire control system One Mk 113 missile fire control system
Surveillance radar:	Either BPS-11A or BPS-15; exact information is classified
Sonar:	Either BQR-7, BQR-15, BQR-19, BQR-21, or BQS-4; exact information is classified
Crew:	142–147

Opposite: *All* Lafayette *and* Benjamin Franklin *nuclear submarines are attached to the Atlantic fleet.*

Ohio-Class (SSBN) Ballistic Missile Submarines

The U.S. Navy's fleet of *Ohio*-class ballistic missile submarines—floating silently or resting quietly on the ocean bottom for weeks at a time—forms an important leg of the United States' triad of nuclear deterrence. In the event of a sneak attack against land-based bomber aircraft or land-based long-range nuclear missiles, this third leg of nuclear deterrence would remain undetectable and could retaliate against enemy targets anywhere in the world.

Operational since 1981, *Ohio*-class submarines represent state-of-the-art technology in everything from weaponry and propulsion systems to sensors and sonars. Nearly a dozen *Ohio* boomers are currently in service, and at present the program calls for a total of 20 boats. The *Ohio*-class submarines were originally designed to replace the older *George Washington* and *Ethan Allen* classes of submarines that could not be converted to carry either the Poseidon or Trident long-range ballistic missiles.

The introduction of the new long-range Trident C-4 missile has greatly increased the range of *Ohio* submarines. With a capacity of up to 24 Trident C-4 missiles or new Trident II D-5 missiles (which should enter service in 1990), *Ohio*-class boats possess a firepower capability equal to or greater than many nuclear-capable countries other than the super powers. Since the *Ohio*-class submarine was designed to carry the new Trident II D-5 missile, the boat's missile tubes have a larger overall diameter than those of *Lafayette*-class submarines. Current C-4 missiles have a length of 34 feet and a diameter of 6 feet 2 inches. The D-5 is much larger overall, with a length of 44 feet and a diameter of nearly 7 feet. The larger size will increase the range of these missiles from approximately 4,000 nautical miles (4,600 miles) to more than 6,000 nautical miles (6,900 miles). Each C-4 missile carries up to eight 100-kiloton nuclear warheads; the new D-5 missile will carry up to 14 150-kiloton nuclear warheads.

Ohio-class submarines can stay submerged at a depth of more than 1,000 feet and remain undetected for more than two months at a time. These capabilities are especially useful for the mission of *Ohio* submarines: to stay hidden and undetected but to be prepared to launch a debilitating nuclear retaliatory strike if necessary.

Ohio-class boats have an S8G natural circulation nuclear reactor that produces up to 60,000 horsepower. The reactor powers two sets of turbines—one for high-speed operations, another for slow and silent maneuvering. *Ohio*-class submarines are capable of cruising at 20 knots (23 miles per hour) or faster.

These submarines are equipped with some of today's most sophisticated sonar detection equipment. *Ohio* boats come with sophisticated listening devices, a towed array sonar system, hydrophone arrays for fire control, side-looking sonars for mapping the ocean floor, and a special sonar that allows these submarines to operate under the polar ice caps. The submarine has two Mark 2 Ship's Inertial Navigation Systems, which receive targeting data via satellite relays to insure the missiles are accurately targeted.

Although defensive capabilities are limited by comparison with surface warships, the *Ohio*-class submarine carries a complement of Mark 48 torpedoes and an array of decoy, deception, and masking devices to better conceal its true position.

Above: *The USS* Ohio *is the lead ship of a new class of nuclear-powered strategic ballistic missile submarines.* Opposite: *The USS* Georgia, *an* Ohio-*class boat, maneuvers off Port Angeles, Washington.*

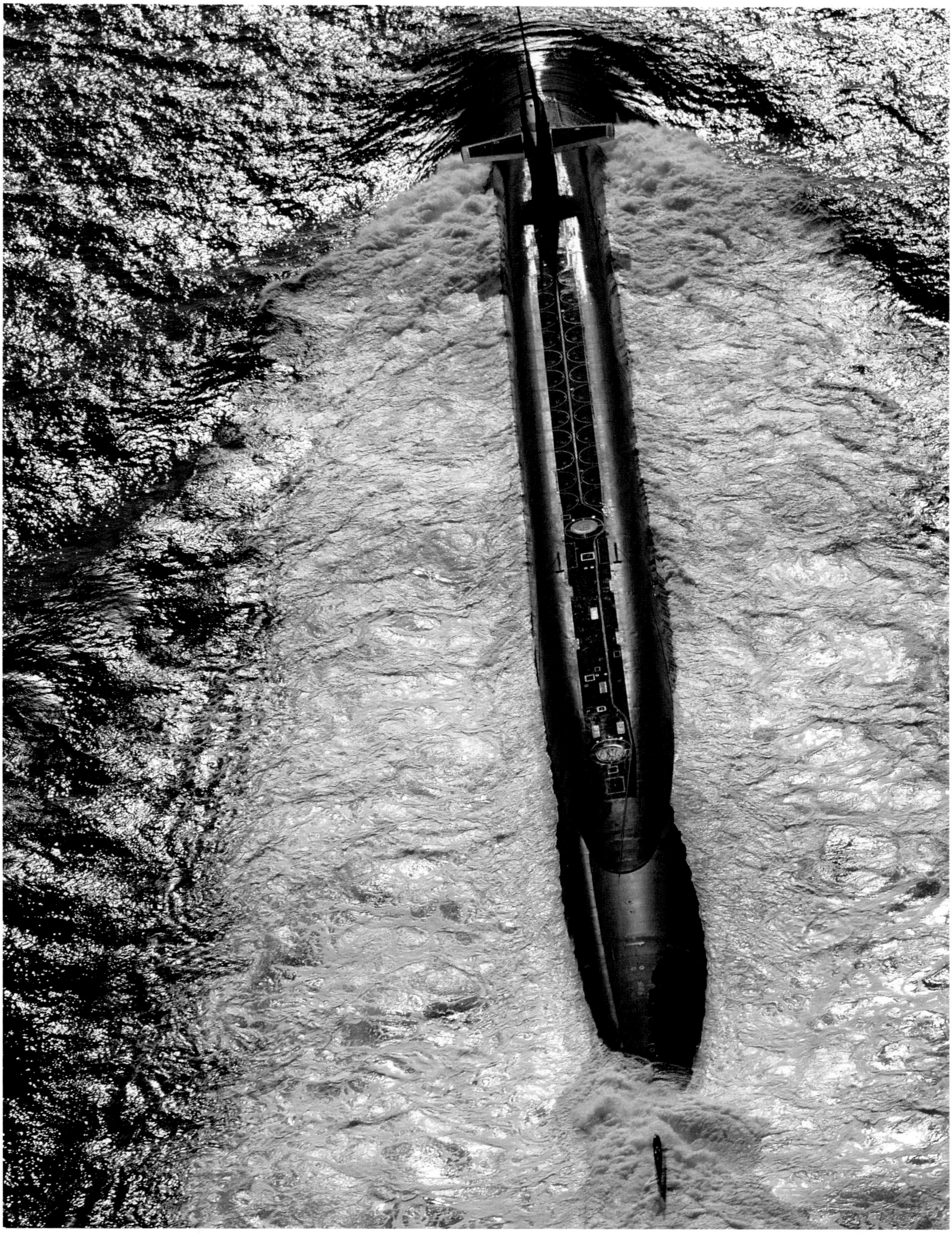

OHIO-CLASS (SSBN) BALLISTIC MISSILE SUBMARINES

Operational (commissioned):	SSBN 726 USS *Ohio* (November 1981) SSBN 727 USS *Michigan* (September 1982) SSBN 728 USS *Florida* (June 1983) SSBN 729 USS *Georgia* (February 1984) SSBN 730 USS *Henry M. Jackson* (October 1984) SSBN 731 USS *Alabama* (May 1985) SSBN 732 USS *Alaska* (January 1986) SSBN 733 USS *Nevada* (August 1986) SSBN 734 USS *Tennessee* (December 1988) SSBN 735 USS *Pennsylvania* (September 1987)	**Planned continued**	SSBN 743 (unnamed) (mid-1997) SSBN 744 (unnamed) (mid-1998) SSBN 745 (unnamed) (mid-1999)
Building:	SSBN 736 *West Virginia* (mid-1990) SSBN 737 *Kentucky* (early 1991) SSBN 738 *Maryland* (early 1992) SSBN 739 *Nebraska* (mid-1993) SSBN 740 (unnamed) (mid-1994) SSBN 741 (unnamed) (mid-1995)	**Displacement:**	
		Surfaced:	16,765 tons
		Submerged:	18,750 tons
		Dimensions:	
		Length:	560 ft.
		Beam:	42 ft.
		Draft:	36 ft., 6 in.
		Propulsion:	One S8G natural circulation nuclear reactor
		Speed:	20 + knots (23 + mph)
		Diving depth:	1,180 + ft.
		Armament:	Twenty-four Trident I C-4 long-range ballistic missiles Four Mk 48 torpedoes
		Fire control:	One Mk 98 missile fire control system One Mk 118 missile fire control system
		Surveillance radar:	Either BPS-15A or WLR-8(V)5; exact information is classified
		Sonar:	Either BQQ-6, BQQ-9, BQS-13, BQS-15, BQR-15, or BQR-19; exact information is classified
Planned:	SSBN 742 (unnamed) (mid-1996)	**Crew:**	157–160

Opposite: *The natural habitat of* Ohio *submarines is the Arctic Ocean. They can surface through the ice to send messages or fire their missiles.* Left: *The* Ohio-class *submarines are the largest submarines ever built in the United States.*

All Ohio-*class submarines are based with the Pacific fleet. This photo shows the USS* Nevada *at its mooring in Bangor, Washington.*

Permit-Class (SSN) Attack Submarines

Above: *Attack submarines, such as the USS* Haddo *of the* Permit *class, are built specifically to raid surface shipping and hunt enemy submarines.*

In the mid-1950s, the U.S. Navy decided to test and attempt to field two very different classes of attack submarines. The first would be a high-performance boat designed to work in conjunction with fleet operations. The other, known as Slow Hunter-Killer (SSK), would be a silent stalker that would sneak up on or lie in wait for an enemy's submarine force. After building the nuclear-powered USS *Tullibee* (SSKN), the Navy realized that, although the idea of two separate attack submarine classes was a good one, funding for the two separate classes was not feasible. The Navy dropped the fast submarine program and compromised the SSK program in an attempt to combine the attributes of both.

Out of this program grew the *Thresher* class of boats—now called the *Permit* class—with a mission leaning heavily toward antisubmarine warfare. The nuclear-powered *Permit*-class submarines entered service in the early 1960s. They are only 278 feet long and displace slightly less than 4,300 tons when submerged. Main propulsion is derived from the S5W water-cooled, pressurized nuclear reactor that enables the boat to travel at speeds up to 27 knots (31 miles per hour). The hull design features a large spherical bow sonar system that caused the torpedo tubes to be positioned in the submarine's midship area. Other construction innovations included the use of new steels in building the boat's single pressure hull. The extra strength gained from these steels enabled the submarine to dive to a depth of more than 1,300 feet. Unfortunately, such deep dives were not without failures. The tragic 1963 loss of the USS *Thresher,* the original ship of the class, only two years after it was built, bears grim testimony to the results of metal failure due to faulty welding.

The Navy was committed to using an existing nuclear reactor for the *Permit*-class submarines rather than investing additional time and money to develop a new powerplant. This raised concern about the vessel's overall speed when either racing in to make a strike or pressing an attack. To address this concern, the vertical fins of *Permit* submarines were redesigned to minimize drag. But there was a trade-off for this increased speed: There were problems fitting the various mast-mounted sensors necessary to operate the submarine when in its attack role.

At first, *Permit* submarines carried a host of conventional and nuclear torpedo weaponry. The torpedoes could be fired from one of four torpedo tubes that were angled ten degrees upward. Although built to handle torpedoes, the tubes were designed to fire the Navy's nuclear-tipped antisubmarine missile SUBROC as well. All SUBROC missiles have now been pulled from *Permit* submarines. Sea Lance missiles were intended to replace the SUBROC missiles, but funding difficulties have put the Sea Lance on hold for now. Since 1976, all *Permit*-class submarines have been modified and retrofitted to carry the Mark 48 torpedo. These same modifications also enable the boats to carry and launch Harpoon missiles.

Including the *Thresher,* a total of 14 *Permit*-class submarines were constructed between 1961 and 1965 at five different shipbuilding facilities. The 13 boats that remain continue to serve a variety of attack scenarios. The final three submarines were built as prototypes for the *Sturgeon*-class attack boats that succeeded them.

Top: *The Navy maintains a fleet of 104 attack submarines, all nuclear-powered. The USS* Haddock *belongs to the* Permit *class.* Bottom: *The USS* Guardfish, *preparing to submerge, is a* Permit-*class attack submarine.*

PERMIT-CLASS (SSN) ATTACK SUBMARINES

Operational (commissioned):	SSN 594 USS *Permit* (May 1962) SSN 595 USS *Plunger* (November 1962) SSN 596 USS *Barb* (August 1963) SSN 603 USS *Pollack* (May 1964) SSN 604 USS *Haddo* (December 1964) SSN 605 USS *Jack* (March 1967) SSN 606 USS *Tinosa* (October 1964) SSN 607 USS *Dace* (April 1964) SSN 612 USS *Guardfish* (December 1966) SSN 613 USS *Flasher* (July 1966) SSN 614 USS *Greenling* (November 1967) SSN 615 USS *Gato* (January 1968) SSN 621 USS *Haddock* (December 1967)
Displacement:	
Surfaced:	3,750 tons
Submerged:	4,300 tons
Dimensions:	
Length:	278 ft.
Beam:	31 ft., 7 in.
Draft:	29 ft.
Propulsion:	One S5W water-cooled, pressurized nuclear reactor
Speed:	27 knots (31 mph)
Diving depth:	1,300 ft.
Armament:	Four Mk 48 torpedoes Four Harpoon missiles
Fire control:	One Mk 113 missile and torpedo fire control system
Surveillance radar:	Either BPS-5, BPS-9, BPS-15, or WLR-1; exact information is classified
Sonar:	Either BQQ-3, BQS-14, or BQR-15; exact information is classified
Crew:	127

The USS Dace *of the* Permit *class sails up San Francisco Bay toward the Golden Gate.*

Two Permit-*class attack submarines at dawn in San Diego; actual day or night holds little meaning for a submarine and its crew.*

Sturgeon-Class (SSN) Attack Submarines

Although *Permit*-class submarines filled the attack role well, they gave up some performance characteristics to maintain higher speeds. The *Permit* submarine lacked room for new, more sophisticated electronics, and the small fin limited available space for mast-mounted sensors. *Sturgeon*-class submarines were built as a follow-on to the *Permit* design. From the late 1960s until the introduction of the highly sophisticated *Los Angeles*-class attack boats, *Sturgeon*-class submarines set the standard by which all other submarines were compared.

Sturgeon boats have an overall hull length of 292 feet and displace 4,640 tons when submerged. These submarines were built using the same basic hull design as *Permit* submarines, but they were given more internal space, which allowed for the addition of new electronics. But this extra space did not diminish the vessel's performance or increase underwater noise levels. Despite their increased size and internal volume, *Sturgeon* submarines are able to use the S5W nuclear reactor and maintain a maximum speed of 26 knots (30 miles per hour). *Sturgeon* boats are deep divers, capable of going down to more than 1,300 feet.

Sturgeon submarines have a large cylindrical bow area occupied by the BQS-6 spherical active/passive sonar system. This sonar system can detect targets as far as 35 nautical miles (40 miles) away by using one of several sensing systems that the Navy calls a "bottom bounce" or "convergence zone" of operation. Unlike *Permit*-class boats, *Sturgeon* submarines have a greatly enlarged fin area to accommodate the larger attack center and control room area with an array of computer consoles and targeting equipment. With the addition of upgraded electronics and sensing/targeting devices, *Sturgeon* boats can engage multiple enemy targets at one time. The larger fin can accommodate more mast-mounted sensors for greater ability to detect enemy submarines. The boat's large fin-mounted horizontal hydroplanes can be rotated downward to allow the submarine to operate under and surface through thin to medium ice packs.

Several of the later *Sturgeon* boats have been modified to carry a miniature salvage submarine. The miniature submarine can be launched and recovered while the *Sturgeon* boat remains submerged. This miniature submarine capability opens the door for everything from rescue operations to salvage ventures, as well as deployment of underwater demolition teams, SEAL (Sea, Air, and Land) teams, or other special operation forces. Several of the *Sturgeon*-class boats have a rear hatch designed to enable people to be transferred while the vessels are submerged and under power.

Sturgeon submarines carry an array of weaponry nearly identical to *Permit*-class boats. There are four Mark 63 torpedo tubes angled ten degrees upward. The tubes can fire the Mark 48 torpedo or the Harpoon antiship missile.

Many of the *Sturgeon*-class submarines have estimated life spans that will carry them to the mid to late 1990s. The Navy is again upgrading some of the submarines in this class with new technology. Tests have recently been successfully completed in which *Sturgeon* boats were used as launching platforms for the Tomahawk cruise missile. Several *Sturgeon* submarines are being retrofitted with anechoic hull coatings that further reduce noise as the submarine powers through the water, increasing its chances of remaining undetected.

Above: *The USS* Sea Devil, *just after surfacing, belongs to the* Sturgeon *class of attack submarines;* Sturgeon *submarines carry a larger sail than* Permit *boats and have better ability to operate under ice.* Opposite: *The long container on the port side of the USS* Drum *houses the towed array sonar system.*

STURGEON-CLASS (SSN) ATTACK SUBMARINES

Operational (commissioned):	SSN 637 USS *Sturgeon* (March 1967) SSN 638 USS *Whale* (October 1968) SSN 639 USS *Tautog* (August 1968) SSN 646 USS *Grayling* (October 1969) SSN 647 USS *Pogy* (May 1971) SSN 648 USS *Aspro* (February 1969) SSN 649 USS *Sunfish* (March 1969) SSN 650 USS *Pargo* (January 1968) SSN 651 USS *Queenfish* (December 1968) SSN 652 USS *Puffer* (August 1969) SSN 653 USS *Ray* (April 1967) SSN 660 USS *Sand Lance* (September 1971) SSN 661 USS *Lapon* (December 1967) SSN 662 USS *Gurnard* (December 1968) SSN 663 USS *Hammerhead* (June 1968) SSN 664 USS *Sea Devil* (January 1969) SSN 665 USS *Guitarro* (September 1972) SSN 666 USS *Hawkbill* (February 1971) SSN 667 USS *Bergall* (June 1969) SSN 668 USS *Spacefish* (August 1969) SSN 669 USS *Seahorse* (September 1969) SSN 670 USS *Finback* (February 1970) SSN 672 USS *Pintado* (April 1971) SSN 673 USS *Flying Fish* (April 1970) SSN 674 USS *Trepang* (August 1970) SSN 675 USS *Bluefish* (January 1971)
Operational continued	SSN 676 USS *Billfish* (March 1971) SSN 677 USS *Drum* (April 1972) SSN 678 USS *Archerfish* (December 1971) SSN 679 USS *Silversides* (May 1972) SSN 680 USS *William H. Bates* (May 1973) SSN 681 USS *Batfish* (September 1972) SSN 682 USS *Tunny* (January 1974) SSN 683 USS *Parche* (August 1974) SSN 684 USS *Cavalla* (February 1973) SSN 686 USS *L. Mendel Rivers* (February 1975) SSN 687 USS *Richard B. Russell* (August 1975)
Displacement:	
Surfaced:	4,250 tons
Submerged:	4,640 tons
Dimensions:	
Length:	292 ft.
Beam:	31 ft., 7 in.
Draft:	29 ft.
Propulsion:	One S5W water-cooled, pressurized nuclear reactor
Speed:	26 knots (30 mph)
Diving depth:	1,300 ft.
Armament:	Fifteen Mk 48 dual-purpose torpedoes Eight Tomahawk cruise missiles Four Harpoon missiles
Fire control:	One Mk 117 missile and torpedo fire control system
Surveillance radar:	Either BPS-14, BPS-15, or WLQ-4; exact information is classified
Sonar:	BQS-6 active/passive BQR-15 towed array Either BQQ-2, BQQ-5, BQS-8, BQS-12, or BQS-13; exact information is classified
Crew:	107

Opposite: *Even at 20 feet above the waterline, lookout duty on an attack submarine can be a wet job.*

Los Angeles-Class (SSN) Attack Submarines

The formidable *Los Angeles*-class attack submarine—drifting silently at deep or shallow depths—likely rates as the quietest nuclear submarine in existence today. As their main mission, these state-of-the-art antisubmarine warfare boats seek out Soviet submarines and ships and sink them before they can attack U.S. aircraft carrier convoys.

The origins of the *Los Angeles* submarine can be traced to the late 1960s. The intended role of *Los Angeles* attack submarines was to travel ahead of a carrier battle group and station themselves in front of advancing Soviet submarines. Called "close-support," these submarines would need to achieve a high underwater speed but not at the expense of being noisy. The result was the *Los Angeles*-Class Attack Submarine, Nuclear Powered (SSN).

Los Angeles-class submarines have a rather large and massive hull of 360 feet in length. These attack boats feature a water-cooled nuclear reactor that produces almost double the horsepower of any other submarine in U.S. inventory. With almost 30,000 horsepower driving the geared steam turbines, *Los Angeles* submarines can achieve a speed of more than 31 knots (35.6 miles per hour). The submarine uses a tactic called "sprint and drift"; it races to a protective area and then drifts quietly until ready to attack an approaching vessel.

While stalking its prey, the submarine's sophisticated electronics, sonars, and sensors serve as its eyes and ears. The entire bow section is taken up by a large active/passive spherical sonar system that helps the submarine listen, detect, and identify enemy targets. That information is then sent to the boat's fire control system, which can simultaneously engage multiple threats and targets with a variety of weapons.

One of the most potent weapons of the *Los Angeles* class is the long-range Tomahawk missile. Against fixed targets the Tomahawk Land Attack Missile—armed with either conventional or nuclear warheads—can be fired from the vessel's standard torpedo tubes against ground-based targets as far as 1,400 miles away. The Tomahawk Antiship Missile can be fired at targets more than 250 nautical miles (287 miles) away. Depending on the specific mission of a particular *Los Angeles* submarine, the vessel can be outfitted with Mark 48 torpedoes or Harpoon missiles. Later versions of the *Los Angeles* submarine can be pressed into service as underwater minelayers.

Most nuclear submarines require refueling every seven to ten years. But *Los Angeles* attack boats have a very efficient reactor fuel core design that enables the submarines to sail for up to 13 years before refueling. The U.S. currently has more than 40 *Los Angeles* submarines in inventory and as many as 30 more on order. Although the class is far from complete in terms of construction, it is the most numerous class of nuclear submarine ever built.

Below: *Wives, children, friends, and alternate crew members greet the USS* Honolulu, *a* Los Angeles-*class attack submarine, as it arrives at Pearl Harbor.* Opposite: *A* Los Angeles *attack submarine receives a new radar installation at San Diego, California.*

65
MISTER MARSHALL

Left: *The USS* Birmingham *surfaces dramatically.*

LOS ANGELES-CLASS (SSN) ATTACK SUBMARINES

Operational (commissioned):

SSN 688 USS *Los Angeles* (November 1976)
SSN 689 USS *Baton Rouge* (June 1977)
SSN 690 USS *Philadelphia* (June 1977)
SSN 691 USS *Memphis* (December 1977)
SSN 692 USS *Omaha* (March 1978)
SSN 693 USS *Cincinnati* (June 1978)
SSN 694 USS *Groton* (July 1978)
SSN 695 USS *Birmingham* (December 1978)
SSN 696 USS *New York City* (March 1978)
SSN 697 USS *Indianapolis* (January 1980)
SSN 698 USS *Bremerton* (March 1981)
SSN 699 USS *Jacksonville* (May 1981)
SSN 700 USS *Dallas* (July 1981)
SSN 701 USS *La Jolla* (October 1981)
SSN 702 USS *Phoenix* (December 1981)
SSN 703 USS *Boston* (January 1982)
SSN 704 USS *Baltimore* (July 1982)
SSN 705 USS *City of Corpus Christi* (January 1983)

Operational continued

SSN 706 USS *Albuquerque* (May 1983)
SSN 707 USS *Portsmouth* (October 1983)
SSN 708 USS *Minneapolis-Saint Paul* (March 1984)
SSN 709 USS *Hyman G. Rickover* (September 1984)
SSN 710 USS *Augusta* (January 1985)
SSN 711 USS *San Francisco* (April 1981)
SSN 712 USS *Atlanta* (March 1982)
SSN 713 USS *Houston* (September 1982)
SSN 714 USS *Norfolk* (May 1983)
SSN 715 USS *Buffalo* (November 1983)
SSN 716 USS *Salt Lake City* (May 1984)
SSN 717 USS *Olympia* (November 1984)
SSN 718 USS *Honolulu* (July 1985)
SSN 719 USS *Providence* (July 1985)
SSN 720 USS *Pittsburgh* (November 1985)
SSN 721 USS *Chicago* (September 1986)
SSN 722 USS *Key West* (September 1987)

Left: *The USS* San Francisco *leaves Pearl Harbor to begin another 30-day Pacific cruise.*

LOS ANGELES-CLASS (SSN) ATTACK SUBMARINES

Operational continued

SSN 723 USS *Oklahoma City* (July 1988)
SSN 724 USS *Louisville* (November 1986)
SSN 725 USS *Helena* (July 1987)
SSN 750 USS *Newport News* (June 1989)
SSN 751 USS *San Juan* (August 1988)
SSN 752 USS *Pasadena* (February 1989)

Building:

SSN 753 USS *Albany* (1990)
SSN 754 USS *Topeka* (1990)
SSN 755 USS *Miami* (1990)
SSN 756 USS *Scranton* (1990)
SSN 757 USS *Alexandria* (1990)
SSN 758 USS *Asheville* (1989)
SSN 759 USS *Jefferson City* (1990)
SSN 760 USS *Annapolis* (1990)
SSN 761 USS *Springfield* (1990)
SSN 762 USS *Columbus* (1990)
SSN 763 USS *Santa Fe* (1991)
SSN 764 USS *Boise* (1992)
SSN 765 USS *Montpelier* (1992)
SSN 766 USS *Charlotti* (1992)
SSN 767 USS *Hampton* (1992)

Planned:	Ten additional
Displacement:	
Surfaced:	6,080 tons
Submerged:	6,927 tons
Dimensions:	
Length:	360 ft.
Beam:	33 ft.
Draft:	32 ft., 3.6 in.
Propulsion:	One S6G water-cooled, pressurized nuclear reactor
Speed:	31+ knots (35.6 mph)
Diving depth:	1,475 ft.
Armament:	Twelve vertical launch tubes for long-range Tomahawk missiles Harpoon missiles Mk 48 torpedoes Mine-laying equipment
Fire control:	Either one Mk 113 or one Mk 117 missile and torpedo fire control system; exact information is classified
Surveillance radar:	Either BPS-15A, BRD-7, WLR-8(V)2, or WLR-12; exact information is classified
Sonar:	Either BQQ-5A, BQQ-5D, BQS-5, BQR-15, or BSY-1; exact information is classified
Crew:	127

A harbor tug assists the Los Angeles *submarine* Honolulu *at Pearl Harbor.*

806
YTB 806

Above: *The* Los Angeles-*class attack submarine USS* Phoenix*—in the water—is dwarfed by two* Ohio-*class submarines under construction at the Electric Boat shipyards.* Left: *The USS* Los Angeles, *the lead ship for its class, powers through the waves.* Opposite: *The* Los Angeles-*class attack submarine USS* Pasadena *was launched September 12, 1987.*

752
752
YTB 834

SUBMARINE-LAUNCHED BALLISTIC MISSILES

The matching of the ballistic missile with the nuclear submarine has proved to be one of the most effective weapon systems ever developed for maintaining peace. The submarine's stealth combined with the ballistic missile's speed and accuracy have strengthened the concept of Mutual Assured Destruction, which has helped prevent a nuclear war since the early 1950s.

As with most modern weapon systems, the submarine-launched ballistic missile was first conceived and designed in Germany during World War II. Plans were developed to arm German U-boats with sea-going versions of the V-2 missile, but the war ended before those plans could be carried out. After World War II, the United States and the Soviet Union each conducted long-term programs to develop submarine-launched ballistic missiles. The Soviet Union deployed the first such missile aboard the conventionally powered *Golf*-class submarine in the late 1950s. Polaris missiles were the U.S. Navy's first ballistic missiles. They were deployed for the first time in 1960 aboard *George Washington*-class strategic nuclear-powered ballistic submarines (SSBN). The Polaris evolved through three series and is now retired from U.S. service.

The Polaris series was followed by the Poseidon C-3 missile, which carried a maximum of 14 Multiple Independent Reentry Vehicles (MIRV). Each MIRV warhead could be aimed at a separate target within the missile's footprint (the area that all warheads could reach). The Poseidon had a longer range than the Polaris and was installed aboard *Benjamin Franklin* and *Lafayette* SSBNs.

To maximize the unique capabilities of the submarine, the Navy developed the Trident C-4—a missile far more accurate and with a longer range than the Poseidon. The C-4 is a three-stage missile with a MIRV warhead. The Trident C-4 is deployed on all nuclear-powered strategic ballistic missile submarines in U.S. service. A follow-on to the C-4—the Trident D-5, which is more powerful and accurate—is in its final test stages. It is due to be deployed to the fleet in 1990.

Above: *The Trident C-4 is a sea-launched ballistic missile carried by the* Benjamin Franklin- *and* Ohio-*class submarines.* Opposite: *The Poseidon C-3 is a two-stage sea-launched ballistic missile.*

UGM-73A Poseidon (C-3) Submarine-Launched Ballistic Missile

The Poseidon C-3 was designed and built as a follow-on to the U.S. Navy's first submarine-launched ballistic missile (SLBM), the Polaris A1-3. Originally called the Polaris B3, the Poseidon was built by Lockheed Missiles and Space Company. The Poseidon was to carry twice the payload weight with double the accuracy for the same distance as the Polaris. Warheads carried to the Poseidon's maximum range of 2,500 miles have a circular error of probability (CEP) of one-third of a mile. (The CEP is the radius of a circle into which 50 percent of all launched warheads will land.)

The Poseidon's main improvement over the Polaris can be found in its payload capacity. The Poseidon can carry up to 14 Multiple Independent Reentry Vehicles (MIRV), each carrying a 50-kiloton warhead. The SALT II agreement imposes a limit of ten MIRVs on Soviet and American long-range ballistic missiles. Each MIRV warhead can be aimed at a separate target. The Poseidon missile can carry all ten MIRVs a maximum distance of 2,500 miles: The range of the MIRVs after being released from the Poseidon missile is classified.

The Poseidon is a two-stage rocket powered by solid propellant motors. The rocket nozzles are mounted on gimbals for steering. Poseidon missiles have been upgraded regularly during their service life, and an improved inertial guidance system has been installed.

The Poseidon made its first flight in August 1968 and completed its testing program in June 1970. The first firing from a strategic nuclear-powered submarine took place in August 1970, from the USS *James Madison* (SSBN 627). *Benjamin Franklin* and *Lafayette* strategic nuclear-powered ballistic submarines (SSBN) were converted to carry the Poseidon SLBM between 1970 and 1978; all Poseidon missiles are operated by the Atlantic fleet. At present, 19 *Benjamin Franklin* and *Lafayette* SSBNs in service carry the Poseidon C-3; each submarine carries 16 Poseidon missiles. There are currently 304 Poseidon C-3 missiles in service. Each Poseidon has ten MIRVs, accounting for a total of 3,040 nuclear warheads.

Left: *The Poseidon C-3, here being launched from the* Lafayette-*class USS* Casimir Pulaski, *has a range of 2,500 miles.*

Above: *All sea-launched ballistic missiles in U.S. inventory are launched while the submarine remains submerged.*

UGM-73A POSEIDON (C-3) SUBMARINE-LAUNCHED BALLISTIC MISSILE

Length:	34 ft.
Diameter:	6 ft., 4 in.
Weight:	65,000 lbs.
Engine:	Two-stage, solid propellant motors
Maximum range:	2,500 miles
Date of service:	1970

UGM-96 Trident I and II (C-4 and D-5) Submarine-Launched Ballistic Missiles

Above: *A Trident I C-4 missile is launched during developmental testing.* Opposite, top: *The Trident II D-5 is a three-stage missile that will become operational in mid-1990.* Opposite, bottom: *This Trident C-4 missile is being loaded into the USS* Daniel Boone, *a* Lafayette-*class submarine.*

In the late 1960s, a new submarine-launched ballistic missile (SLBM) was proposed. The new SLBM, named STRAT-X, would have a range of 6,900 miles, which was more than twice the range of the Polaris then in service or the Poseidon then undergoing development and testing. The new missile would be carried on a new class of submarine. Because of the difficulties in developing such a missile, the Navy divided development into two phases.

The first-phase missile was based on the Extended Range Poseidon (EXPO) program. The first phase resulted in the Trident I (C-4) missile, which has the same capability and accuracy as the Poseidon but a longer range of 4,600 miles. The second phase is to be the Trident II (D-5) missile, which will have a range of 6,900 miles. Deployment of the Trident II is to start in the early 1990s.

Lockheed Missiles and Space Company, which had developed the Polaris and Poseidon, received the contract for the new missile in November 1972. The Trident I made its first flight in January 1977 and was first deployed on the *Benjamin Franklin*-class submarine USS *Francis Scott Key* (SSBN 667) in October 1979. A total of 12 *Benjamin Franklin*-class submarines each carry 16 Trident I missiles. The Trident I is also carried aboard all *Ohio*-class submarines; each *Ohio* submarine carries 24 Trident I missiles. The range and accuracy of the Trident I extends the operational area of current strategic nuclear-powered ballistic submarines (SSBN), which greatly complicates the Soviet Union's problems of identifying and tracking the submarines.

The Trident I is a three-stage, solid-fuel missile. All three stages are powered by Thiokol/Hercules rocket motors. A sophisticated inertial guidance system takes an initial setting from the submarine's main computer. Shortly after launch, the settings are updated when the missile's on-board computer takes a set of star sights. This unique guidance system accounts for the missile's accuracy. The circular error of probability (CEP) is one quarter of a mile.

The Trident C-4 carries the Mark 4 reentry vehicle, which carries eight Mark 500 Evader Maneuvering Reentry Vehicles (MaRV). Each Mark 500 vehicle contains a 100-kiloton warhead. To achieve additional range, a sharp spike—called an aerospike—extends from the missile's nose after launch. This spike reduces drag, adding 300 or more miles to the missile's range. This spike, when combined with the third stage, gives the Trident I a range nearly twice that of the Poseidon.

The Trident II (D-5) missile has a longer range and is more accurate than the Trident I. Its CEP is expected to be about 400 feet. The Trident II will carry 75 percent more payload than the Trident I—up to eight Mark 5 MaRVs with the Mark 87 warhead. The first Trident II firing took place in 1987, and the program continues, although somewhat behind schedule. The Trident II will be carried on *Ohio*-class boats that are fitted for the larger diameter missile. The Trident II is expected to enter service in 1990.

The increased range and accuracy of the Trident II missile will challenge Soviet ground-based missile sites that have been especially hardened against the less accurate SLBMs.

UGM-96 TRIDENT I AND II (C-4 AND D-5) SUBMARINE-LAUNCHED BALLISTIC MISSILES	
Length:	
Trident I:	34 ft.
Trident II:	44 ft.
Diameter:	
Trident I:	6 ft., 2 in.
Trident II:	6 ft., 11 in.
Weight:	
Trident I:	65,000 lbs.
Trident II:	126,000 lbs.
Engine:	Three-stage, solid propellant motors (both)
Maximum range:	
Trident I:	4,600 miles
Trident II:	6,900 miles
Date of service:	
Trident I:	1979
Trident II:	Expected 1990

Above: *The Trident II D-5 carries eight Mk 5 reentry vehicles; each reentry vehicle carries one Mk 87 nuclear warhead.*

INDEX

A

A-4 Skyhawk, 40, 42–43, 48
A-6 Intruder, 40, 44–47, 316, 321, 324, 329, 332
  EA-6B Prowler, 44, 316, 321, 324, 329, 332
  KA-6D, 44
A-7 Corsair II, 40, 48–51, 321, 324, 329, 332
A-9, 52
A-10 Thunderbolt II "Warthog," 16, 40, 52–54, 274
A-11, 58
A-12, 82
Abrams, General Creighton W., 232
Aegis SPY-1 system, 338, 346–47, 366, 370, 394, 396, 456
Aerial refueling, 36, 106
Aerial tankers, 106–11
  KC-10 Extender, 110–11
  KC-135 Stratotanker, 108–9
Afghanistan (Soviet invasion), 315, 332
AGM-86B air-launched cruise missile, 60, 162–65
  AGM-86A, 162
AH-1 HueyCobra, 138, 148–51
  AH-1 SeaCobra, 148, 424, 426
  AH-1W SuperCobra "Whiskey," 148
AH-64A Apache, 156–59
  YAH-64, 156
Airborne Warning and Control System (AWACS), 86
Aircraft carriers, 314–15
  Enterprise-class (CVN), 328–31
  Forrestal-class (CV), 320–22
  Kitty Hawk-class (CVN), 323–28
  Midway-class (CV), 316–19
  Nimitz-class (CVN), 332–35
Air-defense systems, 274-97
  FIM-43A Redeye missile system, 282–83
  FIM-92A Stinger, 290–93
  M48A1 Chaparral missile system, 288–89
  MIM-23B Hawk missile system, 278–81
  MIM-104 Patriot missile system, 294–95
  Roland missile system, 296–97
  Vulcan air-defense system, 284–87
Air Force One, 92
Air power, 6, 14–165, 312
  aerial tankers, 106–11
  attack helicopters, 138–59
  attack planes, 40–59
  bombers, 60–75
  cruise missiles, 160–65
  electronic warfare aircraft, 76–91
  fighters, 18–39
  organization of, 14–16
  reconnaissance aircraft, 76–91
  transport helicopters, 112–37
  utility helicopters, 112–37
Air-to-air combat, 18, 138
Allied Submarine Devices Investigating Committee (ASDIC), 374
Ammunition
  105mm artillery, 210
  105mm tank, 239
  120mm tank, 239
  155mm artillery, 210–12
  203mm howitzer, 213
Amphibious ships, 420–21
  Charleston-class, 434–35
  Dock landing-class, 428–31
  Iwo Jima-class, 422–23
  Newport-class, 432–33
  Tarawa-class, 424–25
  Wasp-class, 426–27
AN/PAQ-1 laser target designator, 272
  AN/PAQ-3 MULE, 272
AN/PPS-5B Battlefield Surveillance Radar, 269
AN/TPQ-36/37 Mortar/Artillery Fire Finder Radar, 270–71
AN/TVQ-2 Ground/Vehicular Laser Locator Designator, 272
Anchorage-class (LSD) dock landing ships, 428, 429
Antipersonnel mines, 264
  "Cupcake," 264
  M16A2, 264
  M18A1, 264
  "Toe Popper," 264
  M14, 264
Antiship guns, 441–43
  Mark 45 (five-inch), 441–42
  Mark 75 (76 millimeter), 441–42
  16-inch guns, 441–42
Antiship missiles, 40, 444–45
  Harpoon, 444–45
  Tomahawk, 444–45
Antisubmarine weapons, 358, 362, 446–49
  Antisubmarine rockets (ASROC), 342, 346, 350, 354, 358, 362, 366, 370, 374, 382, 386, 390, 394, 406, 410, 446–47
  depth charges, 446
  helicopter, 131, 140
  Mark 46, 446–47
Antitank mines, 264–65
  M74, 265
  M75, 265
Antitank weapons, 240–49
  AT-4 Light Antitank Weapon, 249
  M47 Dragon II medium antitank weapon, 246–48
  Tube-launched, Optically tracked, Wire-guided (TOW) missile (BGM-71), 244–45
Arleigh Burke-class (DDG) guided missile destroyers, 338, 374, 383, 396–97, 456
Armored fighting vehicles (AFV), 250–63
  classes of, 250
  Light Assault Vehicle 25, 258–63
  M2/M3 Bradley Infantry and Cavalry Fighting Vehicles, 256–57
  M113 Armored Personnel Carrier, 252–55
  M998 High Mobility, Multipurpose Wheeled Vehicle (HMMWV), 260–63
Artillery, 192–219
  ammunition, 210–13
  Lance Battlefield Support Missile (MGM-52C), 214–15
  M101A1 105mm Towed Howitzer, 194
  M102 105mm Towed Howitzer, 196–97
  M109 155mm Self-propelled Howitzer, 201–7
  M110A2 Self-propelled 203mm (8-Inch) Howitzer, 208–9
  M114 155mm Towed Howitzer, 195
  M119 105mm Towed Howitzer, 200
  M198 155mm Towed Howitzer, 198
  Multiple Launch Rocket System (MLRS), 216–18
  Tactical Missile System (TACMS), 219
  types of, 192
Ashville-class frigates, 398
ASROC. *See* Antisubmarine weapons.
AT-4 Light Antitank Weapon, 240, 249
Atlantic fleet, 310–11, 316, 350, 354, 358, 366, 386, 415, 434
Attack aircraft, 20, 40–59, 274
  A-4 Skyhawk, 42–43
  A-6 Intruder, 44–47
  A-7 Corsair II, 48–51
  A-10 Thunderbolt II "Warthog," 52–54
  AV-8B Harrier II, 55–57
  F-117A Stealth fighter, 58–59
Attack helicopters, 138–59
  role of, 138
Austin-class (LPD) amphibious transport dock, 428, 431
AV-8A Harrier, 55, 138, 422, 424
AV-8B Harrier II, 40, 55–57, 424, 426
AWACS. *See* Airborne Warning and Control System; E-3 Sentry.

B

B-1B, 60, 68–71, 72, 160, 162
  B-1A, 68
  XB-70, 68
B-2 Stealth bomber, 6, 72–75
B-17 "Flying Fortress," 14, 62, 160
B-24 bomber, 14, 160
B-29 Superfortress, 14, 62, 106
B-47 Stratojet, 62
B-52 Stratofortress, 62–63, 68, 162
B-58, 68
B-66, 76
B-70, 68
Bainbridge-class (CGN) cruisers, 329, 342, 347, 354–57
Battle of Britain (1940), 14
Battlefield electronics, 86, 268–73
  AN/PPS-5B Battlefield Surveillance Radar, 269
  AN/TPQ-36/37 Mortar/Artillery Fire Finder Radar, 270–71
  laser designators, 272–73
Battleships, 336–37
  Iowa-class, 336, 338–41
Bazooka, 240
Belknap-class (CG) cruisers, 350, 358–61, 386, 396
Benjamin Franklin-class submarines, 464–69, 494, 496, 498
Berlin Blockade, 222
BIGEYE aerial bomb, 304–5
Bismarck (Germany), 336
Black Swan-class sloops, 398
Blue Angels, 42
Bombers, 60–75
  B-1B, 68–71
  B-2 Stealth, 72–75
  B-52 Stratofortress, 62–63
  F-111/FB-111, 64–67
British Royal Navy, 314, 398
Bronstein-class (FF) frigates, 402, 403
Brooke-class (FFG) guided-missile frigates, 403, 406–9
Browning, John, 172, 174
Browning automatic rifle (BAR), 172, 180
Burke, Arleigh, 374

C

C-1 Trader, 92
C-2, 92
C-5 Galaxy, 92, 102–5, 130, 203, 258
C-9 ambulance, 92
C-17, 92
C-20, 92
C-21, 92
C-22, 92
C-23, 92
C-47, 95
C-130 Hercules, 6, 92, 94–97, 258
  AC-130 Spectre, 95
C-141 Starlifter, 92, 98–101, 130, 201, 203, 258
California-class (CGN) guided-missile cruisers, 362–65
Carrier-based aircraft, 20, 44
Carrier battle group (CBG), 15
Carter, President Jimmy, 68, 160, 162
  administration, 332
Central Treaty Organization (CENTO), 7
CH-3/HH-3 Jolly Green Giant, 112, 120–21, 126
CH-46 Sea Knight, 118, 122–25, 422, 424, 426
CH-47 Chinook, 112, 118–19, 196, 198
CH-53 Sea Stallion/HH-53 Super Jolly Green Giant, 126–29, 134, 135, 198, 422, 424, 426
CH-53E Super Stallion/MH-53E Sea Dragon, 134–37, 258, 422, 424, 426
Challenger (British), 232
Charles F. Adams-class (DDG) guided-missile destroyers, 382–85
Charleston-class (LKA) amphibious cargo ship, 434–35
Chemical warfare, 304–7
  agents, 306
  capability, 304–5
  components, 305
  protection, 305
Circular error of probability, 496, 498
Civil War, 14, 172, 192, 460
Claymore mine, 264
Cold War, 7, 14, 220, 222, 310, 320
College Eye EC-121Q, 86
Colt Firearms, 174
Connolly, Admiral Tom, 24
Counterbattery fire, 268, 270
Cruise missiles, 60, 160–65, 219
  AGM-86B, 162–65
  MX-774, 160
  SM-62A Snark, 160
  SM-64 Navajo, 160
  Tomahawk, 162
Cruisers, 342–73
  Bainbridge-class, 354–57
  Belknap-class, 358–61
  California-class, 362–65
  Leahy-class, 350–53
  Long Beach-class, 346–49
  Ticonderoga-class, 370–73
  Truxtun-class, 354–57
  Virginia-class, 366–69

D

Dash Eighty, 108
Dealy-class frigates, 398
Defense Department, 14-15, 16, 171, 396
Destroyers, 374–97
  Arleigh Burke-class, 396–97
  Charles F. Adams-class, 382–85
  Farragut-class, 386–89
  Forrest Sherman-class, 378–81
  Kidd-class, 394–95
  Spruance-class, 390–93
Detroit Tank Arsenal, 222, 232
Dock landing-class (LSD/LPD) amphibious ships, 428–31
Dorneberger, Colonel Walter, 298
Dragon I, 240, 246
Drone antisubmarine helicopter (DASH), 402, 403, 406, 410

INDEX

E

E-1 Tracer, 80, 90
E-2 Hawkeye, 80–81, 86, 90, 92, 316, 321, 324, 329, 332, 456
E-3 Sentry AWACS, 6, 16, 80, 86–89, 108
Eastern Bloc, 7
EA-6, 90
EB-66, 76, 90
EC-121 Warning Star, 80
EC-135, 86, 108
EF-111 Raven, 90–91
89th Military Airlift Wing, 92
Eisenhower administration, 320
Electronic warfare, 44
  aircraft, 16, 76–91
Emergency Airborne Command Post, 301
Enterprise-class (CVN) aircraft carrier, 314, 328–31, 346–47
Essex-class aircraft carriers, 316, 320
Ethan Allen-class submarines, 464, 470
Executive flight detachment, 140

F

F2H Banshee, 20
F3H Demon, 20
F-4 Phantom II, 18, 20–23, 24, 28, 32, 48
  F-4G "Wild Weasel," 20
  F-110, 20
  RF-4C, 20, 76
F-8, 48
F8U Crusader, 48
F-14 Tomcat, 6, 16, 18, 24–27, 28, 316, 320–21, 324, 329, 332
F-15 Eagle, 16, 28–31, 32
F-16 Fighting Falcon, 16, 32–35
F-102 fighter, 18
F-105, 90
F-106 fighter, 18
F-111/FB-111, 24, 28, 64–67, 90, 162
F-117A Stealth fighter, 58–59
F/A-18 Hornet, 18, 36–39, 316, 321, 324
Falkland Islands War (1982), 55, 138, 200, 310, 333, 371, 396
Farragut-class (DDG) guided-missile destroyers, 386–89, 390
FG42 automatic rifle, 42
First Special Operations Command
  Air Force Special Warfare, 169
  Green Berets, 169
Fighters, 18–39
  F-4 Phantom II, 20–23
  F-14 Tomcat, 24–27
  F-15 Eagle, 28–31
  F-16 Fighting Falcon, 32–35
  F/A-18 Hornet, 36–39
  speed of, 18
FIM-43A Redeye missile system, 282–83
FIM-92A Stinger, 274, 282, 290–93, 450
Fire Finder. *See* AN/TPQ-36/37 Mortar/Artillery Fire Finder Radar.
530M Defender, 152–55
  OH-6A Cayuse, 152
Fleet air defense, 24
Flintlock musket, 172
Flower-class ships, 398
Forrestal-class (CV) aircraft carrier, 314, 320–22, 323, 328
Forrest Sherman-class (DD) destroyers, 374, 378–81, 382
Fragmentation mine, 264
French Navy, 398
Frigates, 398–419
  Bronstein-class, 402
  Brooke-class, 406–9
  Garcia-class, 403–5
  Knox-class, 410–13
  Oliver Hazard Perry-class, 414–19

G

G/VLLD. *See* AN/TQ-3 Ground/Vehicular Laser Locator Designator.
Garcia-class (FF) frigates, 403–5, 406
Gatling gun, 172
Gearing-class destroyers, 390
George Washington-class submarines, 470, 494
Golf-class submarines, 494
Gorbachev, Mikhail, 28
Government Model 1911 semiautomatic, 174
Grenades, 184
Ground-attack aircraft, 274
Guided missiles, 18
Gulf of Sidra, 24

H

Hanazuki (ex-Japanese) destroyer, 378
Harpoon missile launchers, 336, 338, 342, 346, 350, 354, 358, 362, 370, 374, 382, 386, 390, 394, 397, 406, 410, 414, 437, 486
Heinemann, Ed, 42
Helicopters, 15, 112–59
  AH-1 HueyCobra, 148–51
  AH-64A Apache, 156–59
  CH-3/HH-3 Jolly Green Giant, 120–21
  CH-46 Sea Knight, 122–25
  CH-47 Chinook, 118–19
  CH-53 Sea Stallion/HH-53 Super Jolly Green Giant, 126–29
  CH-53E Super Stallion/MH-53E Sea Dragon, 134–37
  530M Defender, 152–55
  SH-2 Seasprite, 144–47
  SH-3 Sea King, 140–43
  UH-1 Iroquois (Huey), 114–17
  UH-60A Black Hawk/SH-60B Seahawk, 130–33
Hellcat, 24
Hitler, Adolf, 310
HMS *Broadsword,* 396
HMS *Coventry,* 396
HMS *Hood,* 336
HMS *Illustrious,* 314
HMS *Prince of Wales,* 336
Hose and drogue, 106
Howitzer, 192
  self-propelled, 201–9
  towed, 194–200
Hurricane fighter, 14
Hydrophone, 374

I

Identification, Friend or Foe (IFF) system, 86, 282, 290
Igloo White EC-121R Batcats, 86
Infantry weapons, 172–91
  M9 Beretta double-action 9mm sidearm, 174–75
  M16A2 rifle, 176–77
  M21 sniper rifle, 178–79
  M24 sniper rifle, 178–79
  M29A1 81mm mortar, 186–87
  M40A1 sniper rifle, 178–79
  M60 General Purpose Machine Gun, 182–83
  M249 5.56mm Squad Automatic Weapon, 180–81
  M252 81mm mortar, 188–89
  Mark 19-3 40mm Automatic Grenade Launcher, 184–85
  Shoulder-launched, Multipurpose Assault Weapon, 190–91
Intercontinental ballistic missile (ICBM), 98, 298–303
Interdiction minefields, 265
Iowa-class battleships, 336, 338–41, 441
Iran-Iraq war, 138, 221
Iron Curtain, 14, 222
Islamic Revolution, 394
Iwo Jima-class (LPH) amphibious assault ships, 422–23

J

James Madison-class submarines, 496
Japanese Air Force, 14
Japanese Navy, 314
Jeep vehicles, 260, 269
Johnson, Kelly, 78
Johnson administration, 332
Joint Chiefs of Staff, 310

K

Kaman, Charles H., 144
KB-29 tankers, 106
KC-10 Extender, 110–11
KC-97 tankers, 106, 108
KC-130 Hercules, 134
KC-135 Stratotanker, 86, 106, 108–9, 110
Kennedy administration, 315, 332, 398
Kidd-class guided missile (DDG) destroyers, 131, 338, 394–95
Kitty Hawk, North Carolina, 14
Kitty Hawk-class (CVN) aircraft carriers, 314–15, 323–27
Knox-class (ff) frigates, 410–13
Korean War, 7, 20, 112, 168, 172, 176, 201, 220, 222, 264, 315, 320, 336, 339, 428
Krag bolt action rifle, 172

L

Lafayette-class (SSBN) ballistic missile submarines, 464–69, 470, 494, 496
Lance Battlefield Support Missile (MGM-52C), 192, 214–15
Land-based intercontinental ballistic missiles, 298–303
  Minuteman III (LGM-30), 300–1
  Peacekeeper (LGM-118), 302–3
Land mines, 264–67
Land power, 6, 166–307
  air-defense systems, 274–97
  antitank weapons, 240–49
  armored fighting vehicles, 250–63
  artillery, 192–219
  battlefield electronics, 268–73
  chemical warfare, 304–7
  fire support, 192–219
  importance of, 168
  infantry weapons, 172–91
  land-based intercontinental ballistic missiles, 298–303
  main battle tanks, 220–39
  mines, 264–67
  organization of, 168–71
Laser designators, 272–73
Leahy-class (CG) guided-missile cruisers, 350–53, 358, 386
Leatherwood, Lieutenant James, 178
Lebanon (1982), 168, 221
Lehman, John, 332
Lenin icebreaker, 346
Lewis gun, 182
Lexington-class aircraft carrier, 314, 316
Libyan MiG-23, 24
Light airborne multipurpose system (LAMPS), 258
  Mark III program, 131
Light Armored Vehicle Battalions (LAVB), 144
Liquid-fueled missile, 298
Loaches. *See* 530M Defender.
Long Beach-class (CGN) cruiser, 329, 342, 346–49
Los Angeles-class (SSN) attack submarines, 486–93

M

M1 Garand, 172, 176
M1 Howitzer, 192
M-1/M-1A1 Abrams Main Battle Tank, 148, 168, 220, 232–38, 239, 252, 424, 432
M2/M3 Bradley Infantry and Cavalry Fighting Vehicles, 192, 216, 250, 256–57, 290
M-4 Sherman medium tank, 222
M9 Beretta double-action 9mm sidearm, 6, 168, 174–75
M14 rifle, 176, 178
M16A2 rifle, 172, 176–77, 180, 184
M21 sniper rifle, 172, 178–79
M24 sniper rifle, 178–79
M-26 Pershing tank, 220
M29A1 81mm mortar, 186–87, 188
M40A1 sniper rifle, 178–79
M-47 tank, 220, 222
M-48 General George S. Patton medium tank, 220, 222–25, 226, 239
M48A1 Chaparral missile system, 284, 288–89
M60 General Purpose Machine Gun, 182–83
M-60 Main Battle Tank, 220, 223, 226–31, 232, 239, 252, 424
M72 Light Armor Weapon (LAW), 249, 338
M79 grenade launcher, 184
M101 105mm Towed Howitzer, 194, 195, 196, 202, 210
M102 105mm Towed Howitzer, 196–97, 202, 210
M107 howitzer, 203
M109 155mm Self-propelled Howitzer, 203–7
M110A2 Self-propelled 203mm (8-inch) Howitzer, 208–9
M113 Armored Personnel Carrier, 184, 186, 214, 252–55, 278, 288
M114 155mm Towed Howitzer, 195, 198, 210
M119 105mm Towed Howitzer, 200, 210
M225A1 vehicle, 186
M128 Ground Emplaced Mine Scattering System (GEMSS), 265
M198 155mm Towed Howitzer, 198–201, 210
M249 5.56mm Squad Automatic Weapon, 172, 180–81
M252 81mm mortar, 188–89
M998 High Mobility, Multipurpose Wheeled Vehicle (HMMWV), 184, 200, 260–63, 269, 284, 290
McNamara, Robert S., 64, 323, 362
Main battle tanks, 220–21, 226–31, 250
Marianas Turkey Shoot, 24
Marine Corps Light Assault Vehicle 25, 250, 258–59
Marine Expeditionary Brigade (MEB), 420
Marine Expeditionary Force (MEF), 420

Marine Expeditionary Unit (MEU), 420
Mark I tank, 220
Mark 19-3 40mm Automatic Grenade Launcher, 184–85
Mauser, Peter Paul, 240
Maxim, Hiram, 180
Mexican War, 192
MG42 machine gun, 182
Midway-class (CV) aircraft carriers, 314, 316–19, 332
Military Airlift Command (MAC), 92, 94, 98, 102
  Rescue and Recovery Service, 94
Military aviation history, 14
Military power, 6–11
Mills Bomb, 184
MIM-23B Hawk missile system, 278–81, 294
MIM-104 Patriot missile system, 294–95
Minefields, 265
Minelaying systems, 264–67
Mines, 264–67
  antipersonnel, 264
  antitank, 264–65
  Claymore, 264
  fragmentation, 264
  land, 264–67
  minelaying systems, 264–67
  scatterable, 265
Minuteman missiles, 98, 298, 300–1, 302
Missiles, 40, 60, 98, 244–45, 246
Multiple Launch Rocket System (MLRS), 209, 216–18, 219
Muskets, 172
Mutual Assured Destruction (MAD), 298, 494
MX-774 cruise missile, 160, 298

N

NASA, 78
National Command Authority, 6
National Reserve Fleet, 378
National Security Act, 170
Nautilus-class submarines, 346
Naval Chief of Staff, 310
Naval Forces Europe, 310–11
Naval Reserve Fleet, 410, 432, 434
Naval Surface Weapons Center, 190
Newport-class (LST) tank landing ships, 432–33
Nike Hercules missile system, 294
Nimitz-class (CVN) aircraft carriers, 314, 315, 332–35
Normandy, 14
North American Air Defense Command (NORAD), 86
North Atlantic Treaty Organization (NATO), 6–7, 32, 232, 250, 310, 311, 420

O

105mm artillery ammunition, 210
105mm tank ammunition, 239
106mm recoilless rifle, 244
120mm tank ammunition, 239
155mm artillery ammunition, 210–12
Observation aircraft, 76
Ohio-class (SSBN) ballistic missile submarines, 470–75, 498
Oliver Hazard Perry-class (FFG) guided-missile frigates, 131, 338, 398, 402, 414-19, 441
Operation Aphrodite, 160
Operation Arc Light, 62
Operation Linebacker II, 62
Osirak, 32
OV-10 Bronco, 424

P

Pacific fleet, 311, 314, 316, 350, 354, 358, 366, 415, 434
Panama invasion, 58
Patrol and special warfare craft, 436
  Pegasus-class, 437–39
Peacekeeper (LGM-118) intercontinental ballistic missile, 6, 298, 302–3
Pegasus-class missile patrol boats, 437–39, 441
Percussion musket, 172
Permit-class (SSN) attack submarines, 476–81, 482
Persian Gulf, 86, 339, 394
Phalanx Close-In Weapons System (CIWS), 316, 324, 328, 333, 336, 338, 342, 346, 350, 354, 362, 366, 370, 394, 397, 415, 422, 425, 426, 434, 450–51
Phony minefields, 265
Point minefields, 265
Polaris missiles, 346, 464, 494, 496. *See also* UGM-73A Poseidon C-3 submarine-launched ballistic missile.
Protective minefields, 265

R

Radars, 269–71, 456–59
Raleigh-class (LPD) amphibious transport dock, 428, 430
RAM, 450–51
Ranger-class, 316
Rapid Deployment Force (RDF), 171, 296
RC-135, 86, 108
Reagan, President Ronald, 68
  administration, 315, 396
Reconnaissance and electronic warfare aircraft, 76–91
  E-2 Hawkeye, 80–81
  EF-111 Raven, 90–91
  SR-71 Blackbird, 82–85
  U-2/TR-1 Series, 78–79
Red Sea operation (1984), 127
Regulus II surface-to-surface missile, 346
Remington Model 700 sporting rifle, 178
Reserve Component, 170
Revolutionary War, 178
RF-101, 76
Rock Island Arsenal, 198
Roland missile system, 296–97
Royal Air Force, 14
Russo-Japanese War, 374

S

S-2 Tracker, 80, 92
S3A Viking, 321, 324, 333
SALT II agreement, 465, 496
Scatterable mines, 265
Sea power, 6, 308–493
  aircraft carriers, 314–35
  amphibious ships, 420–35
  battleships, 336–41
  cruisers, 342–73
  destroyers, 374–97
  frigates, 398–419
  patrol and special warfare craft, 436–40
  submarines, 460–93
  submarine-launched ballistic missiles, 494–500
  weapons and surveillance systems, 440–59
Sea Sparrow (RIM-7), 316, 323, 333, 338, 390, 403, 410, 426, 450–51
Second Fleet, 310–11
Self-propelled artillery, 192
Sergeant York antiaircraft system, 214, 284
Service Life Extension Program (SLEP), 321, 323, 324, 391
Seventh Fleet, 311
SH-2 Seasprite, 144–47, 350, 354, 358, 366, 370, 394, 403, 406, 410, 415
SH-3 Sea King, 120, 140–43, 316, 321, 324, 329, 333
SH-34 Seabats, 140
Shoulder-launched Multipurpose Assault Weapon (SMAW), 190–91
Sidewinder missile, 288, 450
Signal Corps
  Balloon Section, 14
  Dirigible No. 1, 14
Skunk Works, 58, 78, 82
Sixth Fleet, 310–11, 316, 358
SM-62A Snark cruise missile, 160, 298
SM-64 Navajo cruise missile, 160, 298
South Dakota-class battleships, 336
Southeast Asia Treaty Organization (SEATO), 7
Soviet Union, 6–7, 310–12, 336, 494, 498
  Air Defense Forces, 16
  Air Force, 16, 28, 60
  Antonov AN-124, 102
  armored fighting vehicles, 250
  BMP-2 infantry combat vehicle, 256
  main battle tanks, 232
  MiG 29, 16
  MiG 31, 16
  Navy, 16
  Su-27, 16
  Tbilisi, 16
  Tu-95 Bear bomber, 28
Spanish-American War (1898), 14, 192
Special Operations Forces (SOF), 171
Specifications
  A-6E Intruder, 45
  A-10A Thunderbolt II, 53
  AGM-86B air-launched cruise missiles, 163
  AH-1S HueyCobra, 149
  AH-64A Apache, 157
  AN/PPS-5B Battlefield Surveillance Radar, 269
  AN/TPQ-36/37 Mortar/Artillery Fire Finder Radar, 271
  antiship guns, 442
  antiship missiles, 445
  antisubmarine weapons, 447
  Arleigh Burke-class (DDG) guided-missile destroyers, 397
  AT-4 Light Antitank Weapon, 249
  AV-8B Harrier II, 56
  B-1B, 68
  B-2 Stealth, 73
  B-52H Stratofortress, 63
  Bainbridge-class (CGN) cruiser, 355
  Belknap-class (CG) guided-missile cruisers, 359
  Benjamin Franklin-class (SSBN) ballistic missile submarines, 468
  Bronstein-class (FF) frigates, 402
  Brooke-class (FFG) guided-missile frigates, 407
  C-5B Galaxy, 103
  C-130H Hercules, 95
  C-141B Starlifter, 99
  California-class (CGN) guided-missile cruisers, 363
  CH-3E/HH-3E Jolly Green Giant, 121
  CH-46E Sea Knight, 123
  CH-47D Chinook, 119
  CH-53D Sea Stallion/HH-53D Super Jolly Green Giant, 127
  CH-53E Super Stallion/MH-53E Sea Dragon, 135
  Charles F. Adams-class (DDG) guided-missile destroyers, 384
  Charleston-class (LKA) amphibious cargo ships, 435
  Dock landing-class (LSD/LPD) amphibious ships, 429–31
  Garcia-class (FF) frigates, 404
  E-2C Hawkeye, 81
  E-3 Sentry (AWACS), 87
  EF-111A Raven, 90
  Enterprise-class (CVN) aircraft carrier, 329
  F-4E Phantom II, 21
  F-14A Tomcat, 25
  F-15C Eagle, 29
  F-16 Fighting Falcon, 33
  F-111F, 65
  F-117A Stealth fighter, 59
  F/A-18 Hornet, 37
  Farragut-class (DDG) guided-missile destroyers, 387
  FIM-43A Redeye antiaircraft guided-missile system, 283
  FIM-92A Stinger, 291
  530 MG Defender, 153
  Forrest Sherman-class (DD) destroyers, 379
  Forrestal-class (CV) aircraft carriers, 322
  Iowa-class (BB) battleships, 339
  Iwo Jima-class (LPH) amphibious assault ships, 423
  KC-10 Extender, 110
  KC-135R Stratotanker, 109
  Kidd-class (DDG) guided-missile destroyers, 395
  Kitty Hawk-class (CVN) aircraft carriers, 325
  Knox-class (FF) frigates, 412
  Lafayette-class (SSBN) ballistic missile submarine, 468
  Lance Battlefield Support Missile (MGM-52C), 215
  Leahy-class (CG) guided-missile cruisers, 351
  Long Beach-class (CGN) cruiser, 348
  Los Angeles-class (SSN) attack submarines, 488
  M-1/M-1A1 Abrams Main Battle Tank, 238
  M2/M3 Bradley Infantry and Cavalry Fighting Vehicles, 257
  M9 Beretta double-action 9mm sidearm, 175
  M16A2 rifle, 177
  M21, M24, M40A1 sniper rifles, 179
  M29A1 81mm mortar, 187
  M47 Dragon II medium antitank weapon, 247
  M48A1 Chaparral low-altitude self-propelled surface-to-air missile system, 289
  M-48A5 General George S. Patton medium tank, 223
  M60 General Purpose Machine Gun, 183
  M-60A3 Main Battle Tank, 227
  M101A1 105mm Towed Howitzer, 194
  M102 105mm Towed Howitzer, 197
  M109 155mm Self-propelled Howitzer, 204
  M110A2 203mm (8-inch) Self-propelled Howitzer, 209
  M113 Armored Personnel Carrier, 253
  M114 155mm Towed Howitzer, 195
  M119 105mm Towed Howitzer, 200
  M198 155mm Towed Howitzer, 199
  M249 5.56mm Squad Automatic Weapon, 181
  M252 81mm mortar, 189
  M998 High Mobility, Multipurpose Wheeled Vehicle (HMMWV), 261

Marine Corps Light Assault Vehicle 25, 259
Mark 19-3 40mm Automatic Grenade Launcher, 185
Midway-class (CV) aircraft carriers, 317
MIM-104 Patriot tactical air-defense missile system, 295
MIM-23B Hawk air-defense missile system, 279
Minuteman III (LGM-30) intercontinental ballistic missile, 301
Multiple Launch Rocket System (MLRS), 217
Newport-class (LST) tank-landing ships, 433
Nimitz-class (CVN) aircraft carriers, 334
Ohio-class (SSBN) ballistic missile submarines, 473
Oliver Hazard Perry-class (FFG) guided-missile frigates, 416
Peacekeeper (LGM-118) intercontinental ballistic missile, 298, 302-3
Pegasus-class missile patrol boats, 438
Permit-class (SSN) attack submarines, 477
Roland air-defense missile system, 297
SH-2F Seasprite, 145
SH-3D Sea King, 141
Shoulder-launched, Multipurpose Assault Weapon, 191
Spruance-class (DD) destroyers, 390–93
SR-71 Blackbird, 82
Sturgeon-class (SSN) attack submarines, 484
surface-to-air weapons, 451
Tactical Missile System (TACMS), 219
Tarawa-class (LHA) amphibious assault ships, 425
Ticonderoga-class (CG) guided-missile cruisers, 372
TR-1, 79
Truxtun-class (CGN) cruiser, 355
Tube-launched, Optically tracked, Wire-guided (TOW) missile (BGM-71), 245
U-2, 79
UGM-73A Poseidon C-3 submarine-launched ballistic missile, 497
UGM-96 Trident I (C-4) and II (D-5) submarine-launched ballistic missile, 499
UH-1H Iroquois (Huey), 115
UH-60A Black Hawk/SH-60B Seahawk, 131
Virginia-class (CGN) guided-missile cruisers, 367
Vulcan air-defense system, 285
Wasp-class (LHD) amphibious assault ships, 427
Spitfire fighter, 14
Springfield rifled musket, 172
Spruance-class (DD) destroyers, 131, 338, 374, 390–93, 394, 414
SR-71 Blackbird, 58, 82–85, 108
SS11 wire-guided missile, 244
Standard missiles, 346, 350, 354, 358, 362, 370, 386, 394, 406, 414, 450–51
Stoner, Eugene, 172
Strategic Air Command (SAC), 60, 62, 64, 68, 78, 82, 106, 108, 160
Strategic Arms Reduction Talks (START), 302
Stuka dive bomber, 14
Sturgeon-class (SSN) attack submarines, 476, 482–85
Submarine-launched ballistic missiles, 494–500
UGM-73A Poseidon C-3, 496–97
UGM-96 Trident I (C-4), II (D-5), 498–500
Submarines, 460-93
Benjamin Franklin-class, 464–69
Lafayette-class, 464–69
Los Angeles-class, 486–93
Ohio-class, 470–75
Permit-class, 476–81
Sturgeon-class, 482–85
Surface-to-air weapons, 450–55
guided missile, 278
Phalanx, 450–51
RAM, 450–51
Sea Sparrow, 450–51
Standard, 450–51
Sverdlovsk, 78
Swinton, Lieutenant Colonel E.D., 220
Syrian Air Force, 28

T

T-48 tank, 222, 224–25
T-54 medium tank, 222
T-54/T-55 Main Battle Tank, 226
Tacoma-class frigates, 398
Tactical Air Command (TAC), 64, 86
Tactical fighter, experimental (TFX) program, 24, 64
Tactical minefields, 265
Tactical Missile System (TACMS), 219
Talos (RIM-8) missile launcher, 346, 370
Tanks, 220–249, 250
ammunition, 239
M-1/M-1A1 Abrams, 232–38
M-48 General George S. Patton, 222–25
M-60 Main Battle Tank, 226–31
Tarawa-class (LHA) amphibious assault ships, 424–25, 426
Tartar (RIM-24) guided missiles, 362, 370, 378, 382, 406
Terrier (RIM-2) missiles, 323, 346, 354, 358, 370, 386
Texas Towers, 120
Thetis Bay-class escort carriers, 422
Third Fleet, 311
Thomaston-class (LSD) dock landing ships, 428, 429
Thresher-class boats, 476
Ticonderoga-class (CG) guided-missile cruisers, 131, 366, 370–73, 396, 414
Tirpitz (Germany), 336
Titan I missile, 298
Titan II missile, 302
Tomahawk cruise missile, 162, 336, 338, 342, 346, 362, 366, 374, 390, 482, 486
Towed artillery, 192
Transport helicopters, 112–37
CH-46 Sea Knight, 122–25
CH-47 Chinook, 118–19
CH-53 Sea Stallion/HH-53 Super Jolly Green Giant, 126–29
CH-53E Super Stallion/MH-53E Sea Dragon, 134–37
Transports, 92–105
C-5 Galaxy, 102–105
C-130 Hercules, 94–97
C-141 Starlifter, 98–101
Truman administration, 320
Truxtun-class (CGN) cruiser, 354–57
Tube-launched, Optically tracked, Wire-guided (TOW) missile (BGM-71), 240, 244–45
Tullibee-class submarine, 476

U

U-2/TR-1 Series, 78–79
U.S. Division Plan 86, 201, 209
U-boats (German), 494
UGM-73A Poseidon C-3, 464, 470, 494, 496–97
UGM-96 Trident I, II, 464–465, 470, 494, 498–500
UH-1 Iroquois (Huey), 112, 114–17, 130, 138, 148, 424, 426
UH-60A Black Hawk/SH-60B Seahawk, 130–33, 138, 202, 370, 394, 396, 415
United Nations, 310
United States Air Force, 6, 15–16, 18, 314–15, 320, 420
Aerospace Rescue and Recovery Service, 120
Alaskan Air Command, 18, 28, 40
compared with Soviet Union, 16
in Europe, 18, 40
Military Airlift Command (MAC), 92, 94, 98, 102
Pacific Air Forces, 18, 40
Special Operations Forces, 127
Strategic Air Command (SAC), 60, 62, 64, 68, 78, 82, 106, 108, 160
Tactical Air Command (TAC), 18, 40, 52, 64, 86
United States Army, 6
aeronautical branch, 14
Air Corps, 15
Air Forces, 15
Balloon Section, 14
battalion, 169
brigade, 169
company, 169
corps, 169
Dirigible No. 1, 14
divisions, 169
establishment of, 168
heavy infantry, 171
land combat forces, 168–69
light infantry, 171
major commands, 168
Marksmanship Unit, 172, 178
missile command, 244
numbering system, 170
Ordnance Department, 182
platoon, 169
Reserves, 170
Signal Corps, 14
Special Operations Forces, 171
Special Operations Target Interdiction Committee, 178
squad, 169
Standard Hot Day, 156
United States Marine Corps, 6, 94, 420, 422, 424, 426, 428
air power, 15
attack squadrons, 40, 42
establishment of, 168
Executive Flight Detachment, 131
land combat forces, 169–70
numbering system, 170
organizational structure of, 170
United States Navy, 6, 310, 312, 314, 350, 374, 386, 390, 394, 396, 398, 402, 410, 420, 424, 426, 428, 432, 434, 436, 441, 444, 446, 450, 456, 460, 464, 470, 476, 494, 496, 498
air power, 15, 16
attack squadrons, 40
Blue Angels, 42
compared with Soviet Union, 16
establishment of, 168
fighter squadrons, 40
Military Sealift Command, 92
Sea, Air, and Land (SEAL), 131, 436, 482
strike-fighter squadrons, 40
Underwater Demolition Team (UDT), 131
USS *Albany*, 144
USS *Constitution*, 398
USS *Enterprise*, 24
USS *Glover*, 403
USS *Independence*, 144
USS *Nimitz*, 24
USS *Ranger*, 48
Utility helicopters, 112–33
Utility tactical transport aircraft system (UTTAS) program, 130

V

V-1 pulse-jet-powered cruise missile, 298
V-2 missile, 298, 494
V-22 Osprey, 426
VC-25, 92
Vertical takeoff and landing (VTOL) aircraft, 55
Vietnam War, 7, 18, 20, 28, 48, 52, 60, 76, 86, 90, 98, 102, 112, 114, 120, 138, 156, 168, 172, 178, 264, 269, 315, 320, 332, 336, 339, 414, 424, 436
Virginia-class (CGN) guided-missile cruisers, 362, 366–69
von Braun, Wernher, 298
Vought F8U Crusader, 48
Vulcan air-defense system, 284–87

W

War of 1812, 192
War of the Spanish Succession (1701–14), 172
Warsaw Pact, 7, 310, 420
Wasp-class (LHD) amphibious assault ships, 426–27
Weapons and surveillance systems, 440
antiship guns, 441–43
antiship missiles, 444–45
antisubmarine weapons, 446–49
radars and surveillance systems, 456–59
surface-to-air weapons, 450–55
West German Leopard 2, 232
Whidbey Island-class (LSD) dock landing ships, 428, 430
Wilhelm, Kaiser, 310
World War I, 14, 76, 106, 138, 172, 182, 184, 192, 220, 240, 250, 264, 270, 274, 304, 310, 342, 374, 432
World War II, 6–7, 14, 18, 24, 60, 62, 76, 106, 112, 138, 144, 160, 168, 172, 176, 182, 184, 190, 192, 203, 220, 240, 250, 264, 268, 270, 274, 298, 304, 310, 312, 314–16, 320, 333, 339, 342, 374, 390, 398, 402, 420, 422, 424, 426, 428, 432, 436, 440, 494
Wright Brothers, 14
Wright Flyer, 14

X

XH-40 program, 114
XM687E1 155mm binary chemical artillery shell, 304, 305

Y

YF-12, 82
YF-16, 32, 36
YF-17, 32, 36

Z

ZB26 machine gun (Czechoslovakian), 182
Zumwalt, Admiral Elmo, 437